To Mollie —

with respect for your
personal excellence,
and with every good wish,

Mike Greenly

April, 1987

CHRONICLE
The Human Side of AIDS

by **MIKE GREENLY**

IRVINGTON PUBLISHERS, INC.
740 Broadway
New York, NY 10003

Library of Congress
Cataloging in Publication Data

Greenly, Mike, 1944 –
    Chronicle: the human side of aids.

    1. AIDS (Disease) – Popular works.
    2. AIDS (Disease) – Case studies. I. Title
RC607.A26G73 1986   616.97'92'00922
                86-10643
        ISBN 0-8290-1800-X

Printed in the United States of America

Foreword

AIDS, a tragedy of enormous human proportions, has also been a true test of government. More than any public health emergency in memory, this mystifying disease has made heavy demands upon the leadership, character and effectiveness of government.

Because it was and, in large part remains, a medical mystery, confusion was great when AIDS descended upon us in 1982. A disease largely confined to gay men, feelings about it ran high. We were without medical models, facing a disease that always kills.

AIDS was unique. It required public officials to educate themselves about a baffling, unseen and deadly disease at a time when the medical community was itself learning about it. What caused AIDS? How is it transmitted? What is its effect — on individuals and on whole communities?

So many questions — and so few answers.

Knowing only a part of the epidemic's potential, city officials hastily organized a response. We looked for rational programs to meet the need, not preconceived notions or past practices. After quickly educating themselves, city health experts launched crash programs to educate others — while simultaneously deciding and organizing ways to combat an unprecedented public health crisis of unknown dimensions. Without the benefit of scientific data, much was learned by talking to the people with AIDS and the doctors who were treating them.

While officials responded, so did the general public. Without complaints, San Franciscans approved millions to fight AIDS. In 1985, for example: $8.8 million to help develop a hospital ward, hospice and community education and counseling. The public quickly grasped the danger, but without panic — just compassion for the victims and a willingness to learn. The gay community took seriously a responsibility to change lifestyles. Across the city, hundreds came forward and asked if they could help.

Today, San Francisco is held up as a model for other cities to follow in dealing with the AIDS epidemic. Statistics suggest we are on the right track. We pray the model is a good one, because certainly it is imperative that the response be equal to the magnitude of the threat.

In this book, Mike Greenly performs a genuine public service in humanizing AIDS for the adult reader. The diverse cases he presents in interviews reflect a disease with far-reaching impacts. As we read this book, some of the fear of the epidemic is dispelled and our sympathy increases.

The more we all understand about the human impact of AIDS, the more likely we are to meet its challenge, carry on the fight and continue the compassion essential to all of its aspects.

AIDS is still with us, and so are many of the original questions. This book will help answer some of them.

DIANNE FEINSTEIN
Mayor of San Francisco
January, 1986

Acknowledgements

I did not write this book in a "normal" way. I don't think I could have. Most of it appeared on a number of computer screens around the world before words ever appeared on paper.

The new medium of communication that facilitated the birth of *CHRONICLE* is called "computer conferencing." Its application to news and commentaries is called "*interactive* journalism." Using the computer conferencing medium, readers at home and in offices can write back to the reporter and can also dialogue with each other.

Some progressive corporations are beginning to conduct "electronic meetings" among people with different schedules or in different geographical locations. Each participant reads in precise chronological order exactly what anyone else says on a topic — totally at one's own convenience. If you travel, your portable computer allows you to read every new comment, transmitted over the phone in your hotel room, or even from a phone booth.

After leaving twenty years of corporate life behind me, and while earning my living as a marketing consultant, I developed a kind of "hobby." It became a passion, actually — being one of the very first journalists in history to cover computer trade shows and political events via computer. With two colleagues, Sherwin Levinson and Diane Worthington, I co-founded TRANSCOASTAL Electronic News Service.

Eventually I became curious to explore new ways that this "high tech" computer medium could be used for communicating more personal, "high touch" topics. After considering various subjects, I chose AIDS. I could feel the strain on my own doctor, Ron Grossman, of treating people with such a treacherous and little-understood disease. It seemed there was an important human story that was not being captured as fully as it deserved, and I determined to do my best to be its scribe.

What I did not foresee was reader reaction — from England, Japan, Canada, Iowa, everywhere. Their notes began to fill my electronic mail box. They were intense and supportive and hungry for more. Given such strong encouragement, I set aside my consulting business and devoted myself to the task of completing a book The result was often influenced by people I've still not met in person. They nominated ideas for interviews. Sometimes they provided specific individuals for me to meet. They gave me motivation by telling me that this book really mattered, at least to them.

I would not have written *CHRONICLE* without such reader interaction. The book began in "Participate" — a computer conferencing program publicly available on The Source. The Source is a telecommunications network based in McLean, Virginia; it has 60,000 subscribers worldwide. Halfway through its completion, I began to "port" *CHRONICLE* to a second network, Unison, based in Denver. My sincere thanks to the "joiners" on both systems who read the book as it was being created electronically.

On The Source, their names or "identities" appeared on my computer screen this way:

STC-EDIT; DR.KEN; NORMAN KURLAND; MAC; GENJI; ALLAN O'DALE; GEORGE M; DAVE WENTROBLE; WARD; SWANZO; RACOM; STEVE JOBS; PSI DAVE; BRYNY; JEFFREY; SHERWIN; PAT MACKEN; WSL; DAVIDESQ; DOM S.; DR. MEMORY; OWL; KENNY; BOB SANDHAUS; RICH B.; RON TINDIGLIA; BOB*; PHILIP ELMER-DEWITT; HOTSPUR; T/O; MARTHA; ; FINN; WILL S.; DVO; BBH912; ROB H; C.J.; FRANK; DOJ8; STANDOC; CADAVER; LISA CARLSON; P.A.T; JIM ARMSTRONG; TCC; CYNIC AL; T:O:M; LEGION; JIM FRANKLIN; ST3871; IZUMI; JAR; DAVID KNOPF; JENNIFER; BBX395; DAVID Z.; GYM; ALEXIA; JJX; GRAMERCY; BCB860; PEGGY B.; DIANE; CAPT. KEN; PETER THE GREAT; STEFANIE KOTT; CHIRON; PHIL MOORE; BCQ693; BDB268; JIM D; BDA282; DRD; BDE544; BBC956; BDB193; AAH461; SURFER; CRAIG STURGIS; GRENDEL; BCE124; BCX993; BBX738; BDP074; DANA BLANKENHORN; STCMED; ELANA; STEPHEN DEERING; STORM!; DAVE C; BGS;

And on Unison:

GENJI; IDEL; CHEF; SANDY; WEB; FIANNA; PEABO; PEGGYR; STEFANIE KOTT; PATRICIA; DGLAIRD; TINA VOZICK; FTF; MIMIMM; APPLE ANDY; ANDY A; THE MADAM; KATE WHOLEY; SDC; MAVEN; STEVEH; JOEL; TERRY TRAVIS; DAVID TINGLER; SHERM .

Many people helped shaped this book by "networking," connecting me to other people, and offering special assistance in a variety of important ways. Here are people, in addition to conference joiners, to whom I owe *special* thanks:

Nancy Beckman. Peggy Berk. Dr. Steven Billstein. Dr. Stan Bodner. Lisa Carlson. Katie Colino. Linda Cranor. Dawn Debbe. John Doorley. Fred Dudden. Philip Elmer-Dewitt. Mary Fehrenbach. Chuck Forester. Dr. Lewis Greenly. Tom Griffin. Allen Heustis. Dr. Preston Holly. Dr. Phil Hopewell. Frank Ireland. Welton Jones. Art Kleiner. Al Krause. David Knopf. Stefanie Kott. Tom Krakovia. Sherwin Levinson. Sandy Lucot. George Maniscalco. Joe McKay. Phil Moore. Dr. Ken Phillips. Dr. Robert Roth. Kenneth Rhodes. Dr. Chris Ritchlin.

Eric Rosenthal. Dr. Robert Sandhaus. Vivian Shapiro. Jeffrey Silverstein. Paul Stepak. Ron Tindiglia. George Van de Mark. Maurice Villoria. Peter Vogel. Taylor Walsh. Gordon Weaver. Dale Wilson. Diane Worthington. And, David Rodale, whom I miss very much.

I'm also extremely grateful to every person interviewed herein. And most especially to Dr. Ronald J. Grossman.

Mike Greenly

Technical Notes

I composed *CHRONICLE* using three separate computer systems: an IBM XT, a 512K Macintosh, and a Tandy Model 100. The latter is a three-pound portable that I often took to interviews.

After readers of these reports urged me to turn the material into a book, I suddenly began to feel the pressure of a "deadline" (i.e., as soon as possible) that hadn't been an issue when the interviews were electronically available to readers only seconds after being written.

In order to speed the transfer of the material from computer screen to printed page, I used a "desktop publishing" software package, *Pagemaker*, from the Aldus Corporation in Seattle, Washington. With that software, with the Macintosh on loan from Apple Computer, and with a rented LaserWriter printer, I personally set every page of type in this book.

To be sure, some of the margins or sentence breaks may seem a bit homemade in places, but the technology nonetheless let a true "non-techie" like me produce a typeset book in only three weeks. *CHRONICLE* could thus be published in hard-cover format almost half a year earlier than conventional methods would have allowed. Eleven months after the first electronic message (Chapter 1), the material had become a book.

Technology exists to serve people, not the other way around. May technology help speed the discovery of solutions to AIDS.

M.S.G.

Contents

Chapter 1:
Dr. Grossman - The Beginning

Ron Grossman is the reason I began to write CHRONICLE. *He'd been my physician for almost a decade. In the spring of 1985, I suddenly noticed he seemed fatigued and ragged. "What's going on?" I asked.*

"AIDS." I'm amazed I knew so little about it. Patrick Kelley, a wonderful man who once trained me to become a gestalt therapist, had died of AIDS. I'd lost touch with Pat, however. I sent helium balloons to his hospital bed; I wish I had brought myself there.

Except for newspaper articles and distant acquaintances, I was sheltered from the disease until I saw it taking a toll on my own doctor. That's when I realized there was a major human story going largely untold. I asked Dr. Grossman to help me tell it.

(MAY 18, 1985)   The most important chart Dr. Ronald J. Grossman draws on my yellow pad at our first dinner is this one:

Natural history of epidemics

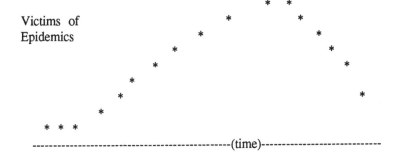

His guess on where we are on the time line with AIDS, the Acquired Immune Deficiency Syndrome? At the fourth star. Yes, down on the left. That's his estimate, now in mid-May, 1985. If he's correct in his prediction, then 10,000 cases in the U.S. today could become 1,000,000 cases by 1990-2000. If you don't know someone with AIDS today, you're increasingly likely to.

Ultimately, Dr. Grossman tells me across the dinner table, an epidemic saturates the available pool of victims. It then continues to exist, but as a "background" disease. There are three ways an epidemic reaches saturation. Its potential victims get sick and die, or get sick and survive, or develop immunity. Saturation is the reason for the sharp drop-off on the chart; the available pool of victims dries up.

Between here and saturation, however -- unless a miraculous cure or vaccine comes unusually quickly -- could lie a society severely dislocated by a mysterious and painful killer. A society of heterosexual and homosexual victims alike.

Is Dr. Grossman right? He fervently hopes not. So far, during the years he's been tracking AIDS, his predictions have actually been conservative.

The doctor's hastily drawn chart lies flat on the table between us. The intimate, brick-walled restaurant and the candlelight flickering in our corner add a cinematic air to my reflections. Can things really be as dramatic as he's telling me? Might the disease really become *so* much more widespread? What would be the consequences?

Ask your parents, he says, about the Great Flu Epidemic of 1917-1918. Who did their families lose when America saw the deaths of half a million flu victims? Had I pondered what happens to a nation's mind and climate, or to a globe's, when an unchecked disease claims lives in mammoth numbers?

He asks if I've ever seen an AIDS victim up close. No, I say, thinking of Patrick. Not yet. I agree to visit a hospital with Dr. Grossman as a part of this reportage.

The earliest case of what we now think of as "AIDS" was recorded in 1961 *Lancet*, a medical magazine. In 1961, I was a freshman at Duke University. I had a part-time job at Duke Hospital to help pay for my schooling. In fact, I remember, I used to page through *Lancet* in the Medical Library. Now I wonder about the articles I casually leafed through. I'd take a mental break from Shakespeare, gazing idly at the photo of a woman with gruesome boils or at a baby with burnt skin. Did one of those exotic picture stories depict a young man who couldn't fight off simple diseases? Perhaps a fellow with blotches on his arms?

Ron Grossman is testing a drug called "Isoprinosine." It was used to stimulate the body's immune system long before AIDS became an

2

issue. Most drugs, Ron tells me, are available in other countries without prescription. So is Isoprinosine. The medicine is not a cure, however, and it's not expected to be. But there is hope it could be a stabilizer of sorts -- like insuline for diabetics. It used to be available in Mexico, at $2.75 for a bottle of thirty pills. Now, young men from Texas and California bring the medicine back illegally: $25 a pill on the streets of San Francisco.

Ron is part of a "double-blind" research project. Half the test patients get the drug; the other half get a placebo. Neither doctor nor patients know who gets what. That's a necessary part of fair testing.

Tuesday night, Ron answered a call from a desperate father. PLEASE help me get Isoprinosine for my son, the father begged him. PLEASE put him into your program.

It doesn't work that way. The drug isn't yet approved here, and it can't be until the research is complete. The testing must, of necessity, include controls. Ron's answer to the father was, reluctantly, no. He could offer the man only his prayers.

Chapter 2:
"Cliff" - Whose Lover Has AIDS

As I began to send articles about AIDS to readers on the computer network, they began to write back with their own suggestions for interviews. A reader in Washington, D.C., for example, arranged for me to meet her friend who lives and works in New York City.

I had still not actually met a person with AIDS. But I was beginning to learn about the disease from people who had. "Cliff" agreed to speak with me provided his identity remained a secret. Here are the reports of our conversations.

June

He is an executive of a New York bank, and "Cliff" is not his real name. He will share the experience of learning that his lover, "Aaron," has AIDS.

We sit in Cliff's office at the conference table where he helps run a megastructure. I type into my portable computer as he answers my request for background. He manages the information calmly, a steady unspooling of the past.

Both men are in their late thirties. Cliff describes himself as has having been "sexually promiscuous" by his own standards until six years ago — three or four years for Aaron. They've been together for two years, living in separate but nearby apartments.

Aaron has been gay since college, Cliff "since eleven". He laughs at himself, and at the definitiveness the young age betokens. He has a silvergray moustache, rich charcoal hair, and clear green eyes. His white shirt and navy blue necktie complete the picture of a competent executive. Nothing flashy.

Three years ago, Aaron first became worried and had tests at a local hospital. Negative. His fear subsided.

I ask Cliff what their relationship was like before AIDS became part of it. It was "normal" he thinks — a few arguments about how much time they'd spend together, a few jealousies, but a strong commitment to each other after only a few months. Cliff had moved to New York from the South. It seemed in those early days that he was always meeting Aaron's "formers." At first it unnerved him, the social chitchat with Aaron's past intimates. Eventually Cliff became surer of himself and things were fine.

~ ~ ~ ~ ~

In the summer of '84, they took shares in a house on Fire Island. That's when Cliff began to notice all the AIDS stories. About people he knew in Washington, or friends of friends in New York City. Not yet anyone close. The topic began to entwine itself, ever-present, into cocktail hours and beach parties. Mostly the conversations expressed concern, but for some the tone was gallows humor. The island woods that were a setting for adventurous "encounters" began to be called "the AIDS House." *"He's going to stop by the AIDS House tonight."* (I feel a chill as Cliff imitates the lighthearted sound of it.)

The more Cliff heard around him, the more a new sense of irony colored his experience. Fire Island is celebrated around the world for its beauty and pleasures. Temptation surrounds the beach like an ocean. Oiled bodies gleam in the sun, hot music tugs you in the night. But Cliff began to picture a "death cloud" hovering over the sexual opportunities.

Cliff thinks the humor that summer was protective distancing, the mind's defense against a frightening truth. People spoke of "they" -- the danger "they" were in by abusing drugs, or by "their" adventurous visits to the AIDS House. Some men, he remembers, would express concern over an evening drink -- and then quietly head off to the woods.

Cliff and Aaron live near a bookstore. A special one, with a Back Room some men frequent for sex. He tells me dryly of the private language he and Aaron came to share. Like when they'd see a man enter the bookstore.

"There goes another AIDS girl," they'd say. They spoke of the men they were observing as "sluts." They took comfort from the fact that their own lifestyle was tamer than that at the book stores, and so much tamer than it used to be.

The disease affects "them," not us.

~ ~ ~ ~ ~

Aaron saw the first spot on his forehead. It was Christmas 1984. They both thought it was just a bruise, a foolish nothing. They referred to it kiddingly as an "AIDS spot."

5

"Maybe we'd convinced ourselves," he says, "given the length of time we'd been relatively careful. We thought AIDS was far behind us." Every time there'd be a new report on the AIDS incubation period, the men would recalculate. One year? No problem. We've been good. Two years? Yah, we're still okay. Like calculating your history -- are you eligible for the vacation?

He remembers the report of F-I-V-E years: five years ago, you might have been exposed to the virus. Is it incubating inside you now? That was scary: they couldn't count that far back with sufficient rectitude to relax.

It wasn't the spot on his forehead that made Aaron see a doctor. It was the "manifestation" in his mouth in early 1985. The first doctor they saw -- of all the many they've now visited -- was the *only* uncaring and callous one they encountered. He did, however, suggest an oral surgeon who proved quite helpful. The surgeon suggested a specialist, and generously went with Aaron to see him. There's probably nothing much to worry about, both doctors said as they took a biopsy. Did they really believe their own words, Cliff wonders. Or did they simply not want to create alarm? Aaron's resulting hopes made the ultimate crash devastating.

Cliff hadn't joined his friend for the visit to the doctor that day; it was probably just a routine sore, after all. Aaron phoned, with unclear sounds in a sea of frightened silence. Cliff left work immediately.

They cried for hours. They hugged and cried.

(As Cliff continues tells me his story so simply, so deliberately, I find my eyes want to mist. My throat feels thick. But Cliff has such a persistent dignity that I squelch my own feelings. I meekly continue to type as he narrates his own documentary.)

Kaposi's sarcoma, that's what Aaron had. Not just cancer, but AIDS. Mid-March, 1985 and the guessing is over.

Within hours, Cliff tells me, in a phase that lasted for weeks, he was consumed by a desire for AIDS information. It was the one thing he could do -- make phone calls, read articles, talk to anyone, learn all he could. At night they'd lie in bed and strategize: which doctors to call the next day, which questions to ask, should there be a second biopsy, should there be a second opinion.

"It kept us busy," Cliff says. "But nobody knew a lot."

Medical terms became the substance of conversation. At first, Cliff was afraid to reveal his own worries -- might he have AIDS himself? Eventually he noticed Aaron insisting that doctors specifically talk to Cliff, addressing Cliff's fears. What kind of physical contact would be safe, for example. Cliff noticed with pleasant surprise that except for that first, brusque doctor, every physician they spoke with accepted them as a legitimate couple. Straight or gay, the doctors readily understood the significance of Cliff's and Aaron's relationship, respecting the central role each man plays in the other man's life.

They were simply like any other couple in desperate fear. Cliff attended every session because Aaron was too terrified to be sure he really HEARD what the doctors were saying.

At about this time, Cliff noticed strange reactions from several friends. Cliff would be talking on the phone about his first biopsy, and a friend would mention someone else: "Yes, Jack had a biopsy, too. They did lots of biopsies, but couldn't save him." Or: "Yes, Herbert had Kaposi's too. God, poor Herbert. You remember him, the conductor? Died in November."

Cliff was amazed that Aaron's friends told such terrible stories in response to his reports. He noticed, almost always, that moments after the conversations, Aaron would hang up the phone and rush to the bathroom for intestinal collapse. Cliff speculates on the psychology of those callers. Maybe they actually wanted to say, "You're not like Jack. You're not like Herbert." Aaron has since learned to ward off others' reactions for his own protection. He has also learned to offer — before people ask — "Naturally you might be worried if AIDS is contagious. Well, if you don't exchange bodily fluids . . . ."

Aaron began to notice persistent weight loss. He is robust, a strapping weightlifter. But he has begun to deteriorate, slowly and subtly. There are heartbreaking mornings when Aaron feels weak. Cliff wants to say, "It's okay, Aaron. It's okay. Rest in bed." Instead he urges his friend to get it together, and not to stop struggling. An attention to bodily details is a round-the-clock focus.

Aaron: "That pimple is new."
Cliff: "No. It's not."
Aaron: "This mole wasn't here before."
Cliff: "Yes. It was."
Aaron: "That spot has changed color."
Cliff: "No. It has not. I am telling you the truth."

Aaron is an architect. They know at his office that he's in treatment for cancer. They also know about Cliff. Surely, Cliff thinks, they've figured it out now. Surely they know about AIDS.

Cliff looks away to the window as he tells me about calls from Aaron's bosses, even from people Aaron views as unsupportive. "If the time ever comes when Aaron needs time off, if he needs contacts — if he needs anything at all, please just tell us." Aaron doesn't know about the calls. They were meant for Cliff.

Aaron is not as depleted as he could be, Cliff says. "We haven't experienced the worst. We haven't gone through what many others have." ("Yet" is the word I hear without his voicing it.)

Cliff and Aaron have "gone shopping" for treatments. Aaron is qualified for Interferon treatments. Interferon is a natural substance produced by the body. Its purpose is to build up the immune system. "The name of the game is delay," says Cliff. "Anything that can stall or stabilize."

Meanwhile, their relationship has changed. Now there's more sharing and tenderness. Suddenly they say "I love you" with spontaneity. They say it much more often.

Cliff thinks about the future, though he tries not to talk about it. Sometimes he walks through Aaron's apartment and thinks how difficult it will be when Aaron's not here. They are both writing wills now. "But at moments I think, I really think, we could somehow beat this." They continue their plans for a weekend house. They must either plan for the future, or admit defeat.

I invite Cliff to talk directly to readers. What would he like to say to you himself?

FROM CLIFF: "There's one thing people can do that is so simple and yet absolutely crucial. That is, to treat AIDS patients like any one who is ill. With compassion. With concern. In effect, say, 'You, like any other sick human being, or or any other person in need of help, you are worthy of your need being acknowledged.' I have been struck by how helpful it's been to have people in my office, even people I know just casually, acknowledge they know it's difficult for us, that the sickness and our fear needn't be hidden. One of the hardest things about this disease is the underground quality of it. That somehow it's not legitimate.

"It's very hard to be both sick and strong. Just simple support — that's enough to give you courage to try to face it . . . ."

July

I phoned Cliff today to see how things are going. Here's what he told me:

"We've been struggling with a remarkable range of options. They just don't go away; the information on new treatments pours in. Everyone seems to have a differing insight into treatments. We feel even more as though we've earned a medical degree -- we are drowning in information. Sometimes we're frozen in trying to make a decision.

"The good news was we were to start the treatment at Sloan-Kettering today." (I notice, and am touched by, his saying "we" were to start treatment.)

"The bad news was, the treatment would probably entail some chemotherapy. There has been so much written to suggest chemotherapy could be detrimental to your general immune system. We had more or less made up our minds not to do that. Then we learned that Interferon would only be available if we submit to the blind research protocol."

Cliff explains what signing up for the protocol means: half the test group gets Interferon only, while the other half gets Interferon plus chemical treatment. The selection of which group you're in is made randomly. If you're unwilling to take your chances with the chemical treatment, then you can't receive the Inteferon treatment either. "You can line up advocates for almost every form of treatment there is. We've spoken to five different people about nutritional methods. They've cautioned us against the medical side. We've found people who are using vitamin solutions. Others disagree with the majority that the problem is even a virus — some say it's bacterial, which means still other approaches.

"One New York doctor told us, `If you don't go to Paris and get the medicine there, you're going to die.'" Cliff mentions there's a potentially very successful treatment in Paris, HPA-23. It is not yet approved in the U.S. They claim to have had remarkable success in the relatively few cases treated. One choice is to wait for the treatment to be endorsed here -- or go to Paris, to the Pasteur Institute, right now.

"These would all be hard decisions for a dispassionate, non-feeling observer. It's even tougher to decide what to do when the questions are for someone you love. I have a feeling we're going to go with intuition and end up with a combined nutritional and medical approach. This is one of those situations, though, where the person receiving the treatment must BELIEVE in it for things to work -- to avoid ending up later with regret or anger at what you've done. Aaron has not yet affirmed any approach at all."

Cliff talks about how he has to deal with his own emotions as these choices are confronted. "On the one hand I catch myself feeling, `Goddamn it, make a decision!' On the other, I have to realize that Aaron has no more information about all this than I do. Of course I'm aware that the decision is really his life. So I bite my tongue and realize that my only real function is to listen. Not to decide."

September

We agree to meet at my apartment this time. Cliff has changed jobs and now works for a university nearby. When he arrives, it is late afternoon. I pour wine, we toast, and step briefly onto the balcony to admire the river. A tugboat pushes a barge that must be a dozen times its own size and weight.

Back inside, I ask Cliff how he's been.

"I've been depressed," he says. "I can't put my finger on it. I think it's a lot of stuff just culminating in feelings of . . . no control over what's going on. It's something I've tried to talk to myself about, and I've dealt with it in therapy. But there's an unabating sadness." Compared to

9

when I first met him, he now speaks in more cautious, pensive fashion. He pauses more often, and his voice has less energy.

"I guess I even feel guilty about my sadness. For the first time since the beginning, I've become fearful about myself. I don't know why. Maybe as I've gotten more anxious in general, those fears have come more to the surface. Last week I made another appointment for a checkup -- to be reassured, I hope. My last checkup was April.

"My anxiety comes at a time I'd have thought would be happier. We're in the midst of closing on a little country house. We're doing it partly because it's pleasant. Maybe also to say we're having good times, no matter what. Maybe to say -- it isn't happening.

"But it's hard to hold back the anticipation of loss. It's hard to push back the fear. I have a new appreciation for people who run away from fear. Myself, I'm getting the 'four a.m. wake-ups.' To a large extent, we've accepted it. It *is* happening. Aaron does have AIDS. But you don't wake up each day and simply say to yourself, `Okay, let me just accept it. Someone I care about is dying.'" This tall, handsome man sits heavily back in the rocking chair. For a few seconds, he stares at the floor. Then he has a sip of wine and continues.

"On the medical front, we're still exploring new avenues, but we're persisting with a macrobiotic approach. Last week, we spent an hour with a physician who's a macrobiotic specialist. I found it the most refreshing hour I'd spent with a doctor for quite some time. I left her feeling that, at last, I can affirm the macrobiotic method . . . there's really some sense to the way we're trying to go about this. What was curious, though, is this: previously, I was the skeptic. But this time, Aaron's the one who left the session discouraged.

"I was taken aback by that. What I finally discovered was, all the things the doctor said played to my value structure, not his. Things like: macrobiotics is not just a medical approach, it's a philosophy about life, and unless you can begin to understand and appreciate the philosophy, the diet's value may be limited.

"All of that made sense to me. I was hearing: this is a way to live a fruitful life as long as you live it. As long as it's working, you are well. But in Aaron's mind, he heard her say: the diet won't work, and this is not a cure.

"We talked about that for a long time. Basically, what Aaron acknowledged, and maybe this is one of the things that depressed me, was that for him, all our pursuits have been alternative CURES. It's a matter of chosing the best cure . . . rather than trying to make sense out of what you want to do with the life you have left.

"For Aaron, following exactly what the macrobiotic cookbooks say is important; but affirming the truth of the precepts is tangential. To me, it's only the philosophy that lets the awful diet make any sense."

"What's the most meaningful aspect of the philosophy?" I ask.

"Most of the precepts are quasi-spiritual, and very compatible with almost any religion. They begin to sound like religious values: 'The eternalness of your life is now.' Whatever is your life situation -- whether it's sickness, health, planning the future, having no future -- it's all just a smidgen of some kind of eternity you have to affirm. You have to believe in 'now' in order to make sense of the limited time you have on earth, eighty years or only two.

"That sort of thinking leads them to say: make good use of your time, whatever you do. Have a diet that lets you to be well while you're here. It's the philosophy that actually gives you the peace. Otherwise, your mind is racing: am I better, am I getting well, how am I today? Worrying is not a peaceful way to live, regardless of what you're doing for yourself.

"In many ways I think Aaron is missing one of the principle benefits. Were he on chemotherapy and being sick or weak a great deal, he'd have all the same mental anxieties. But now he's not getting the mental benefit of avoiding all of that stuff. I think that's what this doctor was trying to say to us."

Two birds fly by outside, past the large glass door to the balcony. Steam from the Con Edison plant next door creates a mist that almost obscures the top of the United Nations. The birds fly into the mist and out of my view.

"Tell me, Cliff. Have you decided just to get the most value out of the macrobiotic approach and stop there?"

"That's basically what we're doing. The macrobiotic doctor told us that some of hospitals in Boston are taking a very aggressive chemotherapy approach to AIDS. But their patients are living the shortest length of time of any AIDS patients in the country, averaging between six and eighteen months. The more moderate chemotherapy people are living longer, she says. Nobody's really monitored people who are doing nothing, or macrobiotics. She's convinced that the patients who've chosen macrobiotics are doing better, and for longer. With chemotherapy, she says, you're treating a poison with a poison.

"Maybe things right now are as good as they can be. Aaron basically feels well off. He's going to work. Nothing has changed, other than the fact that he's lost nearly forty pounds in six weeks. He's down to 155 and he's 6' 1". Right now, it looks okay -- real thin, but attractively thin. If you saw him for the first time you'd say, this is a very slender and generally well-proportioned person. But if you had seen him in May, at 190 . . . . We were afraid the weight loss was AIDS. But the doctor says, people often lose that kind of weight on a macrobiotic diet."

I am curious, so I ask him: "What do other medical doctors think of macrobiotics?"

11

"They won't come out and say its crap," he tells me. "They're smart enough to say they don't know. The better ones say that diet and nutrition are very important, even if they don't think eating seaweed is necessarily any better than eating zucchini. The doctors at Sloan-Kettering were afraid the diet would alter his basic system so as to hurt his response to chemotherapy, if we try that later.

"It's a checker board. People are all over the place. Hardly any doctor will put down nutrition, though. We've been on it for two months. He's had no new lesions for two months. Two months, if you have a two-year life sentence, is a long time. He still feels basically well."

"What about you?" I ask him. He turns to face me straight on.

"When I started this, I envisioned myself as a terribly sufficient person, who could bolster, encourage and assist someone I care about, even in the face of death. Be the good provider. Now, I'm more inclined to say . . . I probably can't do all that. I'm becoming more realistic. I can offer physical, psychological, emotional, and financial support. But I can't make his life come to a nice neat package in the end, if there's going to be an end. I can't do that for him.

"In some ways, I'm measuring how good I can feel about myself by how Aaron feels. Maybe I've made it a goal to help him achieve acceptance because it's so hard for ME to accept. I don't want him to come to an end. However much I put things into the context of 'eternal energy' or any other metaphor that makes people feel better, the bottom line is: there's be a big big void with death. And it doesn't get filled."

It is starting to get dark, and I know Cliff's about to leave.

"I will be very sad to lose him," he says.

"Privately," I ask him gently, "do you ever think, just to yourself, about what you'll do afterward?

"Yes," he says. It is almost a whisper. "And that's why I feel so guilty."

Chapter 3:
Dr. Grossman -
Hospital Visit in July

This is a report of my first hospital visit with Dr. Grossman -- and a followup report on "Daniel" and "Philip," the two AIDS patients I met that night. Biographical details have been disguised, but the spirit of the encounters is accurate.

(JULY 18, 1985) As I've now come to expect, Dr. Grossman is late. We were to meet at 7:30. When he finally calls, it's after 9:00. I enter the dry, hot stillness of his darkened office. The air conditioner's been completely broken all day, he says.

Dr. Grossman sits at his receptionist's telephone. He gestures me in from the waiting room to the small circle of light where he sits with files and notepaper. He is careful not to mention patient names, and I listen as he finishes his phone calls:

An AIDS patient. The man answers the phone and hears good news -- his lover has tested *negative*. Ron speaks with the lover also. "You be his good right hand now, okay?" They agree to regular re-testing, every six months.

Next, a pre-AIDS case of facial shingles. Ron assures the man that an eye specialist predicts there'll be no vision complications. The blistering sores and swelling are just the latest in a series of problems: herpes, anal fissures, more. "Is this just going to continue?" the man asked Ron recently. The patient is only beginning to accept the pattern of what it means to have his immune system weakened.

Now a non-AIDS call, to a seventy-seven year old man in the hospital. He may shortly be having the same surgery as President Reagan's. The man has been quite depressed lately. Ron jokes with him about White House fame and is pleased to have made the patient laugh.

Last, a "newly diagnosed probable AIDS," a young man who learned of his condition in Ron's office this morning. "There's no reason for my call," Ron says, "other than to hear your voice."

It is after 9:30 when we leave for the hospital.

~ ~ ~ ~ ~

The first of two visits is to Bellevue Hospital Medical Center. It's the very same Bellevue featured in the late-night 1930's movies. We head through humid night to the newer, high-rise wing.

Dr. Grossman says that Daniel, a thirty-one year old bartender, has an advanced case of Kaposi's Sarcoma (KS) and may not live more than another week or two.

"Are you sure you're up to this?" he asks me. I tell him yes, with a speed and certainty I don't examine. I have never seen an AIDS patient, and I do feel apprehension, although not for my health. I'm now confident and well-informed enough not to worry because, of course, there'll be no transfer of bodily fluids. I do fear facing someone with no prospect of rescue from death. And I'm afraid of my own fear.

"I worked in a hospital in college," I say to Dr. Grossman. "You'll see, I'll be fine." We walk through a garish lobby. Doors and carpets are color-coded to facilitate directions. ("Walk to the purple door.") All signs are in English and Spanish. We pass through the Bellevue Emergency Room. It is teeming with people on stretchers. They slump in chairs like listless students. They lean against walls. They stand in shadows. Nurses cluster by the command center, shoppers at a crowded summer fruit stand. We hurry through the living painting.

Into the new wing -- hard flourescent squares over colorless walls and carpet. Here and there a smudge, but mostly nothing. There is not one picture or plant in the drabness of the corridor.

"This is a city hospital," Ron explains. "Almost anyone can gain admittance here. Don't be too hard on it, Michael. There needs to be a Bellevue in this city." We come to Daniel's room. I wait outside until Ron confirms I can enter.

I don't know what I notice first. Maybe the irregular, multi-purpled spots that crowd Daniel's arms, legs, and face. Or his smile, sweet and cordial. Or the horrible thinness of his legs and arms. He sits on the bed like a starving Ethiopian symbol. I shake his meager hand. I see the edge of his undershorts under the hospital gown, exposing thighs like blotched and narrow fenceposts. With embarrassment, I note I can glance directly behind Daniel at the patients in the room next door, through large glass panels just above his bed. There is no privacy. Daniel's room was formerly an Intensive Care Observatory.

He complains about an attending physician who failed repeatedly to install the intravenous line now bandaged to his arm. The doctor missed six times. "With YOUR beautiful veins?" Ron asks softly. He holds Daniel's hand in his own. Daniel says with pride that he refused to let the doctor hurt him one more time. An oncology nurse -- "oncology",

I learn, means the study of tumors -- asked Daniel gently if she could use a "butterfly" (a tiny needle with stabilizing "wings.")

"We can try," he told her. She immediately succeeded, to Daniel's relief. The doctor left with a huffy warning that the needle might fall out. While Daniel talks I notice a mouse that skitters from bed to guest chair. Dr. Grossman catches my glance and sees it too. Daniel makes a friendly, clucking sound to the scampering creature.

"He looks well-fed," says Ron. We laugh as though at a cocktail party. Daniel talks with a definite southern accent -- about his mother who's come up to be with him, about the friend who visits daily, about help from a Medicaid payment of $2,500. "Now I can pay some bills, like back rent and electricity."

He is positive and upbeat, even when he talks about the sore now growing inside his penis. He speaks glowingly of the impressive atmosphere at the N.Y.U. Hospital next door, where he recently went for treatment. Dr. Grossman urges him to speak up if he has any trouble urinating. A catheter might ultimately be called for.

I'm self-conscious, at the end of our visit, when Dr. Grossman and I wash our hands at the sink in Daniel's room. I'm sorry we need to wash after contact with Daniel.

"Oh. There's a roach here too!" says Dr. Grossman at the sink.

"That's Harry," Daniel says brightly.

~ ~ ~ ~ ~

Much later, over dinner, Ron tells me more about Daniel. "I don't think he'll leave the hospital," he says. "The pneumocystis will overwhelm and kill him."

"Does he realize that?" I ask.

"I tried to talk about death once," Ron answers. "What he really wanted to talk about was pain. I promised him the actual pain will be minimized. As you saw, he was far more critical of an inept doctor than of his own condition. That schmuck doctor had to add insult to injury by coming in to criticize the successful IV the oncology nurse had established.

"Daniel is a classic case, the ultimate classic. He is wasted. He is riddled with KS internally and externally, with constantly recurring pneumocystis pneumonia. He has a classic no-win situation: the chemotherapy for KS further damages his immune system, and that allows infection. But if we halt the chemotherapy to treat the infection, the KS lesions go on the rampage. So it will go. Until finally, one of the infections will find him in no position to fight it off. He will die of organ failure, from infection or tumor."

Both of us are thinking about the mouse. "The mouse has an

15

endless supply of food," Ron observes. "He probably knows how to go to the toilet and drink. He looked healthy. Did you notice? There was not a hint of despair, pessimism, or depression in Daniel. Nor did he engage you in any dialogue about how he may have gotten here, about meaning or philosophy. His focus is entirely the NOW."

~ ~ ~ ~ ~

We leave Bellevue and head up Second Avenue to N.Y.U. Ron regrets he can't show me their advanced medical equipment at this hour of the night. "Dr. Grossman," he says, identifying himself to the security guard. "Just one of my usual late night calls." The guard nods in recognition. It's almost 10:30. We pass a glass-walled booth with dozens of TV monitors and computer sensors. The decor, the plantings, the texture of the carpet are all many levels richer than at Bellevue. I see why Daniel was impressed with his day trip.

Outside Philip's door is a large yellow trash can on a cart. "DISPOSAL" is printed on it. "Yellow is the accepted code color in New York City," Ron tells me. "That means AIDS, and appropriate precautions." As I wait outside for Ron to clear my visit, I look down the long corridor and am saddened to see four yellow rigs at other doorways.

"Come in, Michael," Ron says to me. I enter to shake the hand of yet another extremely thin man in his early thirties. He is lying flat on his back. His right arm is bandaged; he extends his left to me with an apology.

His room is different altogether from Daniel's at Bellevue. It could be a luxury motel with a spartan designer. I realize when Philip speaks that he is vastly unlike Daniel -- culturally, educationally, experientially.

"Philip is a world class expert in classical drama," Dr. Grossman tells me. He is also a personal friend. They talk together about the famous institution where Philip teaches and directs. They mention theatrical personalities whose names you would instantly recognize, people who work with Philip directly, who respect his talent and knowledge.

I learn that Philip has suffered an unusual case of arthritis despite his young age, and also extreme anemia. He recently experienced a rare tumor — Burkitt's lymphoma — normally found in Africa and hardly seen on this continent. The tumor had swollen on Philip's stomach and was literally, they both assure me, the size of a watermelon. Ron gently lifts Philip's nightshirt and shows me where the growth used to dominate: now the soft hill on the man's fair skin is the size of a walnut.

Philip speaks in cultivated fashion — his vocabulary and pronunciation are impeccable. He is light of breath as he tells a joke

16

about the gruff oncology specialist working on his case. Philip had told the doctor that his friends think Philip is looks better these days.

"Your friends are sycophants," the doctor replied, staying in character. Philip laughs as he tells this story.

He used to have brown hair, I learn.But the chemotherapy, nicknamed "CHOPP" for the chemicals involved, caused Philip to go bald, after which his hair came back blond. His sister visited from out of town to negotiate with Philip's personnel department. I gather it's very important not to have his case labeled as "AIDS". He tells of his sister's enormous firmness: Philip has arthritis. Philip has a tumor. Don't you dare call it anything else! The theater complex has been generous. (Later, Ron tells me of another patient working for an oil company; this man, despite his badly weakened condition, is forcing himself to return to work for the months it will take to re-validate his insurance.)

Philip has agreed to let me question him. I'm not at all sure what to ask. I've been impressed, however, with his humor and affable spirit. "Well . . ." I say. "I guess I'm curious to know how you are coping."

I am startled by his reply.

"For one thing, I don't have AIDS," he says. There are specific conditions he's been fighting with success, he tells me. And he has so many aspirations ahead of him. Ron interjects that the progress Philip has made is remarkable, as is the case itself; Philip will surely be documented in medical journals for the rareness of his tumor.

"I want to write a book on 18th century Renaissance theatrical convention," he says. "There are many places to which I still plan to travel. And -- I'd like to think it's not to much to ask, at my relatively young age, to find a close, personal relationship."

Ron tells Philip that when he leaves the hospital for home, there are many kinds of care services Ron can help him locate and acquire. No, Philip says with a smile. "My sister, my friends -- I think THEY have a need to do things for me. I'll let them take care of me for a while, rather than hiring someone. They'll care for me till I go back to work."

Again, we wash our hands before leaving. Philip's room has a separate, private bath. I notice elegant brand names on his toiletries. We say good night, and he sways his left hand as we exit.

~ ~ ~ ~ ~

"Philip and I have talked at length about death," Ron tells me later. "Philip is denying he has AIDS. Daniel is not.

"We would all like to think there's some sort of ingrained human code. A code that says, if you are upbeat and positive and optimistic, good things will happen to you. Mostly it doesn't work that way. The

17

shits of this world can become successful, too. Joan Baez once said, `We need leaders and we get gamblers instead.' People who take super care of themselves *can* get sick. Nice people do get sick.

"How promiscuous do you suppose Philip is?" he asks me.

"Not very," I guess.

"You are right," Ron replies. "But that doesn't mean he avoided AIDS. The CDC definition," he cites the Center for Disease Control's widely noted standard, "is: cellular immune damage, but with no apparent source other than AIDS for it. Not damage from taking drugs, or from X-rays. The immune damage must be coupled with either KS or other rare life threatening infections. Philip DOES fit all of that. He's got the immune problem. And he has the other, rare tumor. But he's had three years of other diseases also -- Reiter's arthritis, and a profound anemia that can easily cause immune damage. So . . . is he a `manufactured' AIDS?"

"If he survives this treatment, I desperately want to give him an anti-virus. But I'd have to test him first. He *will* test positive for AIDS. His treatment so far has caused him nausea, weight loss, diarrhea. He can't walk. The chemotherapy and spinal fluid killed his legs. He can't go the bathroom himself. But he'll leave the hospital in three weeks."

"When will he go back to work?" I ask.

"Never," says Dr. Grossman. "He will never go back to his desk. That doesn't mean he won't freelance or consult. But he will not go back to his desk -- he will not be able to walk." By this time, we are in a Mexican restaurant near the hospital. It is after midnight. Music videos blare and flicker in the background. I have never seen Ron Grossman so down.

"When will you tell him?" I ask.

"After he's home. When he's plugged back into his more familiar environment. He may still write his book. But he'll never work in the theater again. He'll never again work on a show. He'll never travel. And I don't think he'll find that relationship."

"He obviously doesn't know all that yet," I say. I am thinking about how I would feel, if I were Philip. How would I want to feel. What would I want to know and when?

"You mustn't take hope away," Ron says. "Both of those boys showed extraordinary trust. They are really, both of them, managing their own medical treatment." (I think back to Daniel refusing to allow a doctor to bruise his veins one more time.)

"I am astonished," Ron says, "at the number of times that the content and quality of treatment is influenced by patients' personalities. The crusty old oncologist temporarily taking care of Philip -- his skin is a mile thick. But he finds it within him to kid Philip, to say his friends are `sycophants'. Both those boys you saw tonight have a spark within them that people respond to.

18

"I've seen AIDS patients die like they lived. Some are angry, some depressed. Some are noncomittal, uncooperative, and obstructive. People die the way they live, for the most part. There are usually no surprises. No matter. A person at that age just should not have to deal, even remotely, with planning for death."

"Daniel" - Aug. 15, 1985

Telephone Message from Dr. Grossman: "'Daniel' died quietly at Bellevue yesterday morning. He had gone home for a few days, but returned when he deteriorated. 'Philip' has also deteriorated, but is still hanging in there. Thursday next week is fine for another meeting. Much to talk about. Bye."

Follow-up on "Philip"

Two months after I met him, he's receiving care in his West Side apartment. His mother has come from New Mexico; she'll bring him back there in less than two weeks. "This will likely be your last chance to see him," Ron tells me. Philip understands I've disguised his name and biography. He'd be pleased to see me again.

As Philip left the hospital, an in-dwelling catheter was placed in his chest: a tube to insure nourishment, since he wasn't eating at the time. Before I know it, I'm hearing an explanation of the catheter. I don't ask to know about it, but a description pours forth from the doctor the way a friend might tell you about the engine of a car he particularly admires.

"It goes through two incisions -- first, a shallow incision below the breast. The catheter is pushed under the skin; it's almost painless. The catheter is sewed to that incision. Then a somewhat larger incision is made right under the collar bone. The sub-clavian vein, which is a branch of the jugular vein, is identified. The catheter is pierced into the vein, then *fed* right into the right side of the heart. Then it's sewn into place again. All you see on the outside is a short length of rubber tube dangling."

It's so easy for him to describe. So established and simple. He takes for granted a process I find it difficult to hear about.

"The patient now has a permanent, in-dwelling catheter which serves three functions. One: if you want to draw blood out of it, you don't have to puncture their veins any more. For the patient, that's not so trivial. Two: it allows you a line for live-saving procedures. Three: it allows you to put in large volumes of high-concentration fluids which would destroy the average vein in a day. Why? Because the fluid is diluted with the blood that is right inside the heart."

He tells me about the doctor who invented this catheter. There are several physicians who have catheters named in their honor.

As Dr. Grossman talks, I find myself tuning out. It isn't easy for me to picture a tube puncturing the thin, pale man I'd met . . . in truth, it isn't easy for me to picture the process on anyone. How many other people are squeamish about these things? I've worked in hospitals. I can maintain external composure, no matter what. But I allow myself mental withdrawal as the doctor chats about this technique.

As he talks, I remember -- I was eight years old, and a fourth-grader. It was my turn to read aloud from one of my favorite books, *Robin Hood*. It was the last chapter, and Robin was dying. I stood at the front of the room on that hot Carolina morning, reading about Robin's weakness, his loss of blood . . . I could no longer continue. I was dizzy and I couldn't stand. Someone else took over. I lay my head onto the cool, thin slab of the desktop. I thought of Robin lying helpless, the fluids leaving him, his muscles weakening. How could I read, as Robin lay dying right *then* ?

I haven't thought about that moment in years, but somehow the catheter explanation -- my vision of Philip's frail body -- brings it back. Dr. Grossman continues explaining the benefits of the system.

"I must have six patients right now who have this catheter," he tells me. "It's usually done for people who are starved, wasted from chemotherapy, or who have bowel disorders, which means they should *not* eat. My longest patient survived six months with no oral food. Philip was woefully wasted. He'd lost another seven or eight pounds after you met him, and you remember what he looked like then."

The nurturing fluids cost hundreds of dollars a day at home, Dr. Grossman mentions. "Much less than in a hospital," he adds when I gasp. Philip was set up with a nurse at home, an electric bed, commode, wheel chair, and other such trappings of the confined under treatment. At this moment, he's off the catheter and eating again.

I remember how distinctly Philip had told me that night, "I don't have AIDS." Dr. Grossman alerts me once again of his need to deny it.

"He sees his situation as, `I had cancer, and now most of my problems are due to chemotherapy.' He sees his situation as simply recovering from the severe effects of chemotherapy."

"He's going to New Mexico, he thinks, to . . . ?"

"Hopefully to get his strength back. To go into rehabilitation therapy. His mom has a ground floor apartment, and Santa Fe in winter is sure a lot warmer than New York!"

"What do you expect will happen, really?"

"In New Mexico? I expect there will be a limit to his

improvement. He will reach a certain level, which will probably mean walking with the walker. He'll get a psychological lift. But it's an odds-on bet he'll never come back to New York.

"Given that he does have AIDS . . . he'll get other diseases next, yes?"

"If he doesn't first just waste away."

~ ~ ~ ~ ~

It is an old West Side brownstone -- built in large scale for its six-story height. It has plenty of what real estate agents call "character," though it lacks the comfort of an elevator. The building is not in prime condition, but the block is clearly experiencing 'gentrification' . . . an influx of professionals with taste and money.

I walk up the six flights of stairs. I'm a few minutes late, so I hurry. My aerobics instructor is right: I need to more training. I can see how much of a barrier these stairs would be for someone in a wheelchair.

At the top of the sixth floor landing, the door is open and Philip's mother greets me. Surely that's a wig, those long auburn tresses. She's over seventy years old. With a friendly smile, she mentions that the apartment's been burglarized several times. She leads me past theater posters and porcelains, through a spacious living room with antique couches and chairs, to Philip's bedroom.

The bedroom walls are pink-and-white, cheerful in all the light from the windows. The wood furnishings are painted white. There is a cushioned wicker chair at the bedside. There are large, fluffy pillows, expensive artwork, soft floral quilting . . . this could be the boudoir of a highly refined prince in the south of France.

Except for the figure, like a spaghetti man, in the bed. I can't believe how thin his arm has become. I take the hand gingerly; I have a fantasy it will snap off in my greeting. How could there be room for the necessary biology in this flat, drinking straw of a human body? His eyes seem magnified in huge, round glasses. Green orbs suspended on paleness. They are friendly and clear, and he is gracious as he invites me to sit. I am startled by his condition -- sharp and raw. Bones in the midst of luxurious softness. I cover my surprise by fiddling with the tape recorder's extension cord.

"Tell me about you since the last time I saw you."

"I had more chemotherapy." His voice is round, somehow. From this spindly, angular body comes a sound with no corners, no push. It is a monotone of softness. "It's bad enough having the chemo. Eight days later, you develop fevers, the low blood count. You just feel really lousy. I was getting weak. They wanted to give me a fifth dose of chemo. I felt I couldn't handle it. The doctors, both Dr. Grossman and

21

the oncologist, didn't think so either. We decided to get me well enough to come home. I'd been in the hospital since the middle of June, and this was the end of August. That's a long stay."

"Yes, it is," I agree. I am becoming more comfortable with his other-worldly appearance.

"Finally I left with the ambulance, the porter chair, my nurse, in a parade up here to my apartment. Everything had been readied; my mother had come from the Far West.

"I was glad to be home. Ultimately I got off of the catheter, though it was hard to eat. I still had lesions in my mouth from the chemotherapy, but I had to keep up my strength. Eventually the sores disappeared, but I still have to be careful about my stomach. My strength is slowly coming back, even if it's hard to sit up. I've got to work on that. I'm feeling well enough that I'm grumpy. I can't kick the dog, because there is no dog. But I bark at my mother, and I bark at my nurse. They're handling it fine.

"I've had trouble getting good nursing. Whether that is a question of AIDS or not, I don't know, but I think it is. You say `age thirty-five, white, gay male' and they think you have AIDS. A couple of the older nurses practically did everything but wear a mask. I would explain to them that my cancer is not Kaposi's. It's Burkitt's lymphoma, and very different. But they still looked at me suspiciously.

"I'm trying to build myself up, and I think I'm making progress. We decided -- and it was a tough decision -- that I'm going to New Mexico for the winter. My mother has a very nice house on the ground floor, which is large enough that I have my own bedroom and bath. And a big terrace in the back. It's only going to get darker and colder in New York, and I'm trapped in this apartment. Mother is seventy-three. She can't care for me here without a dish washer, without a clothes washer and dryer, without the conveniences that we New Yorkers forget about. And she needs a swim every day for her arthritis.

"I don't like the idea of leaving my friends, or my doctors. But they've set me up with a well-known oncologist down there, a famous researcher on lymphomas. I already have an appointment to see him. Dr. Grossman is getting my records ready.

"It'll also be a savings for me financially. Better nursing care is less expensive there. I have to be careful about that. I don't want to go into debt to my friends. I don't want to drain my family's finances. So this will be better. I have someone to sublet my apartment, a good friend, while I'm away.

"The people at the theater have been wonderful. Naturally, their number one question is when I can come back. I think it'll take me a year to get my strength back to where I was when I got the cancer. I think it'll be late spring before I can go back to work. There's no sense in coming back here till I'm ready to do the job.

"It's frustrating for me. There are some wonderful repertory pieces I would normally be working on . . . a very well-known theater troupe is coming over from England and, normally, I would be the one to work with them. But I have to settle for waiting till next year." He pauses and looks at me mildly with those enormous green eyes. "What else can I tell you?"

I will not let myself dwell on any difference between his expectations and what may actually be his circumstance.

"Let me ask you this, Philip. A lot of people -- myself included -- hardly know what chemotherapy is. What happens? What's the experience of it?"

"It's a mixture of chemicals," he says. "They're placed in an IV that they pump into your system. My particular cancer is one of the fastest growing there is. The relevance of the chemotherapy is that it does more harm to fast-growing cells than to slower ones, so it's actually targeted to my disease."

"Now, the balance, *la balance* "-- I remember that he speaks excellent French as well as Italian -- "*la balance* of chemicals is difficult to determine. They don't know exactly what proportion to make up. And these chemicals are HEAVY DUTY." His voice drops deep as he talks about them.

"When I went into the hospital on a Wednesday, I had a rock-hard abdomen, a huge lymphoma cancer. By Saturday they'd given me the first chemo-treatment. Frankly, it was so strong I don't remember much of it. The first batch of chemicals was very heavy, to try to knock as much of the cancer off as possible. It was a 'knock' all right!"

"You get chemotherapy," I ask, "through an IV needle?"

"Right. It's dripping into your arm."

"How long does it take?"

"A couple of hours."

"Are you aware of it while it's happening?"

"Not really. It's like getting any transfusion. You don't really feel it. Then -- there's a waiting period. The reason your hair falls out is that follicles are among the fastest growing cells of your body. So when they hit you with chemicals that attack rapidly growing cells, the hair follicles automatically get affected. In the hospital, hair covered my pillow. I would turn, and chunks would fall out. Your beard comes off, too. I'd brush my face and there'd be hairs on my hands. Finally, my hairdresser friend came to see me, and we just got rid of it all."

"Philip, you mentioned a waiting period?"

"Right. There's a recovery period after the chemo. You're very weak. And you have fevers. Your white cell count goes way down, which makes you feel even weaker. When your count gets up, finally,

23

they hit you with chemo again! Maybe a different formula this time. You do the whole process again. It was at least four times for me, during the two months in the hospital."

We talk again about the reactions of people who believe Philip has AIDS.

"I was sick last fall," he says. "I was out for several weeks; it was before I had the cancer. I got a piece of hate mail from someone at the theater, threatening me not to come back. I was very upset by it. The letter said I had a communicable disease that I could spread to everyone at the theater . . . that I belonged in a hospital, not at work. And that I'd better not come back. I did go back, naturally. My boss was upset someone had sent it.

"I've had friends die of AIDS, including a department head in the theater complex. The theater didn't call the disease by its real name, though. They used euphemisms. That shows a lack of courage, I think. Unless the AIDS patient, for reasons of family or privacy, specifically requested it.

"I think it's important that people know how broadly AIDS is spread through all strata of society. It's not just homosexuals in bars and backrooms doing nasty things, and it's not just intravenous drug users. It's the creme de la creme, in many cases, of creative people. This should be known."

I know Philip has friends from Paris coming to see him tonight, and I shouldn't keep him much longer. "You've been through a very difficult experience so far. What might you say directly to people who have read about you?"

He is unexpectedly silent, considering my invitation.

"I think the number one thing that I had to do, in order to keep strong and keep fighting, was to accept help from other people. I'm a person who's used to being in control. . . I like being in control. . . I'm good at being in control.

"When you're hit with something -- arthritis, cancer, or even just a weakened condition -- there are things you can't do. There are things you have to depend on others to help you with. It can make you very bitter. It can make you resentful of the people who are helping you.

"I had to stop myself. I had to say to myself, don't be resentful that all these people are coming up and doing your laundry. That they want to help. That they're doing what they can because they want to. If the situation were reversed, I'd be the first person doing their dishes.

"That is a very important lesson to me. You never realize how many people care for you, until they see you fighting. When I finally went back to the theater . . . I would take my cane. It took me a full half hour just to get down the stairs here, these few little flights. A half hour. I could climb back upstairs faster because I could pull myself.

24

"So I'd finally get down the stairs. I'd hobble to the bus stop and I'd get on that damn bus. I'd stand -- if I were to sit, I'd not be able to get back up." He is telling me the story slowly. He pauses slightly after each step, almost resting as he remembers it the struggle.

"Eighty year old women were offering me their seats. You've got to keep your sense of humor about that. One eighty-eight year old offered me her seat. I said, 'Honey, shouldn't it be the other way around?' She said, 'I think you need it worse than I do!'"

"Then . . . I'd get off the bus, by the theater. I used the back entrance. It has a long corridor, underground, past the guards. Only staff goes there. It would take me from twenty minutes to a half hour just to get from the back gate to my desk, on my cane. My assistant offered to meet me with a wheel chair. I said no, I've got to push my limits.

"While I was slowly walking -- they could see the small steps I had to take -- the guards, guys from Brooklyn and Queens that I didn't know, they were saying" (Philip's voice sings out) "'Good morning, sir! You look great today.' 'You're moving faster. . . glad to see it!'

"They gave me every homemade arthritis remedy they had, the worst being cod liver oil and orange juice!" I laugh along with him. His ghostly pale face is alive and joyous with the memory. His eyes are sparkling. "That was from someone who couldn't move even as quickly as I could, and the mixture gave me diarrhea like nothing. But, suddenly I realized that these men and women were actually concerned with my progress. Not just the theater management, not just the actors I've worked with, not just the people you'd expect, my peers.

"But these were guys who knew I was a gay man. That's no secret at the theater. It doesn't need to be. They could see my struggle. And they could give me their affection. It was their affection . . . that's what got me from the back gate to my desk.

"It was totally unexpected. I really couldn't have imagined it. I'd thought, these are big brawny Irish and Italian men. They are guards and stagehands. They move heavy sets and equipment, and I have this refined and distant profession. I thought, what do we have in common?

"What we have in common is this: we are human beings. We were both making contact. We were both extending friendship. That is something I didn't expect. And won't forget."

We share a last, friendly look as I say good bye, drawn together by the memory he's just shared with me. I time myself heading down the stairs. It takes me only twenty-six seconds to reach the lobby.

Chapter 4:
Dr. Mathilde Krim

When I spoke with her in the summer of 1985, she was the Chairman of the AIDS Medical Foundation, a not-for-profit organization founded in 1983. By the fall, the organization had joined forces with several others, including the Rock Hudson Foundation, to form the American Foundation for AIDS Research (AmFAR,) a national organization concerned with both research and education on AIDS. Dr. Krim became Co-Chair of the new entity along with Dr. Michael Gottlieb of U.C.L.A.

Portions of the author's royalties are being donated to AmFAR in tribute to Dr. Krim and in recognition of the outstanding work this organization is doing. (You will find an interview with Bill Misenhimer, the Executive Director of AmFAR, in the Los Angeles chapter of this book.)

AmFAR's address for contributions is the American Foundation for AIDS Research, 40 West 57th Street, New York, New York 10019.

I had seen Dr. Krim -- honey-colored hair, black evening gown and pearls -- as she welcomed us from the stage of an AIDS benefit at a Broadway theater. She is often quoted in print and she appears on television discussions of AIDS. Ron Grossman speaks of her with so much respect, I finally asked his help in obtaining an interview.

"He is one of my favorites" said Dr. Krim as her distinctive accent rattled gently over the telephone. I dared to sprinkle in a few French sentences. She switched with me instantly, then glided courteously back to English when I lost my nerve.

"Is there a time I can talk with you when we can be a bit more leisurely?" It was easy to hear frenzy all around her -- multiple suitors for her time and attention.

She considers my request for only a moment. "OK, come to my home," she says. "It will be quieter."

The brick and stone townhouse is unmarked outside its discreet 1907 facade. Its simplicity is easy to pass on the sidewalk. The only ornamentation is black iron leafwork twined across the window fence. No name adorns the large black door, only a peephole.

Joseph, a big formal man, meets me at the doorway. Intricate blue tatoos scroll prominently up both of his arms. He wears a white short-sleeved short and dark pants. "Dr. Krim has been delayed," he tells me. "She phoned from Queens" (it sounds like "Kwunhtz" in his Hungarian accent.) I enter the foyer and watch the white marble floor extend to a hallway cavern. "She asks you please to be comfortable."

We walk back, back, back -- to a spacious wood-paneled kitchen. Joseph searches for spare batteries for my computer. Not much luck. I should have remembered them myself.

"We go upstairs now," he tells me. We ascend a wide staircase past an alcove enclosing some flowers. They seem almost to float in their spotlight against dusky walls. Thick peach carpet gives way to dark, wide floorboards. Joseph leads me into a den. Glass doors at the end of the room border onto a patio. He gestures me to the couch and brings a Perrier in from the pantry.

"Yes, Dr. Krim was originally Swiss. She speaks French, Italian, maybe six different languages. Her husband, Mr. Arthur Krim, is a lawyer."

Joseph isn't happy with the few old batteries he has provided. "We need them anyway," he says politely. I am certain that this man will fetch as many as I specify of the very freshest batteries. ("I'll take 600 double-A batteries, please, Joseph.") My murmurs, "I'm really fine," will not stop him now. He takes an elevator I hadn't noticed to go downstairs to the neighboring drugstore.

After Joseph leaves, I hesitantly walk back through the upstairs hall to a living room facing over the street. On a table behind one of the couches are framed, signed photos. "To Arthur," each one begins, with warm inscriptions from Lyndon B. Johnson and John F. Kennedy. Restlessly, I return to the den, with its African masks on stained, pine paneling. I hear her voice from downstairs. "Is the gentleman here?"

In moments, she has come softly up the stairs. I stand to greet her; she is shorter than I expected. Her face is pale and round, and her hair is a paler white gold. I'm surprised by the strength of her handshake.

"Please just let me wash my hands," she says, crossing over to the pantry and closing the door. "I'll be right back with you." I sit down once again and fiddle nervously with the tape recorder, breaking the silence with clicks and whirs as I wait for Dr. Krim to return.

~ ~ ~ ~ ~

She sits across from me in a chair at the end of the very long couch -- with her ash tray, cigarettes, and the fresh coffee Joseph has brought to the den. She follows intently as I give her background, how I'm writing CHRONICLE and who is reading it on their computers. I ask her to tell me something of her own biography. "It's a long story," she says with a laugh.

"I was born in Italy, of a Czechoslovakian mother and an Italian father. I went to school in Switzerland, and graduated from the University of Geneva. I am a Ph.D. in Biology.

"I married a fellow who was Jewish and went to live in Israel. I followed him and lived there for seven years, worked at the Weitzman Institute of Science. And then, uh, I dropped him" (she laughs, hearing her own phrase) "soon after getting there. I lived alone for a while, and then I married my present husband, Mr. Arthur Krim. I came to the U.S. with him, and I've been in research all my life -- mostly biology, related to cancer.

"Over the last ten years I worked in interferon research. Interferons are natural substances, you know. I became interested in them because they can suppress the effects of tumor-inducing viruses. But interferons are actually induced by viruses themselves."

She talks so readily of "tumor-inducing viruses." It seems to me that all my life I've heard, like an ancient myth, of doctors who are looking for a "cure for cancer." People joke about it, even. At Lever Brothers or at Avon, someone desperate for a way to sell an ordinary new bar of soap, or an uninspired change in a body lotion, might say with a laugh: "Try our Fresh New Spring Bouquet fragrance. AND, It even Cures Cancer!" Ha,ha. Back to work. We can't claim the cancer thing, huh? Well maybe we can do more with the fragrance.

Now I consider, as I listen to Dr. Krim speak, that what I have known about cancer is nothing. As a boy, when my grandmother died of cancer, I wasn't allowed to see her. How shielded and fortunate I have been.

What is a virus anyway? Something you get a needle for. "He's just got a virus; I gave him a shot. He'll be better in a few days." Here I am at forty, naive and uninformed. I am trying to imagine a virus: an inert bit of genetic matter, protected by an outer layer of protein. I want to have a mental grasp of these tiny bits of danger, part of a lifetime of study for the scientist sipping coffee across from me as I type.

Once inside my body, where would a virus reproduce itself? Only within living cells. Creepy thought: it infiltrates in order to prosper. I fantasize one little virus, as in an illustrated water color for seven-year-olds. Little Virus wears a multi-colored protein jacket. He hunts around and finds a cell he considers cozy. He sneaks inside.

I am typing on my computer as Dr. Krim talks of her work, and I am thinking that my fantasy -- See Little Virus Make More -- is the story of a killer. How can a cell defend itself? The body can produce interferons. I wonder if they're so named because they "interfere." They can prevent a virus from multiplying. The immune system also forms antibodies, proteins that attach to a virus to neutralize it. My fantasy now has Little Virus wearing an Interferon Chastity Belt, and Antibody Handcuffs. Color coordinated.

I don't discuss my childish pictures with Dr. Krim. I've seen the title of a paper on which she collaborated:

Purification of Human Leukocyte Interferon Alpha
by Carboxymethyl Controlled Pore Glass Bead Chromatography

That's the kind of world she lived in while I studied Shakespeare and marketing. Now her study is urgently relevant to "the disease of the decade" because HLTV-III, a virus, is what appears to cause AIDS.

Can Dr. Krim's study of interferons help lead to a cure or vaccine? Can the foundation she has helped to begin be helpful to another scientist who'll succeed?

Her friend, Dr. Joseph Sonnabend, had been in interferon research as well. The two have known each other twenty years. Dr. Sonnabend had to go back to private practice, she says, because "there was no money in interferon research." She tells me he came to see her in 1981 and said, "You know, there is something bizarre going on in my practice. I see all these young men with lymph nodes and large spleens."

"Those were exactly his words," says Dr. Krim.

"I don't know what's going on," Dr. Sonnabend had continued. "But it's something very peculiar because all of them are gay, all the kids with these symptoms. You know, Mathilde -- we have to look into this. It's new, it's strange, I've never seen this before. Would you collaborate with me?"

Dr. Krim had said, "sure." Sonnabend obtained other researchers as well -- immunologists, virologists, others. Her role was to explore whether or not the young men's symptoms were an immune reaction to a virus infection. She started to look for interferon: if she found it, she'd have a clue that a virus was actually present and had engendered the interferon.

They did indeed find interferon in Dr. Sonnabend's patients, and Dr. Krim remained involved. For two years, all their work was strictly voluntary. No money at all was available from the government. Dr. Sonnabend studied hundreds of people without pay.

"He also is a guy with principles," she tells me. "He felt he should not ask them to pay him for a study he was doing on them -- but he got very close to bankruptcy. It was draining on all of us, actually.

We decided we must incorporate into a foundation, so at least we could ask people to support our work. By then, after two years, it was getting known this was a serious situation: people started dying.

"That is how we formed the AIDS Medical Foundation. In addition to research, we began to be involved in other aspects -- human and social. Psychological, political, educational. That's how it started."

I ask Dr. Krim if lots of scientists have now begun doing research on AIDS. Is each researcher working in isolation, or do they share results? "People are doing research, yes, but actually not so many," she says. "I don't think it's enough. They work in isolation. This is not unique to AIDS. Research is a cottage industry. I've always tried to work with others, in a team rather than as separate individuals. It's more efficient, but a team approach is not a popular notion yet."

What are some of the topics being researched? For example -- an AIDS vaccine. Will it really take till 1990 to have one? That's the date I've often seen estimated.

"I think it's going to be faster now," she says. She is matter-of-fact, but her answer surprises me.

"Why?"

"Because" -- she chuckles to herself -- "I know the people going after this like crazy. I know how long it takes when industrial companies begin to go for something quickly in order to beat the competition. It's a big market, you know. We're all going to have to be vaccinated."

"In the country? Everyone?"

"EVERY-one. It is going to have to be done shortly after birth, you see."

I wonder if I'm pushing unduly, but I press ahead. "But what is really your guess -- knowing it's only a guess -- for WHEN?"

"I think within one year we're going to have particular proteins identified and cloned. It will take maybe another six months to a year to purify them, depending on their properties. But it's not going to be very difficult, because we have a specific antibody already. So I think two years from now or even less, we're going to have the first batches of vaccine to be tested."

Only two years! Not 1990, but maybe 1987.

"How long does testing take?" I ask.

"Usually a very long time. But that's because vaccines are usually prepared for use in people who are absolutely at no risk -- totally healthy, even babies. With this one, we can test on people who are at very high risk. There'll be no lack of volunteers." (She laughs ruefully. Of course there'll be plenty of volunteers when you consider the horrible consequences of not being immune to AIDS.)

She explains that the vaccine won't be available to the general population or to "little children," until much later.   Slow and thorough testing will be required.   For truly high risk groups, there's the need and, hopefully, opportunity for protection much sooner.   If not in 1987, then by 1988.

What about people hanging on right now, I wonder.   People who'll not make it even another two months.   What about people who don't have AIDS yet, while the virus quietly incubates inside them. Someone just noticing recurrent fatigue.   Or who just awoke with night sweats.   Or sees a strange purple spot that wasn't there not long ago.

And -- "What about people with ARC?" I ask.   What about the large number of people with Aids-Related Complex: swollen glands, yeast infections of the mouth, and other symptoms not yet AIDS.   "I met someone with ARC who's afraid there's such interest in a vaccine to *prevent* the disease,   that the people already infected will be forgotten. Does his question make sense to you?"

She pauses to consider it.   Then: "Yes it does.   But -- not in this case.   Usually a virus -- let's take polio virus.   The natural infection with polio either paralyzes and kills you, or you produce an antibody against it. Your own antibody neutralizes the virus, and destroys it.   From then on, you'll be protected.   You can become reinfected, but you would not be sick.

"With this particular virus, HTLV-III, it's a darn thing about it: it does induce the production of an antibody, but the antibody is mostly NOT neutralizing.   With this one, people can have antibody and infectious virus, both at the same time."

"So," I say, "a NORMAL antibody would counteract the virus . . . but not with AIDS."

"That's right," she says.   "In this case it doesn't do that effectively. For a while, therefore, we thought a vaccine just wouldn't be possible.

You see, if the antibody has no activity, if it doesn't do anything good for people, then it's no use vaccinating them."

"Fortunately -- by studying more carefully what kind of antibody was being produced, and by what protein it is induced -- ."   I am getting a better idea of how intricate her work is.   She interrupts herself: "'Antibody' is used in the singular," she says.   "But it's really a family of different immunoglobulins.   Each of them is capable of binding to one part of the protein."

I picture that protein outer jacket worn by my image of Little Virus.   It's as though Dr. Krim is searching for a tear in his protective jacket -- where a dart can pierce through and penetrate.   Or a key to unlock it.

"There are probably thousands of different forms of antibodies against one single virus," she says.   (Thousands!)   "But it was found that among all the antibody molecules induced by HTLV-III, *some* are actually neutralizing even though the bulk of them are not. So now, the trick is to find WHICH protein, exactly, induces the neutralizing antibody. Once we have identified it, we can clone the gene for such a protein. After that, when we can produce the protein in very large amounts and purify it -- we can use it as a vaccine.

"So, for your question about people with ARC, this vaccine would actually be the kind we could give to people *already* infected. Because, in this case, it wouldn't be infectious. It would be entirely safe. And it would induce the production of much more of the Good, neutralizing antibody. Even in people who today produce mostly ineffective antibody.

She, too, is telling me the story in terms of Good protein and Bad protein. There is some kind of hero -- a little Mighty Mouse character in my fantasy, with a Power Protein sweatshirt. He can sneak up on the lurking Little Virus and punch through that impervious slicker jacket. The question is catching and growing the right Mighty Mouse.

"What do you speculate would happen," I ask her, "if you gave the vaccine to someone with ARC? Could it actually reverse the illness?"

"Yes, quite possibly. I'm speculating, mind you. But, yes. Because ARC people are already having a violent immune reaction to the virus. They are probably full of the virus. In fact, one can more often isolate virus from them than from people who've gone on to have AIDS. That's because people with AIDS already have most of their T-cells destroyed, so they don't produce a lot of virus anymore.

"The good thing about ARC symptoms is that at least they show people's bodies are still responding. Some of them, you know, from five to twenty percent, lose the battle. They go on to get AIDS. But if we could give them a vaccine, even at a late stage of ARC, we could also give them passive immunization, the antibody itself. If we could produce the vaccine in the first place, we could probably also produce antibody for the ARC patients. And at least neutralize the virus.

"Our immune systems have reserve cells, you know, in the bone marrow and in other organs. It's quite possible that when the virus itself is gotten rid of -- when it stops killing lymphocytes -- the bone marrow would replenish the system." She has a sip of coffee. "And the ARC patients could eventually go back to normal."

Reversal! Not just a way to prevent healthy people from getting AIDS, but a way to undo the damage to people already infected. THAT's what this cheerful blond woman is searching for. It's one of the goals her foundation helps others pursue too. As she sits in late afternoon light, she looks like a younger and more wholesome Simone Signoret, not so much a scientist fighting death.

"You seem so relaxed," I say. "How do you do that?"

"I learned to close things out." She nods. "Once I'm doing one thing, I concentrate on it and forget about the rest." She makes a sweeping gesture, shoving aside extraneous issues and problems. "Besides, I was born with a nice round face. Even when I'm deadly worried, when I'm sick, tired, no matter what -- people say `you look so well!'" She exaggerates their honeyed tones as she says it, and we laugh.

I ask her about our government's response to AIDS so far. "I have to tell you frankly, the Reagan Administration has been stupid. What this disease would amount to was actually obvious two years ago, maybe three."

"Really?"

"Yes. From the moment you know every case you're observing is progressive. From the moment you know the disease is transmissible – that we knew even before we had the virus. There was plenty of evidence: you could look at people who'd been infected and see they'd been related to each other sexually. When you have that kind of evidence . . . . To have thought this disease would remain limited to gay men is stupid, too. They probably hoped it would just `Stay there!'" She gestures with her hand, keeping the sickness safely at bay. "Thinking, you know, `it's their problem.'"

Dr. Krim is not a slick or particularly flashy speaker. Her accent thickly covers her every word. She doesn't dazzle the listener with fancy vocabulary or image. But I notice instinctively that I trust her sincerity. Whether right or wrong, she's telling me what she really believes.

"So they missed, for example," I ask, "the fact that some gay men do, also, sleep with heterosexual women?"

"Yah, that's first of all. And what about the IV drug abusers? As soon as the first IV drug abuser was infected, we knew this thing would move out to others. Because these guys are heterosexuals, most of them. Some of them are women. And some of the women are prostitutes. So how could they think in Washington that the disease would remain safely confined?" She shakes her head and frowns.

"Secondly, I also think the Jerry Falwell kind of attitude . . . `Serves them right. They brought it on themselves'. . . those are actually the kind of words that were used, you know . . . that was very short-sighted. That attitude was reflected in the lack of strong support for a long time. The idea was that this was a disease of the underworld. . . of sleazy people."

"Do you perceive now that the government has come to care sufficiently?"

"Mmmmm. I don't know if I call that `care.' I perceive that the government now knows the public is really alarmed, and that political pressure will mount. Absolutely. One of these days, AIDS is going to hit some Senator. Or a general. Or their wives or their kids. So, now they're afraid of that."

While we are talking about heterosexuals getting AIDS, I decide to ask her directly a question about male-female transmission.

"What exactly would you speculate," (I'm not quite sure how to dance into this question) "is the transmission of AIDS from, let's say, a woman prostitute to a suburban married man? I've heard that's a way that AIDS can sneak into `normal' homes. How? -- going from her to him?"

She chuckles softly at my discomfort. Still, I'm not sure I've been clear enough. "I mean if anal receptive intercourse is the most vulnerable way a man or woman can sexually receive the virus from a man, how is it transferred, heterosexually, from a woman b-a-c-k to a man?"

She leans back reflectively to answer me. My fingers are alert at the keyboard in front of me.

"One thing our dear government has not done . . ." She interrupts herself and sits up with force. "You might imagine one of the first things they would systematically study is, under what conditions does this bug survive in the environment? Under what conditions does it not? What the public needs to know are things like whether the virus is sensitive to kitchen detergents, to ordinary soap, to toothpaste. Everyday things like that. Those kinds of questions were never studied, you know. We have only empirical evidence."

"Even questions like, how to wash the dishes in dealing with an AIDS patient? I have to tell worried people, when they ask me all the time, that I've been drinking out of coffee cups where many AIDS patients have drunk before, and I didn't get sick so I guess it is safe. THAT is the level of scientific information we have! There have been no studies of the susceptibility of this virus under conditions of a normal household environment in the presence of normal cleaning materials. That is criminal.

"OK! But at least we do have empirical evidence for four years now. We know there are hundreds of thousands of people infected with the virus but who are not yet AIDS patients. Many are people who still do not even know they're infected right now. They've been living all around us, right? We kiss them every day, probably. And -- nobody has come down with this disease *other* than from sexual transmission, or from blood, or from needles.

"That means contagion is, in fact, very unlikely. Instead, it is *direct* transmission of the virus from one person to another. That's what leads to infection, and that's probably fairly difficult to do in everyday household or business living."

She pauses to see if I am following her. She wants to be giving me a very thorough answer to my question about heterosexual transmission.

"Probably," she continues, "the transmission really requires blood-to-blood transmission. Also -- if this virus hits any cell other than an activated T-4 cell, it does not infect it. So it doesn't infect skin cells, or cells of the mouth lining, or cells of the cornea. A point of entry for many viruses is the eye. Tears are a physiological solution. Viruses survive in tears. That's important with other viruses, like the flu, the common cold -- but it's not significant with AIDS.

"This is a virus that needs to go from blood to blood. So really people must have a laceration, or a wound of some kind, for this virus to enter. You start thinking, you know -- where are these kinds of lacerations? Who is likely to have them? This is where the anal intercourse comes in. The rectum does not have the kind of defense against 'bugs' that is built into the fluids of the vagina. Both women and men could have a fissure internally that provides a point of entry during anal intercourse. It's all a question of mechanics and of tissue structure.

"But what about vaginal intercourse? Well what if a woman is menstruating? What if she has a tiny wound? A herpes lesion, you know, that oozes. That is enough to create a port of entry or transfer. What if the man has even a scratch? Warts? Any little something -- it does not have to be big, Mike. The port of entry can be minuscule.

"Therefore any form of sexual intercourse, homosexual *and* heterosexual, can lead to transmission of infection, including from women to men." I have decided during this interview that I will make a point of speaking with a female prostitute who has a heterosexual clientele, and also to married bisexuals.

Dr. Krim tells me it's clear that much of the homosexual world has changed its sexual habits. The changes will at least help diminish the spread of the disease. "The percentage of IV drug abusers who are getting AIDS is increasing much faster in New York than the percentage of gay men now. And it will increase among the heterosexual population, also. Fast for a while, until they get the message that they'd better change their ways too."

"Wouldn't you speculate," I ask her, "that the heterosexual population, at least the better educated ones, have also changed their sexual habits?"

"No. I don't think so. No. I think the better educated ones now may think twice before they go with a prostitute. But that's as much as they do. They will still go to 'call girls' because they're such 'nice, clean girls,' you know. They don't realize, of course -- yah."

"You believe they wouldn't consider the idea of a little wart or tiny fissure, the kinds of areas you say could be transmission points?"

"No. I don't see any feeling for example" -- she sighs with fatigue -- "in the heterosexual world that it's time to go into colleges and high schools and tell kid, Watch it! When I was young we were terrified, especially young women, of venereal disease and pregnancy. We were educated because we had to be. It was certainly not virtue that kept us from fooling around with the boys. It was fear. We lived with it and we learned to cope with it. We knew what to do about it.

"Nowadays, kids sleep around like crazy. I don't see any understanding that it's time to go back into the schools and say, 'Look, the sexual revolution has come a little too early. Contraceptives and antibiotics have given us the impression that we were protected. But it's not so.' Even the herpes scare has died down."

I ask her how she feels personally about the idea of tamping down the sexual revolution.

"Unfortunately, we're going to have to repress people's sexual pleasures and enjoyment, but it's a necessity, not a question of morality."

"Speaking personally, though, Dr. Krim, would you say that at whatever time a vaccine is available --?"

"Yes," she replies. "I would say then, follow personal choice and do what you please. But not now! We live in a tragedy now. I've known many people who have died. I wish medicine could do something right NOW. Immediately. But at least I believe biology has the power to solve the problem ultimately.

"And at least I feel satisfaction that the Foundation is making a difference in some way. For example, one of the grants we gave is to the first guy who noticed that there was neutralizing antibody in people's blood. Now I pray for his good health and that he continues to achieve fast progress with his work. We have not been able to give him enough to cover all his work, but at least we could help him start sixteen months earlier than if he'd waited for an NIH grant. Sixteen months is something one can count in lives. So we've been able to make a difference.

"At the NIH, the procedures are `business as usual,´ eighteen months between application and grant. They could use machines like yours --" (she gestures to my little machine) "to get answers quickly by computer, without even needing travel by an Approving Committee, with no hotel reservations, and so on."

I lean back into the couch. It is time to go. "One last question. I invite you to say whatever you'd like, directly to anyone reading this. What might you like to tell readers, yourself?"

It is the longest pause of our talk. She makes a little grunting sound to herself. She stares through the French doors leading out to the patio, at the graying sky of early evening above the East Side brownstones. Another little sigh. Then --

36

"Well, I do know what message I want to send them," she says. "I think the heterosexual public is in danger. We have a big scientific and medical problem on our hands. It can be solved, although that will take some time. But I see another problem people don't perceive. It's also important, like the scientific issues. Many of the by-products of this disease that will create havoc in this society -- come from prejudice.

"To give you an example. The fact that AIDS is associated in the public's mind with gay men makes it impossible for some patients to come out and say, `You know, I have been at risk. I am at risk.´ But there can be serious consequences of his reluctance.

"The blood test for AIDS gives false positives and false negatives. A false positive can affect one individual by creating worry that they have AIDS when they don't. But a false negative is even worse, it can affect *hundreds* of lives. The test measures antibody, you see, but it takes time for antibody to be produced. If you take a person who is actually infected, but you give the test before antibody's had time to develop, then you will not see a positive test. So you will not reveal the infection. That's the `false negative.´

"Now picture a person who lives a covert lifestyle that puts him in a high risk group. But his test is negative -- it says he's not infected. He might be infected anyway and be capable of transmitting infection to someone else. But it could take up to six months before his antibody develops and would test positive.

"If this man, say, were not worried about revealing himself, he might confess, `I can't give blood. I'm in a high risk group. I am gay.´ Or, `I've taken drugs. I can't give.´ But people are *afraid* to reveal themselves. They're afraid of repercussions because of society's prejudice. So they might go ahead and feel forced to give blood. Or they might have sex and put others at risk. Take an office, for example. Where the boss comes around and says, `Everybody is going to give blood tomorrow.´ A man might do it not because he wants to, but because he's afraid for his reputation and job if he identifies himself as being gay or bisexual.

"He's afraid because there is prejudice. Do you see the chain? I think the problem of AIDS cannot be solved in its entirety, or at least will be solved later, because of prejudice that makes people hide. If we really want to solve AIDS, we have to solve the political problems too. To create a climate that is not prejudiced. To give people their civil rights, their human rights, so they won't feel afraid.

"It's as simple as that. It's a link I see every day."

I want to be very sure of what she is saying. "You're certain, are you," I ask her, "that -- given what you know about the test -- some blood *is* being given that we think is okay, but it's actually not?"

"Oh, yes. It MUST be that way."

"Because the test is not 100% perfect?"

"That's right. No test is perfect. This test is quite sensitive, it's a good test. But it has a certain threshold, below which it doesn't measure anything. And that's in addition to the timing issue, the fact that antibodies may not yet have been produced at the moment the test is given. This is a new infection and it is spreading very fast. The number of reported AIDS cases is doubling, so the spread of infection is also doubling each year.

"Since there is exponential growth, it means half the people infected today were infected within the last year. Developing antibody takes from weeks to months. So there are plenty of people you could test who do not yet have enough antibody to test positive. The numbers must be very large. And if the infected blood is used for the preparation of a blood product, it is pooled with many other blood donations. It can affect hundreds of other lives.

"If prejudice prevents people from admitting they're at risk, from admitting that they shouldn't give blood or even from having non-"safe sex," then we should stop the prejudice! Tell that to your readers for me."

I assure her firmly: I certainly will.

Chapter 5:
Jenny - A Theater District Prostitute

As I and everyone else learned more about AIDS, the possibilities of heterosexual transmission of the virus became a much more frequent media topic. There was increasing evidence that anal intercourse could be especially dangerous, because of the access it can provide for virus transmission right into the blood stream. Dr. Mathilde Krim, however, had stressed that any sexual intercourse could conceivably transfer the virus, including from females to males. I decided to interview a female prostitute.

SCREW" is a newspaper containing several dozen pages of ads, many with explicit photographs, of female (and some male) prostitutes. The women are called "hostesses," "models" and "escorts." It is harder than I expect to find an interview.

One woman I call has already given me her address. A luxury, high-rise building in the east 20's. She recites the rates for the six girls who work there: "$80 for French, Swedish, Straight, 69, Deep Throat, and an extra $20 for Greek." It is "Greek" -- anal intercourse -- that I'm particularly interested to talk about. I tell her the reason I'm calling.

"We all have families, and none of us wants to interview!" says the receptionist, "not even anonymously." She slams down the phone.

At another East Side address, my request seems amusing. With calls from other clients ringing in the background, I hear several women giggle at the idea of this journalist, wanting to talk about Greek.

"Wanna PARTICIPATE in some Greek?" asks the voice, laughing hard on the phone. "Come by and see what happens, honey!"

I call another number. The ad's headline:

GREEK SEX
24 hours

is accompanied by a photo of a naked woman, her behind very prominent to the camera. She bends over, and her breasts hang down lavishly. Her forehead and hair are just visible behind them.

I Like It

Up The Rear

Or Anyway.

Call

ANGELA

By now I realize that "Angela" is really a group of women working together at one address. This one is in the Times Square area, right across the street from a Broadway theater. Not as elegant a neighborhood as the earlier places I've telephoned -- but here they're at least willing to have me interview someone.

"It's a special request. You'll pay accordingly, right?" I assure her I understand. "Then come on over anytime. We've got plenty of girls who fit the bill."

~ ~ ~ ~ ~

Park Avenue is almost deserted on this Saturday afternoon. The office towers are empty. The hot dog vendors are elsewhere. I walk west, past the Newsweek building, NBC News, Time-Life, McGraw-Hill. The icons of media stand tall above the empty lanes of concrete.

New York clusters itself into mini-neighborhoods. Soon I'm on a street with six or seven music stores that tightly face each other. Electric guitars crowd window after window. I'm only a few blocks west of Park Avenue but it's a totally different universe. I approach Times Square and the traffic around me bustles. Signs on marquees display gold and red "flames" -- for HOT steaks on one corner, for HOT sex movies on another.

I cross Broadway and reach the address from the ad. The theater audience is just leaving the matinee across the street. I ring the bell; a buzzer unlocks the door. Up the gray, narrow steps with faded carpeting to a gray, chipped door with a two peepholes.

"Just a minute, hon."

The room I enter is red, with low benches and chairs. Seven or eight women sit around it, as in a crowded steam room. Someone removes a purse from an empty chair and nudges me into it. I am trying to project a friendly safety. I feel a tension between my early training ("A polite gentleman doesn't stare") and the fact that these women are on display, quite prepared to be scrutinized. Each is doing her best to be chosen.

"Are you going to pick someone?" asks a blonde in pink lingerie. A wispy orange shawl is draped across her body. I notice through a fuzz of anxiety the attractive jet-black woman on my left, a Hispanic on my

40

right, and three or four other faces staring at me from across the room. A tall black woman in curlers, high heels, and a bathing suit enters the room.

"You're the one I talked to?" she says. "These are my friends. We want your book to be real successful. So pick somebody and start chapter one!" I realize now, she thinks my talk of a book is just another gimmick.

"Well . . . ." I'm nervous at the thought of selecting. I remember when I was one of the last ones chosen for a baseball team at, what, the age of nine? The blonde woman who first spoke to me has a nice face and an interesting, husky voice. I could imagine a suburban executive choosing her. "Maybe we could start," I say, nodding in her direction. "And go from there."

"Ah, The Prologue!" exclaims the woman in curlers. "Okay you two." The blonde is plainly happy I chose her. She stands and leads me down a corridor to a small windowless room with green plaster walls. There is one large lamp on a simple table, and the dwindling remains of a roll of paper towels. The lamp base is purple, the bedspread is purple, the carpet is purple. The ceiling is green with areas of white, where the plaster has been repaired. Two paintings of reclining nude women are near the bed, along with two large mirrors on other walls. That is the room.

"Make yourself comfortable," she tells me. "I'll be right back."

"I'm really here only to talk with you," I say.

"Fine. But make yourself comfortable." She leaves the room. I plug in the tapecorder, slip off my sandals, and sit on the bed. There is no chair. I set the recorder as discreetly far away on the nighttable as I can and stretch the microphone back onto the bed. The blonde comes back into the room.

"You're not comfortable," she says.

"Yes I am."

"No. I mean `Birthday Suit Comfortable.'"

"But --"

"Those are house rules. We can't go any further until you're `Birthday Suit Comfortable.' I'll explain it all to you after you do it. I promise I'll be honest for your interview."

"Okay," I say. "I understand. In that case, just give me sixty seconds. I'm all set to talk with you." She leaves again. I quickly strip, tucking my wallet into the bag in which I carried my tape recorder. I am consciously not listening to whatever I'm feeling. Whatever my concerns or anxieties, I will not let them get in my way now. I sit, an embarrassed Buddha, cross-legged on the bed. The microphone extends out on the bedspread like a -- she enters the room.

41

She sits across from me on the bed, glancing quickly at my genitals. Soon I can see she understands: I am genuinely and earnestly just here to talk. She explains it's really important that I'm naked. If I were a police officer, it would be harder for me to "bust" her that way.

"An officer could come in here and have a session and *still* bust you. If they have a badge on, they can bust you. So you get him naked first -- no badge, no nothing." She's become nervous as we've talked about cops and busting. "I want to see some identification," she says suddenly, concerned that I'm really a policeman. I've brought the April, 1985 *Portable 100* magazine, just in case. There I am on the cover, typing something about Reagan's Inauguration in front of the Capitol building in the freezing cold. The photograph makes her happy, and she visibly relaxes. She lets the orange drape slide away from her body and I see -- can it be? She is pregnant! She sees me staring in surprise at her swollen belly.

"I do `Mother's Milk Sessions,'" she explains, to my total surprise.

I can envision the answer, but I ask, "What is that?"

"Mother's milk, right from the breast, along with Oral-Manual Release." She says the words with only a hint of timidity. Mostly it's as though she's talking about manipulating an automobile latch under the hood.

"How long are you . . . um, when are you due to have your baby?" Clearly, of the two of us, it is I who feel more awkward.

"January," she says. I calculate -- she's about six months pregnant.

"And . . . how long are you going to be doing this? How close to the time you actually have your baby?" I try to keep the shock out of my voice, as varied thoughts swirl through my mind. I am wondering if I've made a mistake in choosing her -- how atypical will she be? How experienced was she prior to being pregnant?

I'm also struck at how unprepared I was for her current specialty. You begin to think, after twenty years of living in New York City, that you're sophisticated, confident in your knowledge. My surprise makes me wonder: how many other habits there are, sexual and otherwise, that human beings share and of which I lack even an inkling? Plenty, I suppose. My erstwhile business trips to Japan and Korea, those cherished vacations to Tahiti, Granada, Egypt -- I'd developed a pretense of being a Traveler, remarkably open and cosmopolitan. But here, mere steps away from Popeye's Fried Chicken, are the Mother's Milk Sessions I never imagined. $100 a half hour, including tip.

"I'll do it as long as I can," she says. "That's why I don't have intercourse right now." She asks for the $100 before we go further with conversation. "This is more like an airplane ride than a restaurant," she says. "You pay before getting the service. I could give you a big pack of lies for $10, but I won't. If you pay me in advance and give me the full $100, I'll tell you absolutely anything you want."

"How long have you been working at this?" I ask her, wanting to be sure I've made a wise choice.

"Four years. I did all kinds of things in this business before I was pregnant." I am feeling like Jack in the Beanstalk, trading money for the brightly colored beans. But I agree.

"I'll be back in two minutes," she says. The thin door creaks, then slams behind her. I sit alone in the box of green and purple.

~ ~ ~ ~ ~

Her name is Jenny and she's from upstate New York. She says she's twenty-three; I would have guessed thirty. She laughs with a nice, throaty giggle when I ask about her hair. "The real stuff," she says, delighted. She fingers the luxuriant blondeness. It's swept dramatically to the right side of her face, a Las Vegas nightclub look. She wears a large, blue plastic barrette. The hard, child's blue is incongruous with her fair skin and gauzy pink and orange outfit. She has deep brown eyes. "I started at nineteen."

"Four years, then," I say. "How did you get into this?"

"I started off on, like, drugs. I was having some heavy emotional problems, and I got into drugs. I started turnin' dates, to buy the drugs. When I got off of drugs, I was already used to the money. I have a kid who's five. My son has everything. That's because I work doing this, and I make good money. Once I found I could make this kind of money, I kept doing it. I take a couple months rest now and then."

"What kind of drugs were you on?" I ask her.

"I was doing heroin."

"At nineteen? How'd you get into heroin?"

"Oh, I was in the wrong environment. Upstate, just the wrong people. I had a friend who -- her old man used to sell it. She used to turn me on, you know. One snort, then another. You don't have to inject it. It's like the best drug in the world, I still believe it. Because it's like a reallllly floating feeling. It shuts off all your emotions, and I had a lot of things on my mind where I didn't want to think about anything. So it was just getting high, getting high."

"How did you get off it?"

"I had a good friend who was on it at the time. He did `rehabs' and all that, and he got off it. Then he locked ME in a room for three days. I went cold turkey. I just stopped.

43

"Until then, I was losing lots of friends. Nothing mattered to me. I was almost getting to the point where I didn't care about my son. My mother had him. I was holding down a job, miraculously, but I was not working to my potential." She speaks with no irony about working to her potential.

"How did you first find customers, when you started this?" I gesture to the room around us.

"I used to -- in the town I lived in, it's like really obvious. The main street is only about ten blocks long. So if a man was looking for a girl, he'd ride up and down the street. If he saw you walking by yourself, he'd stop and talk to you. Either that or a local bar."

"And how long have you been here?"

"I've been working for these people for three years now. Not at this location, but for this specific enterprise."

"Do they have more than one location?" Visions of Burger King come to mind.

"Well, no, not exactly. They had another place on the east side that got busted. Then they moved the operation over here." Busts happen when customers complain, she tells me. If enough customers complain, the police feel they must do something.

"What's the typical reason a customer complains?"

"If he's not satisfied with what he got for what he paid. If he didn't get enough. Or, some particular women steal from the customers -- they might complain then. That doesn't happen often though. More likely, he's just not satisfied. Maybe a girl charges $150 for a half hour and only jerks the guy off. So he'll complain."

She shifts heavily on the bed and touches her stomach. "Who is the father?" I ask her.

"My boyfriend. I could be married to him, but I don't feel right about marriage just now, even though I'm having his child. Marriage is totally different.

"He doesn't like it, my doing this. I didn't meet him here. I met him down in Miami. Down there, they don't have houses like here. I used to be a nude dancer there. He was a real playboy type guy, but we started falling in love and stuff. He didn't want me doing this no more. Before I was just a chick he was going out with, but he got attached to me. Right now he's in the process of getting TWO jobs, so I don't work.

"What does he do?"

"He's just a baker's helper," she says. I feel a pang at the flat way she says it. "He'll get a factory job too. He's not skilled."

"He wants to work that hard, so that you won't do this?"

"Yeah."

"How do you feel about that?"

"Ohhhhhhhh," she says with a light moan of regret. "See, my problem is, I'm too used to the money. He gave me a whole paycheck of his from two jobs -- maybe it's $150 and $150. But that's still only $300. I can make that in a day."

"That you can KEEP? And not give to the management?"

"Yeah. Depending on how well the guy tips me. Depending on what they want and what they'll pay for."

"So, in a typical week, what can you make?"

"I'm only here for a couple of days. I stay straight through, you know, like twenty-four hours straight for three or four days."

"And, during that time?" I ask her. I'm noticing a general flatness to her voice. She is no longer trying to get me to select or to pay. She is now simply talking about her life, and her voice is almost a monotone.

"It's been fluctuating a lot," she says. "A lot of the publicity about AIDS. Business has really been hurt."

"When did you start to see a change in business?"

"Oh -- in the last year I think. You expect some drop-off in the summer, when people go away. But not this much." My mind drifts back to margarine seasonality curves at Lever Brothers. To ceramics buying patterns at Avon. Jenny is like any businessperson, noting a sales slump.

"In a typical week, in the old days -- I used to make $1500 to $2000. The least I'd make EVER was maybe $700 or $800. All of it off the books. But that was spending day and night in the house."

"And now? At the current rate?"

"It's down, for sure. For my three to four days work now, I'm only getting $200 to $700. The AIDS thing has hurt."

I decide to establish more of a context first, before asking about AIDS specifically. "What kinds of clients do you personally get, anyway?"

"It varies really. Right now, because I'm doing Mother's Milk, I get the older men who -- I don't know. Mother's Milk, you know, it's weird. He's either sucking on me, or I'm squirting it out. They want MILK, you know. They want MILK." The intense way she says it makes me imagine the pressure of providing it. "That's what turns them on . . . the milk. Watching the milk."

"Oh."

"It has probably somethin' to do with their infancy, or their childhoods. Something they needed. So now I'm getting the older man, the man who was breast fed as a child maybe."

"And before you were pregnant? What kind of person did you get then?"

"Mostly the younger type, 'cause there are a lot of older girls here.

Sometimes young coke dealers. Some times middle-aged guys like, at thirty, post office workers." (I feel regret, hearing her label thirty "middle-aged.") "I get a lot of computer guys," she says with a giggle. "For some reason. Guys who work on computers. Programmers, analysts, executives, computer salesman. Some from out of town. Some local. I used to do my eyes different so I looked Oriental. I was a brunette, then, and I'd get lots of Orientals and foreign guys."

"Now that you look different, a different group picks you."

"Yeah."

It is basic marketing, after all. I know all about the power of packaging, and of product "signals". If the speckles in the detergent are green, you believe the shirt smells fresher. If the speckles are blue, you think the underwear's whiter.

"Thinking back to the time prior to your pregnancy, Jenny, when you used to get a more typical kind of customer -- can you define for me in percentage terms what your clients usually wanted of you?"

"Yeah. Well, I'd say about . . . ummmm . . . 50% want intercourse. Or `half and half,' which means blow job and intercourse. Maybe not even 50%.

"2% jerk themselves off. 10% just want blow jobs. And, maybe 5% want `Greek.'"

"That's 67%," I say. "What are the others?"

"They're Miscellaneous. Freaky things. Like, guys with two girls. Or, guys who want bisexual women. Or, fantasies. Like, I had this guy the other day who wanted to do me between the feet, like this --" She rubs her index finger back and forth between her two big toes.

"That was a weird one! I've never had that one before. But I've had guys who wanted to soap my feet up. Or they just want to touch your legs. I had another guy, I used to lay over him and snort his coke and smoke his cigarettes; he'd get off on that."

"Okay," I say. "Let me ask you now about the ones who want `Greek.´ You said 5%. That's not so popular, then."

"No. That's what most of the other girls would tell you too."

"What kind of men *do* ask you for that? What can you say about that type of customer?"

"To me it's scary. Because AIDS has been around for a long time, as long as I've been in the business. And anyone who wants Greek, it makes me wonder if they're not a faggot. Though most of the guys that I've had just wanted to try it. You ask 'em if they've tried it before or not." Her voice lowers, as she shares a confidence. "If they say no, you really don't have to do Greek because they won't know the difference. I don't particularly like it. I don't do it with my boyfriend, so I'm not gonna try to do it with a stranger.

46

"So far, I've only had two instances where I've faked Greek with the guy and he knew it. They'd done it before, so they were into it. They're the only ones who knew they weren't getting the real thing. The other guys, you just let 'em lay on your back, you put it in the other hole. They think they're getting it from behind, when they're really not."

"Yes."

"From that position, you can work your muscles really hard, to make them tight. They get the idea they're doing Greek, and with the tightness, it makes them come quick. One time it really upset me. The rubber broke. I always think about, if this guy's a faggot and if his rubber broke inside me. It freaks me out. Now I use double rubbers.

"Every girl's different in the room. Every girl does what she does. Some girls will give a blow job without a rubber, or do real Greek without a rubber. Me, I won't even touch his thing without a rubber. I'd say the majority of the girls, though, will not do real Greek -- unless they like it, or unless they don't know how to fake it. I know a couple of girls that really do like it.

"About half of the guys who like Greek I think may be faggots. The other half tend to be really Macho." She deepens her voice as she imitates them, "`Hey, I wanna getcha in the ass, woman.'"

"What percent of the men who want Greek are married would you say?"

"Oh -- I'd say 75%."

"Really?"

"Sure. Because they can't get it at home. Their wives won't do it. About 80% of the guys who come here are well-off financially. They've got their own money to spend to get whatever they want. If they can't get it at home, they can buy it. And they can pay extra for special requests. Like, if the guy requests no rubber, and he's willing to pay a $100-$150 extra, maybe the girl will go without a rubber." What else might she be getting with the extra amount of cash, I wonder. What else might she be giving?

"What about AIDS?" I ask Jenny. "Is that a topic of conversation here?"

"EVERY DAY!!" she says. "Every day. It's really scary. Like I said, I've had two rubbers break on me in the past six months. It doesn't matter if it's straight intercourse or Greek -- if the guy's got AIDS, and his body fluids get in me, it's the same thing. So when a rubber breaks it means I have to worry for another SIX YEARS. Because the two rubbers that broke on me were two guys who I was faking Greek with. Usually from that behind position, there's more strain on the rubber. That's when I started using doubles. So now I have to worry for the next six years."

"Jenny. The girls who don't use rubbers, why don't they?"

"Here most of the girls prefer to use them. But there are houses in New York where they do it without rubbers. We were just talking about it, about other places to work. Like in Queens where the clientele is more Latin, Italian. Those guys don't like to use rubbers. So they have houses where that's how the girls work.

"One of the girls here was telling us about it. And we said to her, `But don't those girls get sick?' And she said, `Well, they check 'em out first.' Usually you can tell if a person has gonorrhea or syphilis. You can tell right away if you know what you're doing. But you never know if a guy has AIDS. So that's just a chance they take, and it's only a $20 house. The guy pays $20 for a room and then tips the girl.

"Down on 11th Avenue, this other girl was saying if you ride by there, you can see the guys in their cars looking back and forth. You can tell he's getting a blow job right there. And then somebody spits out the car window. It's really disgusting. But there are girls who do it.

"But, all this about AIDS. I just want to say that the majority of the women who work in houses are very clean, very sanitary. We're aware of these things. We wash after each customer. Wash hands, whatever, depending on if you have intercourse with him. The publicity about all the AIDS and stuff. . . that would pertain to Street Whores. Women that work on the street. There's not as many of them as the ones in houses."

"Tell me, Jenny. Why do you say the concern is really for the women who work the street?"

"Because they don't use rubbers. Usually that type of woman is more of a low life. Probably doesn't even know about rubbers. Or doesn't want to buy them. They have drug habits, and they need the money for drugs. Or they only give guys blow jobs and they don't want to bother with rubbers. I don't know too many street girls. Because I've always worked in the house."

"Have you ever known anyone with AIDS?" I ask her.

"No, not personally. A girl I works with says she knows three people who've died from it. She's older. She's been in the business about ten years. She knows this one particular girl who was working in a twenty-dollar house. The girls worked her way through school and became an engineer, got her degree. Had a position and was getting ahead. Then she died of AIDS. She was under thirty."

"What percent of your customers come in and refer to AIDS?"

"They usually don't," she says. "I refer to it! They'll always try, about 75%, they don't want to use a rubber. So then I get into AIDS. That does it!" She laughs. "I'd say about 10% of all the men don't even know what AIDS is. They don't even acknowledge it. I had this one man say, `I don't give a shit! You gotta die one day anyway.' I said -- 'Yeah, but what a way to go!'"

"So 10% don't care. But most of them, I say, 'Well it's for your protection and mine.' They say 'Are you clean? Do you have AIDS?'

"I tell them, 'I don't know if I have AIDS or not. Do you want to take this home to your wife? This is for *your* protection too. How do I know where you've been? Maybe you're bisexual. Maybe your wife's bisexual, and she's done it with someone else and it's a whole, big chain.' Usually, they let me leave the rubber on 'em."

She is looking at my watch on the bed. I explain that the main topic I'm writing about is AIDS, and I'd like to give Jenny a chance to say whatever she'd like, directly to you, the reader. She considers for a moment, smoothing the wrinkled shawl, then says --

"It's scary, all the way around. But I don't feel it's right for the health officials or the public to link prostitutes with AIDS. Because from my statistics, I'll bet you any one of the other girls is similar to me -- as far as Greek and AIDS and rubbers and all that."

"You think your attitudes are typical?"

"Oh, yeah. Besides the street girls, anybody who works in a house, I think they'd be pretty safe. It's not fair for them to link us with AIDS. It's really hurting the business and it's not fair. Health officials can only theorize what goes on, unless they actually come here and interview. They'll never know how a girl behaves or what precautions she takes."

"You think they -- the health officials -- aren't so aware of the precautions here?"

"It's like, I think when I see a study, or statistics, I think -- where do they get this? WHERE? From the girls off the street? Or do they come here? I read once in *People* magazine, out of twenty-five prostitutes, ten have AIDS or will contract AIDS. Where do they get that figure, you know? How do they know? I just don't understand how they can come to those assumptions. They're just theories. But now they came out with it in Atlanta two days ago -- `Link Between Prostitutes and AIDS.' I don't understand how they can do that.

"I know prostitution's not legal, but that hurts! It's not fair. It's like saying, `homosexual lawyers -- you can contract AIDS from them.' It's the same thing. I can understand that a prostitute sees a lot more men, but the articles aren't noticing the precautions we take."

I decide to ask her another question. "What would you say to the wives of men who go to see prostitutes? What would you say to a woman to explain to her why her husband might come here?"

"The woman . . . . The wives . . . . It's for so many different reasons. Some men come because they're not satisfied. Some men come because they're having marital problems. If I was to say something to the wife, I would be really -- how can I say -- I would feel for her, of

49

course. I know if I had a husband, I wouldn't want him coming here if he meant anything to me. Maybe all these wives don't really care about the men who come here.

"It's difficult -- some guys just come to get a change of pace. Some guys have a lot of things on their mind. They tell me things they wouldn't think of telling their wives."

"Really?"

"Sure! Like that he's not satisfied with her. Or that he wants Greek. Or that he wants to do it more than once a week. Or, I had this guy the other day. He was really a happy-go-lucky. Said, `I just had the urge to come. I got this fantasy about my wife and this girl I work with. This girl I work with is BI-, and so's my wife. I've got this hangup about it. She's trying to get together with me, but my wife -- I don't know if she'll go for it. But I want her to get together with my wife.' He just spilled the whole beans, painted the complete picture which neither the wife   nor   the   other   woman   knows."

"Let me ask you another question." She is tapping meaningfully on the edge of my watch.

"You used to be on drugs. One of the ways AIDS is contracted is with needles. Do you know any people today who are drug addicts? And whether they're trying to be more careful or not?"

"Well, no. I do know one person who used to work for this place. She used to do a lot of work. She came here recently; she looked terrible. She was sickly looking. She had some kind of scabs on her. I'm pretty sure she was still doing drugs. She was thin. The girl who was on duty here put her outside. It was scary because of the way she looked, you know? Knowing that she injects herself."

"Do you think she might have AIDS?"

"It's possible. She's the kind of girl who would go without a rubber. She injects heroin. She injects needles. I do know she's used needles with other people, shared it. So -- she just looked in too bad a shape. Sickly. Like the scabs all over her arms and neck and stuff."

I wonder about those "scabs" -- is she talking about Kaposi's sarcoma, the all-too-frequent AIDS lesions?

"What are those scabs, Jenny? Do you mean scabs from the needles?"

"No, no. From like -- just these weird scabs. Like all over her. Blotches, like."

"Were they purple or brown?"

"Yeah. Brownish blotches, all over her."

"Why did she come here, do you know?"

"I think she just came to hang out, 'cause she didn't have anywhere else to go." I conclude for certain: the woman had KS I feel a pang for her, this thin, weakened woman -- turned away from the house where she'd worked through how many nights? Where next did she go? Was everyone revulsed at the marks on her arms and her neck? Did she find someone to care for her?

"She was just stopping," says Jenny. "Middle ground." Between what and what, I wonder.

"Ever see anyone else with those same kinds of blotches?"

"No. Oh! I did have one guy. Yeah."

"He was a customer?"

"Yeah, he was a customer. But he was a male prostitute. Oh-oh. It's 4:35. We only had a half an hour." She is chiding me now. I've had my share of the afternoon.

"We're going to have to stop then. I've run out of money."

"I'm sorry," Jenny says simply.

"But is there more you can tell me about that one guy?"

"Oh, he was a male prostitute. He just had these weird things on his hands. Blotches and stuff."

There is a clear, sharp knock at the door.

"OKAY!" Jenny calls out. It is the end of the interview. I reach for my shirt.

51

Chapter 6:
Four People Who Care

Here are the perspectives of four different people, none of whom has AIDS but all of whom have been affected by the disease because of people around them. All four interviews were conducted in the early summer of 1985: Paul, a heterosexual medical resident in San Francisco; "Jake," a gay lawyer who does volunteer work in Washington, D.C.; Mrs. Rae Walsh, a heterosexual woman whose good friend is a gay man with AIDS; Dan Bloom, a gay psychotherapist in New York City.

All four helped me begin to understand some of the human consequences of the disease.

Paul - A Medical Resident
He cautions me at the beginning. "What you're hearing are not the words of an expert on AIDS. This is someone who has the experience of a medical residency, dealing with AIDS patients and treating aspects of the disease -- not someone who knows the latest in research data."

I know him personally to be smart, caring, and especially concerned with social and public policy-setting. To me, he looks like a burly, blond lumberjack. Indeed, during his off-years away from school, he was a mailman, a carpenter, and a mill hand -- living in poor sections of Boston and elsewhere. We both suspect that his experience of being a low-income laborer adds something valuable to his empathy as a physician.

He talks about the trap a clinician can fall into. A doctor who was trained to always live 'on the right track' can unconsciously become angry or judgmental with patients who hurt themselves . . . too much smoking, too much drinking, too much promiscuity. A doctor, leading his own virtuous lifestyle, might overlook the *reasons* that lead a patient toward habits that are harmful. Empathy can be tinged with disapproval.

Paul is glad for the perspective and toleration that his own personal struggles may help to give him.

During a week on the ward of his fairly small hospital, Paul treats one to four AIDS patients a day. He remembers the first AIDS patient he ever saw -- July 1982, during his internship. AIDS was just coming into public awareness. A very young man was defined as having an infection of the central nervous system. Paul now realizes, he had AIDS.

Paul remembers what the fellow went through, receiving an unusually potent drug. Every day, the man endured an hour and a half of violent shaking, frenzied enough to knock over the table lamp by his bed. The man accepted daily misery as the unavoidable cost of treatment. It shocked Paul to see a young person suffer so, enduring agony that would perhaps have been less startling in an elderly patient in the final throes of cancer therapy.

That's one of the frequent characteristics of AIDS, Paul says, seeing someone who by all rights and purposes should be "a healthy, thriving individual, functioning in the world with no particular thoughts of his own mortality."

We talk about people who professionally treat AIDS patients. "When hospital staff come up against this disease," Paul says, "there's an enormity to it that's hard to cope with. On a typical medical ward, you don't regularly work with diseases that rip people apart. It's very stressful for staff to deal with. AIDS is such a new disease, it's not yet thoroughly characterized. That uncertainty in itself creates more stress.

"People are uneasy and afraid. They're wary, no matter how much reassurance they get from NIH that AIDS is not communicable in normal contact. Like the nurse who's assigned to change the bedclothes of an AIDS patient. She's told that if she maintains routine blood- and secretions- type sanitation, she is not at risk for fluids in the air. She is not at risk of breathing AIDS-related particles. But go try and convince her. She may feel, understandably, that she has maximal exposure to a disease that's poorly characterized. She is afraid. She is seeing her patient deteriorate right before her eyes. Someone in her position can feel defensive, worried, suspicious, superstitious, uneasy, disquieted."

I invite Paul to make a direct statement to readers.

"I don't want to get on a grandstand. Had you not asked me about this, I probably wouldn't have sought out a place to vent my feelings. But my impression is that many in the gay community are suspicious that medical doctors in general are not sympathetic to AIDS patients, and to the problems of gays. That isn't so.

"Beyond any problems of gay people, it is extemely difficult for any doctor to deal with p-e-o-p-l-e who would otherwise be young and healthy and who are under a death sentence. No matter how frenzied the doctor's efforts are to cure them, or to sustain them, the patients can fall apart. That's hard for us to cope with. They're dying on you, no matter how you struggle to deal with their disease. You cannot get ahead of it. It's one of the most demoralizing experiences you can imagine for a physician.

"Doctors like to be able to offer the hope of success, or health, or a cure. But in this group of patients, you cure one thing, and something else comes up. You gain a little ground on that, and a third thing happens. You have the little gains, but the losses are larger.

"Aside from the stress, the experience of treating AIDS is, if anything, *humanizing* for most physicans. It's such a harsh and unforgiving disease. Frequently, all you have to give is compassion. `I will hang in with you as far as we go. I will give you comfort as far as we can. If there is anything I can fix, I will fix it. Beyond that, I will care for you. That is all I can do."

"There are so many questions. Like for someone who gets pneumonia, the decision to give or to withold `invasive therapy.' It's a stressful decision. Should you make him endure a tube down his throat? Should you put him on a ventilator? What good will it do him versus the misery it will give? Are you offering him four extra days of life by 'intubating' him, the quality of which will be abject misery and discomfort?

"You can't hope to figure out why people ended up the way they have. All you can do is offer what you've got, if you have any ability to help with their problems. It's just that with AIDS, what you offer isn't nearly enough. You are . . . sweeping the tide with a broom."

"Jake" - Washington, D.C.

We're in an authentic old Washington Inn. We move past clusters of ancient armchairs to the outside courtyard. Jake selects a wood-slatted picnic table beneath a giant mimosa tree. My computer looks incongruous on the old, weathered boards of the table. A billowing, colored parachute stretches above us. Through an opening in the chute, I see hundreds of pink and white flowers, fragile tiaras. We order cranberry bread and coffee and begin our talk.

Jake is a lawyer for a Federal agency. He is thirty-five, weighs about 150 pounds, is 5'8" and looks very healthy. He goes to the gym regularly and has reduced his coffee consumption to two cups a day. (This news makes me wistful about my own lavish habits.) Now he smokes only sporadically. "When you work as an AIDS volunteer," he tells me, "you become a lot more conscious of good health."

He remembers July of 1983 when a friend in San Francisco, a fellow Princeton graduate, said, "I have KS, Jake." Jake was so startled he had to hang up the phone, collect his thoughts, and call back later.

When he eventually visited the West Coast, Stan was weak and could no longer work. Jake remembers his friend participating in a hot linguistics argument at the time, about what people with AIDS should be calling themselves. From those discussions came the term PWA's -- People With AIDS.

"Victims" is politically incorrect, Jake tells me. The word sounds hopeless. "People with AIDS do have hopes," he says "even if hope dwindles to a small objective: just to live to your next birthday. Or you hope you can get out of bed to make an omelette. 'Victim' makes it sound as if there's nothing you can do on your own."

"`Patient' isn't always good either," he says. "Many PWA's are not patients -- they may not be in treatment since there may be no treatment to give them. Both `victim' and `patient' imply a lack of control. Control is a major issue for people at a young age just becoming independent. Suddenly, they're at the mercy of a disease, doctors, nurses, and social workers. They feel an acute lack of control over their bodies and lives. There's no need for language to take away more of their own control."

After that visit, Jake eventually lost contact. When he finally called, no one answered Stan's phone. Within a few months, he learned that Stan was dead. Jake felt enormous regret that he hadn't done more to help. He decided to do something for his friend, even after the fact.

"People with AIDS are often too weak to shop for groceries, unable to clean their own bathrooms, not competetent to drive to the doctor's. If I couldn't do those things for Stan, I would do them for someone else. In his memory."

He began to learn more about the disease -- that you can safely touch people with AIDS. You can hug them and hold them and not be placing yourself at risk. He read about the morticians, ambulance drivers, and nurses who refused to handle AIDS patients. He felt the media was more sensationalist than educational, and he saw fear of AIDS growing all around him.

Jake got involved with the Education Fund of the Whitman-Walker Clinic in Washington, a health clinic with some 100 volunteers who work as `buddies' and `case managers.' Some of the people they support aren't gay at all. Some are homeless drug addicts, often black, who may at first be hostile to a gay volunteer. Sometimes people with vastly different lifestyles form a bond of closeness begun with AIDS. Sometimes a volunteer tries to compensate for family members who need to deny the disease:

"Dad. Mom. We need to talk. This is really serious."

"Hush, son. Don't even think that way. You'll be fine, you'll see."

Jake tries to alleviate the isolation AIDS can bring, but he doesn't always succeed.   He remembers a client named Michael who had "candida," a yeast infection of the mouth.   Michael could hardly talk, but he wanted to say things to his parents.   The family brought flowers and happy `Get Well Soon' cards -- but they couldn't face the boy for a personal conversation.   Jake spent time walking the hospital with Michael's mother. She was sobbing and he tried to console her.

Michael never got the chance to say, "Look, Mom and Dad, I am going. There are things about me you need to know. About who I am." Soon, with his throat disease, all he could do was grunt -- yes and no. It was too late to talk.

Jake has this message for readers:

"Tell them, it will not be long before this disease touches them in a personal way, gay or straight.   Given the spread of AIDS, it is bound to become less of a distant media `event' and be closer to home.   My experience as a volunteer has helped me grow a lot.   There is a tremendous need for volunteers. Not only with AIDS work -- but with the American way of shunting death off into a corner as a taboo subject.

"Many people are dying of cancer, leukemia, all kinds of diseases -- people who don't have anybody to talk to because nobody wants to face the fact that they're dying. If you don't feel comfortable getting involved with people with AIDS, there are plenty of other needs among those who are terminally ill.

"My experience has brought home that fundamental lesson -- all we really have is the time we have now. I'm trying my best to make the most of it."

During our brunch, mimosa blossoms have dropped regularly onto the table. I notice them on the ground around us. Mostly, they are dead ones, old ones. Their spindly tassles are brown like late August cornsilk. Only a few are tender and lush.

As Jake talks, I assemble a diminutive bouquet. It is two inches high. I mix the older, brown blossoms with a few of the soft, crimson ones, fallen prematurely in the breeze.   I wrap them into a napkin and idly put the bundle in my jacket pocket.

Two days later, the napkin unfurls and you can't tell the difference among them.

Mrs. Rae Walsh

I await her at the table for two I carefully pre-arranged: the best corner window of the Edwardian Room.   Today there's scaffolding all around the Plaza Hotel. It blocks out the light and turns the huge and splendid dining room, with its high wooden ceiling and its deep red walls, into a dim and gloomy cavern. The boards and railings outside the window obscure the Plaza fountain along with most of the morning light.

That's appropriate, I think to myself. I am about to interview a woman whose close friend is dying of AIDS. She is straight; he is gay. They are friends; he is dying. No wonder my table for a tete-a-tete seems subdued.

She'd come up from Puerto Rico to surprise her friend on his birthday. That much I know already. She returns home tomorrow and doesn't know when she'll see him again.

"She will ask for your table, Mike. She's attractive."

Mrs. Rae Walsh is escorted toward me by the Captain -- he in his black jacket, she is in tropical white. She is a middle-aged woman with her short white hair in a youthful, zesty cut. She wears a lively rose lipstick with no other makeup, no eye shadow, no liner. Her thick gray eyebrows give her a natural, unaffected look. I notice gold and silver bracelets, and a number of rings. Her gold hoop earrings are the size of silver dollars, but the jewelry is simple. Its glitter is soft and quiet in the strangely darkened room.

She has a firm handshake, and a direct and friendly nod. I think to myself, she has a classic 'sunny smile.' I like her right away.

We sit. The captain, who spotted me as a good tipper this morning, makes an extra fuss to adjust her chair.

I often feel I'm fumbling when I hand someone my business card. I think I'll never handle that ritual as gracefully as I'd like. Now, I'm struck at how easy it feels that suddenly Rae has produced, just to the left of my saucer, a light beige card with sunbrowned ink --

Rae Walsh
the   Owner
b e a c h
h o u s e
~ ~ ~
a small and special guest house right on the beach
San Juan / Puerto Rico

The tops of some of the letters reach up and turn into umbrellas. A sun rises just above them. The word "house" floats on three brown waves.

"We cater to a primarily gay clientele," she says. "My friend and I had worked together in a gay operation. That was the kind of following we had. It was the market we wanted, and we went after it with the guest house."

"But . . . you yourself are heterosexual?" I ask, confirming my information. How does one inquire so it doesn't sound so self-conscious?

"Oh, yes," she says with a smile. "But I find being around gay people a joyful thing. Maybe because they're often single. They're more unconventional than most people."

I am alert to see if I feel uncomfortable -- as I did growing up in the South, hearing locals talk about black people's "traits." But I feel nothing when she talks except a sense of her friendly sincerity.

"Was that awkward for your husband?" I ask. "Your being in a business with gay men as your market?" I'd been told that she's a widow.

Again, she smiles. "Never," she says. "My late husband -- he just died recently -- was a commercial artist, an Englishman. His brother was in the theater. Gay people don't have horns!" She laughs. "When you grow up in London or New York, your attitudes are shaped by the city. I was in Greenwich Village. It was never odd, being around gay people. It's simply nice."

I ask her about her friend with AIDS. "He is James Carlton. Jim. He won't mind my using his name. He's been on TV in the Boston area a lot. I'm here because he just had his thirty-eighth birthday. Another one of his friends, a man who lives in California, called to say, wouldn't it be wonderful to meet in New York and surprise Jim for his birthday. Birthdays, to someone with AIDS, you know, take on a special significance." For the first time, her voice becomes muffled.

"He's living on his father's farm in Pennsylvania. So the other friend, Michael Doyle, came in from California. I flew up from Puerto Rico. We brought Jim to New York, and we're having a marvelous time." I notice how readily she says "a marvelous time," and how bittersweet, in fact, the experience may be.

Rae tells me she had arranged to meet Michael at Newark airport. The two of them rented a car and drove together to Jim's family farm. "That was no easy feat," she says. "It's just out there, somewhere.

"So we pulled into the yard. His father understood we were coming, but Jimmy knew nothing at all. We'd brought party hats and noisemakers. There he was, in the vegetable garden. At first, we were just two strangers, arriving in an unknown car. We stepped out with our hats, we were blowing our little party horns. Oh, it was wonderful! He cried and just kept saying, `Oh, Jesus! Jesus!'"

I am typing steadily as she talks, but I am sharply hit with emotion. I imagine Jim Carlton looking up from his vegetables . . . to see the warm and perky woman across the table from me now, stepping forward in the farmyard with her shiny, dime store party hat. And I am thinking about Jim's father. What did he feel for these two people, friends of his son, who'd come so far, determined to surprise him.

"Jim is my family," she says. "I love him. He was first positively diagnosed in December of 1983. The year before that he'd come up from Puerto Rico. He'd been managing the Beach House with me. He went to New York to have some tests. He'd had symptoms that disturbed him: night sweats, swollen glands. They told him then that he was pre-AIDS. He later went on to get Kaposi's sarcoma on the leg.

"I remember when Jim told me. It was the middle of the day at the Beach House. He offered me a drink. I asked him, `Are you going to tell me something I don't want to hear?' He had difficulty getting the words out. He was very, very upset. Life has never been the same since."

The waiter removes our half-filled cups and brings back empty ones for hot, new coffee. "The Plaza," she says. "It may be dim in here today, but they always keep their cachet." The waiter re-arranges the tray of croissants as though for a photograph. We talk about how fast I can type, the legacy of studying English literature. The waiter leaves, and she says:

"I'd known about AIDS for only about a year. I knew what the letters stood for. I knew it seemed to be mostly in the gay community at that time. But I didn't know much more about it. I don't think I realized it was fatal. I found out a lot in a hurry."

I am aware that Rae maintains very definite eye contact. Whatever she says, she seems to say frankly.

"Jimmy had to stop working immediately. He had to sell his house, which was awful. It meant so much to him. I don't think anyone can know the terror he went through. He was thirty-seven years old and everything was being taken away from him. He's a worker who couldn't work. So he let go. It was hard for him to see the Beach House being run without him.

"Through the intervention of some good friends, he got into an experimental program at the Deaconess hospital in Boston. They were using gamma interferon, and some of the patients showed improvement. So did he, in a way. The Kaposi went into remission, got under control. But now he has a form of leukemia. He has a low blood platelet count. His blood won't coagulate. He bleeds frequently. He bruises. He's tired.

"He looks wonderful," she says. "Everybody seems to delight in saying, `You look wonderful, Jimmy!' I hate to hear it; it's so ironic." Now she does look out the window, at the scaffolding barring the view. She turns back.

"He stayed with friends for a while, in Boston. Money quickly becomes a problem, of course. I have the highest praise for the AIDS program in Boston. They have an emotional support system. Even down to what they call 'Sleep Buddies.' If you're up in the middle of the night because you have the screaming meemies -- you can't sleep, you're terrified, and you call the number they've assigned to you. Your volunteer will come stay with you, and put their arms around you.

"I slept with him and held him when I went to see him in Boston. We touch each other. We acknowledge that we love each other. That's very important. You know, having AIDS is so isolating. Even among gay people, once you have AIDS, you're not so desirable any more. For a man who has had a healthy sex life," (she chuckles to herself) "and Jimmy certainly had one -- all of a sudden you are celibate. You cannot in good conscience have sex with anyone without telling them you have AIDS. Jimmy never could or would do that. So you're suddenly so much more alone.

"Telling your family, that's hard too. His parents took it rather well. The population in their town is only 250 people! It's a farming community. Their other sons are all heterosexual. Just as he was different from his brothers in his preferences, he was different in other ways too. He's more clever; he's artistic. He paints quite well. Having grown up on a farm, he does all kinds of things. Plumbing. Electrical work.

"Now he uses his talents for `projects'. He doesn't have a real goal any more. The longer you last with this disease, the more you wonder when the other shoe is going to drop. Whenever I travel and phone home, the moment I hear any hesitation, the moment I hear a pause, I think: Jimmy is sick and they don't want to tell me. They don't want to spoil my trip and have me come running back.

"I have straight friends who've asked, `Don't you feel there's some risk for you, Rae?' I say no. They have fairly well determined it isn't transmitted that way.

"What worries me is that straight people, who already regard homosexuality as an aberation, are going to use this as further ammunition to strengthen their ideas that gay people are something to avoid or shun. One of the boys from Puerto Rico who died in Boston of AIDS, who'd in fact worked for me at one time, displayed great courage at the end of his disease. He was being interviewed. The reporter asked him, `What do you think about the attitude of people who think that you're being punished for a lifestyle?'

"He said: `This is not a punishment. We're being tested.' I thought that was quite an answer."

"There are plenty of cases down in Puerto Rico, too," Rae tells me. "It just isn't discussed. There's a large gay community. Things are pretty open. We have a section of town with plenty of gay bars. There's no question about it when you're there. Nothing official is ever done against it. The attitude is mostly leave it alone. People don't parade or

60

have Gay Pride marches. The family is the reason. There's such a strong family emphasis. It's not uncommon, when someone develops AIDS, for him to leave the country so that it won't be discussed in the community, for the sake of the family."

Of the many people Rae knows with AIDS, none are heterosexual. "I suppose I will eventually, though," she says. "One hears that it is moving into other sectors. But I know so many people with AIDS, it's hard to get it off your mind.

"In the beginning, it seemed to be striking heavy drug users, the very promiscuous, the people who haunted the bath houses. But I've known some young men -- very, very conservative people -- and they've gotten it too. So, it doesn't seem to be following some clear and particular pattern."

We are nearing the end of our time together. I mention to Rae that her gaze is very frank and direct. For example, when she'd told me so simply that she holds her friend Jimmy, and they say they love each other.

"Oh, you don't know me!" she says. "I'm Irish. That's the way we are. Feelings out front." She slowly caps and uncaps the miniature jar of honey she had chosen from the Plaza assortment.

"Jimmy, last year, sent me a letter telling me what I meant to him. It was beautiful. He said I'd given him something that no one else had -- confidence in himself.

"I wish more straight people could get involved with the volunteer aspects of this thing. It would mean so much to a young man -- a straight woman helping him could be like a mother, or a sister. Me, I can't help myself. I can't even pass a stray dog or cat without doing something about it." She laughs at herself. "I have eight dogs and six cats. If I pass an animal that's injured or obviously alone, I take it home and take care of it. It he's too ill to get well, I'll take him to the vet and have him put to sleep instead of suffering in pain. You don't know me!"

I explain to Rae that I'd like her to have the opportunity to say whatever she'd like to the people reading this interview. She looks at my fingers, poised on the portable computer. Then she says, looking right at me:

"I think people should deal with this as they would with any life-threatening disease . . . and try to separate in their minds and hearts the fact it showed itself first in the gay community. It's very complex, because there are people who are prejudiced in their thinking about gay people, and now this is another potential dimension of their prejudice.

"But I've seen what the disease does. I've seen people with it, shortly before they die. It's a terrible thing. How anybody could withhold compassion and love and support from these people is beyond me. I have the feeling we will look back one day and regard those people like witch-hunters, like the people who used to stone those who were different. It's the most horrible prejudice.

"It's terrible that AIDS had to hit the straight community before people or governments started to do anything about it. People with AIDS have everything taken away from them. First of all, their health. Most of them find it impossible to work. Most are young people faced with the prospect of an early death. Many people die young, but they don't usually know it's coming. It's one thing to be hit by a bus on your way to work. It's another to spend the last two years of your life knowing you're about to die. I wish more people, straight people, would get involved."

I pay the check. Everyone on the staff, it seems, nods as we leave the dining room. Outside, the morning seems brighter than I'd expected.

Dan Bloom - Gestalt Therapist

I'm sitting on a couch in Dan's office, a second bedroom of his Greenwich Village apartment. Stacked up near my feet, like doughy lumps of paisley, are the cushions he uses for group therapy. Each patient will commandeer a soft, individual island on a maroon carpet sea.

He's an instructor at the New York Institute for Gestalt Therapy founded by noted pioneer, Fritz Perls. His practice of heterosexual and homosexual patients is thoroughly established, and he supervises other therapists in training. Gestalt therapy works with "here and now" much more than with the patient's past. Prior events can be re-experienced as if immediate. Patients notice body sensations and feelings, and learn from them. ("That is no longer an empty chair. Your mother is sitting in it. What are you going to say to her, right now?")

Dan's patients come to him for a variety of reasons -- employment problems, social isolation, unsatisfying relationships, depression, drug and alcohol problems. If asked, he never hides his own homosexuality from his patients. In gestalt's humanistic approach to therapy, he says, "anything personal about a therapist matters. I struggled with my own sexuality and now I use that experience in supportively working with any patient, regardless of their personal orientation."

Dan agrees to talk about his patients, while disguising their names and circumstances. He muses about the impact AIDS is having on the people with he works.

"People are now frightened of sex in a way they absolutely hadn't been before. There's a feeling of gloom and an ongoing anxiety about AIDS. And now more people are dying. Before there was fear of illness. Now there's the actual experience of death. People who were suffering from feelings of isolation before are finding real reason to remain isolated. No one in my practice is unaffected today."

A few examples:

"`Joe.' He came to therapy because he's very lonely. He had been `out' as a gay person for ten years or so. He was running around with a couple of buddies and they did everything together -- barhopping, movies, whatever; they were comrades. This winter first one friend, then the other, was diagnosed as having AIDS. Within weeks one died, then the other.

"Joe, who has no family, now has also lost his two best friends. He is left to bear his grief alone. His complaint is that he's so lonely and so depressed, he can't bring himself to meet anyone anymore. This twenty-eight year old man shouldn't be facing the death of his peers for another thirty years or more. He's not only facing them, but he hasn't the basic social foundation to support his grieving and his loss.

"He came to a gay therapist because in the gay community," Dan says, "because we are the outposts for those who are isolated."

"Lewis" has had AIDS since March after pre-AIDS symptoms of fatigue, muscular aches, and pains. Dan talks about what he himself feels in treating Lewis: "sad, helpless, and in terror of looking across the room to see this person for whom there's at least a 50% chance of being dead in a year or two. I know I may be watching him waste away in front of me, wanting desperately to stop the process, wanting to make him well."

Dan paraphrases what Lewis has said to him: "I've just gotten over the pneumonia and any minute I can come down with a diarrhea that will kill me. Or another bout of pneumonia could put me on a respirator. Or I can get brain fever. I look forward to the future as a succession of horrible diseases."

"What do I say back to that?" Dan asks me. "There's no response that can do anything but acknowledge that I've heard what he said."

Dan responds to my invitation to address *CHRONICLE* readers directly. "Take a look at the gay community and see how it has responded to its own potential annihilation. This community has come together and established dozens of organizations like the Gay Men's Health Crisis all across the country and world. The comunity is responding as a community, people helping each other creatively. These organizations are models for the straight community, too, in how to address the threat of AIDS."

As I leave Dan's apartment, I decide I will definitely be investigating the Gay Men's Health Crisis, given the constant praise I am hearing of their work.

Chapter 7:
"Wade" the L.A. Hustler

When the interview with "Wade," a male prostitute, first reached the electronic mail boxes of readers following CHRONICLE via computer, some expressed concern about the frankness of the conversation. However as people began to exchange messages on the topic, as a public group, and in private notes, a kind of consensus developed: it is important to be able to talk openly about sexual practices in dealing with a sexually transmitted disease that kills.

What follows is the conversation with Wade, Dr. Grossman's perspective, an interview with a client, and a brief follow-up with Wade himself.

Wade

He has sex with men for money, a specialized 'Private Dancer.'

He is visiting the east coast and agreed to be interviewed about himself and AIDS when a reader asked him to do it for*CHRONICLE*. He suggests I call him "Wade" in honor of Wade Boggs, third baseman for the Boston Red Sox. He is an avid sports fan -- football, tennis, basketball, almost everything. His lifestyle gives him plenty of leisure time to enjoy this enthusiasm.

If you saw him, I think you'd be surprised at how he earns his living. He looks like a conservative Danish athlete. He is 6'2", weighs 200 pounds, and works out at the gym five days a week, up to an hour and a half each session. He's done weight training since he was twenty-four (he is thirty-eight now.) He says his close-cropped hair is the color of Clairol's "Winter Wheat," but in his case the silvery blond tones are all natural.

Wade has lived on the west coast for fourteen years, having grown up in the east. He's made his living as a hustler for five and a half years, placing ads with his phone number in various gay newspapers. He meets clients at their homes or hotels, or they visit his L.A. apartment. Most of his clients live in California, with a sprinkling of out-of-state businessmen.

How did he get into this? He begins to answer me by saying that at the age of twelve or thirteen, he knew he was different from other boys. His first sexual experience didn't occur till he was seventeen. He was walking through his town's financial district one afternoon when an executive approached him and offered to "give him a tour." The man suggested they stop first at an office upstairs. The tour was a visit to the company men's room. Wade was scared, but drawn to the experience.

A year or so later, Wade quit college and enlisted in the Navy. He'd been bored with school and felt he could do something in Vietnam that was both useful and exciting. For classified reasons, he says, he was later transferred to the Marines. He received a high level security clearance for communications work in Vietnam and Korea. (His experience talking to unseen associates with code-named "handles" via teletype machines gives him a sense of computer conferencing, he tells me.)

Wade had only a few sexual experiences in the service, with both women and men. He didn't yet feel comfortable with himself and his impulses, but he did know he wouldn't have been allowed to do his job if he'd been labeled as "gay." After four years of successful performance, Wade received an honorable discharge from active duty and from the reserves. He moved to San Francisco at twenty-two and became a bank teller, then head teller. He felt frustrated by bank bureaucracy and by wages that were conservative no matter how hard he worked.

He quit and became a bookkeeper for a printing firm associated with several west coast newspapers. He continued for eight years, though he eventually considered the job tedious. One day he heard a psychiatrist on a TV talk show. The doctor advised discontented people staying in jobs they disliked to be more true to themselves. "If you're unhappy in a job and you have a chance to move on without hurting anyone else, DO IT," the doctor said.

Wade did it. First he took a vacation, simply to travel. Then he moved to Los Angeles to seek a new career. While he was looking for work, a friend surprised him by suggesting "hustling" for extra money. Wade's friend was now working fulltime for an airline, but had earlier been a hustler himself.

"Don't get too attached to it," said the friend. "You could grow to like the free time so much, you won't want to go back to regular work." That is precisely what happened.

Originally Wade planned to be very active and set aside lots of money. But as he gained experience, he enjoyed the ease with which he could pay bills and still enjoy leisure time. He became more selective and took fewer clients than he had planned. He rejected inquiring callers for lots of different reasons -- age, color ("yes, I discriminate"), type of sex desired, attitude. He wouldn't see a prospect older than fifty. And he always said no when a client wanted him to be a "bottom," i.e., wanted Wade to take the passive role in anal sex. "I'm always a `top,'" he says.

I find it easy to talk with Wade because he's so matter-of-fact about his experiences. I notice my mind free associating as he speaks. As I silently type his comments, I hear my myself humming merrily from Cole Porter, "You're the Top, You're the Eiffel Tower."

"It's a lot easier being a bottom than a top," he says. "There isn't as much demanded of you. You're the passive one. You can just lay there and they fuck you. You don't have to be the powerful and dominant one. It's work to be a good top."

"I always say no to fist fucking," he tells me. The music has stopped in my head. "And I don't have that many clients I've hurt."

One man, a twenty-four year old gemstone craftsman, wanted to be hit with boxing gloves. Others have wanted to be hit in the stomach, or slapped on the backside, sometimes with verbal abuse. Mostly, though, he doesn't accept clients who ask for S&M. I ask him to tell me about his typical clients. He is readily able to categorize and quantify them; I'm reminded of his professional experience as a bookkeeper.

He estimates he's had 300 men as clients since he started this business, although that number might actually be low. He guesses he's repeatedly seen about sixty of those. He has cut back this year, he says, and has seen no more than twenty clients in 1985. Also this year, he's had sex with maybe ten people he was interested in personally, maybe eight of them being repeat experiences.

Wade's youngest client ever was sixteen (he rejects younger callers) and his oldest so far was sixty-five. Usually the men are in their late twenties or early thirties. Typical clients are successful, lonely, and "married to either sex." Sometimes they are single. Almost always they are dissatisfied with their status, whatever it might be. He guesses that one out of every twenty are married to women. Some clients tell Wade nothing about themselves; others tell him a lot. "I'm not the typical hustler," he says. "The clients I see realize that." I ask him to explain.

"I don't treat someone I'm with for money much different than someone else I meet on my own. I'm basically very honest and open. Sometimes that's a turn-on to them. But others actually want to dislike you since they're paying you money."

The "typical" hustler isn't open at all, he says. "Many street hustlers are runaways or abused children. They're usually very young, insensitive, and uncaring. A lot are into drugs or alcohol. I'm into neither. They are not above board about themselves. They're not honest or truthful. They would rip a client off if they could. They'd take

66

advantage of any situation they could gain from -- money, a new car. They'll tell the client anything to get what they want."

"I'm very old for a hustler. At twenty-four, I was asked. Back then, when someone was attracted to me and asked if they could pay me, I said no. But, even at thirty-two I was asked to do porno flicks. I said no, but it was flattering. It was a turn-on to be a thirty-two year old and be paid to do that kind of work. Today a lot of my clients are younger than me, although they don't know it. I tell them I'm only thirty and that's okay with them. If they knew I was almost forty they'd die."

For the sake of discussing AIDS and sexual practices that could transmit the virus, he categorizes his clients' interests for me:

1% - Light S&M.
This client likes to be dominated, told what to do, perhaps even be struck physically. The process gives the client sexual satisfaction.

1% - Just Talk.
This client doesn't care about sex with Wade. He merely wants someone to listen.

5% - Affection.
This client simply wants to be cuddled and held.

10% - Non-Touching Sex.
Typically, the client masturbates while Wade talks about the military, about father-son relationships, pretends to be an older brother, etc. "A lot of it has to do with acting and fantasy."

30% - Oral Sex; Wade is Serviced.
"Basically, that's just me lying back and them servicing me. I may play with their butts or something, but mostly they do the work. That's what they want."

53% - Anal Sex; Wade is "Top."
"Often these are men who are dominant on their own. They're usually a top. They never get thought of as a bottom. They want a change. They may be extremely goodlooking. Some of the most macho men come to me because what they really want is to get screwed."

"Some clients just cannot be satisfied, period," he says. "Instead of wanting sex from an anonymous person, they want more. They want the whole gamut -- meeting someone, closeness, like a real relationship -- yet they also want you to stay aloof. They want you to be dominant, but soft and tender too. They want everything, but you just can't be everything.

"These days I'm taking only enough clients to get by. It's not that I don't enjoy what I do, but I'm getting less comfortable doing it."

I ask Wade to tell me how AIDS has changed his practices, if at all. He notes two changes:

"First, I don't swallow at all now when they ejaculate. Second, I don't fuck as much." He's also cut down on the frequency with which he accepts clients, and he's raised his fee. When he started, he charged $50 a session. Now his fee is $100 and up.

He's noticed that clients have become more careful over the last two years. More of them ask now that there not necessarily be physical contact. Or they'll say, "If you're going to fuck me, fine, but pull out before you come. Or let's just beat off together." Still today, Wade says, he gets new clients who do not ask him to withdraw before ejaculation. If they don't ask, he may not withdraw.

"It depends on how I feel about it also. I'm not really worried about giving it to them because I feel I'm healthy. I really don't think I have it. Normally my chances might be considered a very high risk. But with my track record, I'm pretty confident that I'm safe."

As yet, no one close to Wade has gotten AIDS. He's never observed symptoms on another person, other than on television. "I'm focusing now on reevaluating my lifestyle. I'm thinking about going back to a normal job. That's one reason I've cut down on clients. Gradually I'm getting myself out of it and focusing on another life, because I'm getting older and I'm almost bored with it. The problem is, it's difficult to get out of such an easy lifestyle. Where else can you be your own boss, make good money, and hardly ever work, yet still be able to survive and have lots of free time?

"There are a few guys that do it -- they meet somebody rich, and end up being subsidized almost. I know guys that end up with a Mercedes or big homes. They've found somebody that's willing to take care of them."

I ask Wade how many of his clients openly talk about AIDS. Most don't even mention it, he says.

"They say, `with what's going around now,' meaning all the diseases. Including a new strain of hepatitis I hear is a real killer. They don't want to say you might have it, or that they might. They want to ignore the problem in their own way, but be more careful too."

I ask what he thinks of his own vulnerability to AIDS, given the long and uncertain incubation period of the virus. "There is the possibility," he says. "They say there are hundreds of thousands of people that are infected with the virus in their systems. But I think it's more the people who don't take care of themselves, the ones who party too much, who don't get enough sleep, who take drugs -- I think they're much more susceptible than those who don't live that way.

"Also, I figure: when it's time to go, it's time to go. When I go, it'll be in a blaze of glory. I'd take every credit card I own and go to the limit. I'd have a lot of fun, travel a lot, and that would be the end of it. I don't have symptoms. So if I do come down with it, there's the chance that by then there'll be a cure. Then again, if you're the chosen one, let it be. I could be in a plane crash or run over by a car, too, you know. I believe in destiny. If it was meant for me to die from AIDS, I will die from AIDS. Or in the plane crash. Or in old age.

"I'm not crazy about death. Although it might be a very relaxing move, since I like to sleep so much." He chuckles at the joke.

What if one of his clients gets AIDS?

"What if? It doesn't mean I gave it to him. He's taking his chances, just like I am in seeing him. Maybe he's giving it to me. I would feel bad for him, but like I said before, when it's time to go, it's time to go. If I definitely knew I was responsible, I would abstain from sex on a contact level, and just go to work in a job, period. If I knew that I was going to give it to someone else, I wouldn't do it. But I don't know that, do I?"

"So you are gambling."

"Yes," he says. "So is everyone else out there having sex with anonymous strangers, or even with their lovers. I'm not just gambling with their lives; I'm gambling with my own."

He estimates that one out of twenty of his clients are married to women. We talk about how AIDS might spread through them to heterosexual families.

"I see men all the time, afraid of coming out of the closet. They're afraid of the fact that they're gay. They want to be straight, or they want families. But acting that way just isn't fulfilling enough for them on a sexual level. Maybe appearing straight is good for business -- they're afraid if they don't do it, they won't get ahead with the company. Or, they have a position as a politician or an actor, in the public eye. They have to be known as a womanizer, or be married and have children. So they get married. You'd be surprised at some of them. The real macho type guys tend to like to get fucked. Otherwise they wouldn't be calling me."

Wade says he's had some very famous people as clients, politicians and theatrical figures who are universally considered to be heterosexual. I ask him to speculate, especially about those with whom he's had anal sex, what if they've received the AIDS virus from Wade? What if they are now passing it along sexually to women in their lives?

"It seems pretty far-fetched," he says. "We're talking years for this to happen. Between the time I give it to him, he has an incubation period. Then a long period of time before he gives it to her. You're talking about a very long connection that would need to happen."

Would Wade like to say something direct to you?

"The people out there who are gay could be your husband, your daughter, your father, your grandfather, your brother -- and you might not know it. There isn't a limit on who it can be, or who the disease is going to affect. The person AIDS research could save may be someone you care about and know.

"The life you save may be your own."

He adds, just to me, "I always wanted to use that line."

Dr. Grossman's Perspective

"I was left absolutely cold by the Wade story. I conscientiously and forthrightly trimmed the Wades out of my practice after I realized they were unreachable. I can't imagine getting through to him. Finally I decided to stop banging my head against the wall.

"Can you appreciate what that boy told you? What if large numbers of others share his viewpoint? It would mean we can't touch this epidemic. It would mean we couldn't do one thing to stop it from growing or not growing.

"I saw an interview with a bunch of kids on sexuality last month. There was a drop from the previous monthly average of six partners per month to five in 1984. It's still at four and a half this year.

"So how are we going to stop the disease? What's out there to stop it? The number of partners still seems to be a key factor. And there are a lot of people carrying the virus who don't realize they are.

"The spectrum of this disease is huge. Those of us involved with it are sometimes given to despair about how to stop its progression. We are years away from any drugs or vaccine to halt the spread of the virus.

"Wade just adds to my despair. I can't imagine breaking his behavior. I can't imagine undoing what he has done. He shows no fear. His arguments may be beautifully constructed, but he's a sad, lost person. Of course it's hard for him to stop. Look at the incredible seductivity of that life: non-taxable money and no structure. He does what he wants when he wants. But, you know, that can very commonly end in overt suicide or indirect suicide by alcohol or pills.

"Meanwhile, my advice to Wade's customers is very simple: STOP!"

"Vince" - One of Wade's Clients

He is nervous about being interviewed. "The ironic thing," he tells me, "is that I handle enormous professional responsibility. The people who work with me are in awe of my competence, and I work very hard to deserve that respect. But if I were known as a gay person, I think they'd suddenly doubt my skill. And if they knew about Wade . . . ."

Vince is thirty-four years old. He's a senior production executive for a large consumer products company. You have at least one of the firm's brands in your larder, if not a dozen. Vince is responsible for making them, getting jars and cartons to match caps, labels, and contents, shifting inventories with costs and brand changes, etc. The company has a plant in California. When Vince visits the west coast office, he often sees Wade and sometimes other male prostitutes as well.

"I would never call a hustler in New York," he says. "My doormen know too much about me already." He asks me to give no physical description of him, and to confine our interview to Wade alone. How long has he been seeing Wade, I ask. And what is his perspective on their transactions?

"I've been seeing him for years, actually. Three or four. I guess you could say I'm a workaholic. I travel a lot. I haven't had a successful relationship since I was twenty-two. That one lasted three years. I work hard on the road. I work hard in New York. The pressure in my job is enormous. When I'm out on my own, I just can't picture renting a car and cruising around in some hunt for bars and discos. Especially in L.A. Do you know how spread out that place is? I'd spend the whole night driving."

"I'm lonely. I'll admit it. There's only so much TV I can watch. Someone like Wade gives me an evening in which I'm appreciated, a night that's got some excitement. He's nice. He's good looking. He's masculine. I like that. You know he was a marine, right? And he's very good in bed.

"I have a great time and still get to bed at a reasonable hour, get up bright and early, jog around the hotel, and get to my business breakfast. It all works fine. It's a convenience that keeps me going, and frankly it doesn't hurt anybody."

"What about you?" I ask him. "Have you thought about danger to yourself?"

"Of course! I've seen things change these past few years. People don't do all the things in bed they used to. But it's important to me still. I *need* to see Wade.

"What am I supposed to do? It's easy for straight couples in their comfy middle class homes and their Sunday School classes and *Good Housekeeping* pattern for living. They've got a clearcut way they're supposed to live. But they don't feel what I feel. I picture if any of them reads this they won't understand one word I have to say.

"It's different for me. It'd be different for them too if they lived in a world where people beat them up after school for being a 'fag'. I used to get that plenty. Or, if they ever got fired just because of their personal sexual desires.

"I had a good friend who got fired as a phys. ed. teacher when a private letter to a friend got returned to the school -- it was a Catholic school -- and the principal opened it, although he shouldn't have. Bang!

The guy is fired. This friend of mine is as super conscientious as you can be. He would never abuse his position. He never even had a chance to defend himself. Gay? Gone!

"So I don't care about the normal lifestyles of the straight and narrow. There were so many times when I was with my friend, the guy I used to live with all those years ago, when I wanted to hold his hand. Just like the straight couples do in public. Just hold his hand because I cared about him. No can do. Like, that would be so terrible. So I make my own path and try not to hurt anyone. And if that means I pay to have sex with someone gorgeous, well I work hard for my money, and I'll pay.

"If you ask the people who work for me, they'll tell you -- and it would be true -- that I'm kind and fair and smart and I help develop my people so they can get ahead too. It's truthful to call me an asset to society, to the economy, to my employees' lives, even to my country. And, yes, I sleep with a prostitute now and then. So?"

I ask Vince to address the AIDS question more specifically.

"Well I won't deny it. I was surprised to read in your article that he's had so many customers. The thing I most like -- being screwed -- is unfortunately what seems to be the most dangerous for catching AIDS. Now he pulls out before coming, we agreed on that. He doesn't like a condom. But I've been worrying lately, this is very recent, about little cracks inside my body I may not know about, or ways that AIDS could get in if he has the virus. And I've been worrying about pre-ejaculatory fluid. It's creepy, all of it."

He sighs, a long sigh.

"Look. What if I have it. It does frighten me a lot, in fact. What if I have it? I didn't start being as careful as I am till a year or so ago. What if this thing has a very long waiting period? What if it's inside me now, and I just don't know it yet? I do think of that.

"But what am I going to do? There's nothing to stop it. From what I've read, it'll be years till they have a vaccine. All those early years this disease has been around and nobody cared about researching it. I don't think Mr. and Mrs. America care about me or my kind. It's like being black, in a way, except nobody even knows it about you. They think you're white, and you do your best to pass.

"Ever since I knew I was gay, I've lived with prejudice. How funny if that prejudice should causs this country to lose so many of us. They'll discover then that people they liked, people they cared about and counted on, were gay all the time. Only it'll be too late.

"That's pretty gloomy. I do worry. And now I'm doing my best. I'm trying to be careful. I have been wondering about my next trip to California. Do I want to see Wade again? Do I want to see any hustler again. I don't know. Don't ask me about my future, 'cause I don't know.

I've thought about psychotherapy again. How do I find a relationship? All the stuff you think about when you're worried. I hope it's not too late, now that I'm being more careful. I hope I don't have it already."

At first, Vince says he doesn't have anything to say to readers when I invite him to. Then, as an afterthought:

"Listen, whoever you are. I know I'm not like you are. But I'm really not a bad person. If you've ever made fun of a gay person, you've made fun of me and it hurts a lot. Of course I don't want to die of AIDS. I don't want to get it. I don't want you to get it either. But if you're judging me because I see a prostitute now and then, well -- are you so proud of everything you do?

"That's it. The end."

Phone Call to Vince

He answers the phone immediately. He tells me he's been thinking about our interview a lot and about his situation with Wade. "I wasn't all that comfortable when we spoke in person," he says, "because talking with you made it all very conscious."

I tell him several readers have sent notes asking how he can tolerate Wade's not using a condom.

"That's one of the things I've been thinking about," he says. "For a long time, after I started to get careful, I felt safe. I asked Wade to pull out before coming, and now he does. So I thought it didn't matter whether he used a condom or not.

"But I'm hearing more talk about the danger. Being passive with anal sex is one of the highest risks there is, and I can't stop wondering if I have a skin fissure. If his pre-ejaculation gets directly into my blood stream. . . . well, I thought I was safe, and now I'm not sure.

"Maybe your readers won't understand this, but I like to please Wade. I'm paying him, yes. But I enjoy the idea that he gets pleasure from me too. It makes me feel sexy, which is part of why I call him.

I hear a small sigh.

"I'm thinking I'm going to have to do without something. Either he'll have to wear a condom, or I can't get screwed anymore, or I'll have to find someone else more careful. It not's a big deal to anybody else, I know. But Wade used to be an important consolation for me on a tough, lonely night. My days are hard, as you know. But an evening I used to count on may have to be cut back." He laughs, harshly. "I almost said, 'may have to go the way of all flesh,' but that sounded so grim."

"As I'm talking to you now, I'm pretty sure I'm going to change. You can put me down into your statistics book. One more guy who cuts back 'cause he's scared." We are both silent.

"When do you think they'll solve this thing?"

Wade - December

"Do you like my moustache?" he says over his drink. I can feel the sting to his question. In truth, his moustache is scraggly and accidental. He no longer has the life guard's body, the physique to envy if a bully kicks sand in your face. He is puffy and hulking. Soft. The moustache is just a blemish on the memory of his former appearance.

"Well, truthfully, no, I guess I don't." I realize I'm stroking my own moustache unconsciously. I move my hand quickly back to my drink.

"Good for you," he says with heavy sarcasm. "I don't like it either. I look at it every day and hate it. But I'm not going to shave it off until I lose weight."

He has stopped being a hustler. No, our interview had nothing at all to do with it. He'd told me he was thinking of quitting anyway, remember? But he's had very bad luck these past months. The boss he's been working for is unreliable, hasn't paid him, and can't manage the company's money. Wade's vision of a future "legit" business opportunity has crumbled. He has five years of no real work experience on his resume, just hustling. How is he going to get a job from scratch at nearly forty? How is he going to start all over?

No, he doesn't see "Vince" anymore. He assumes Vince comes to California for his company but, evidently, he's no longer phoning hustlers. Because of AIDS, obviously. Wade still doesn't know anyone directly who's gotten the disease. And except for gaining too much weight, and except for being too depressed to go to the gym, Wade himself is still "very healthy." No, he hasn't had a blood test.

He can get himself back in shape, he's done that before. He may have to go back to hustling, though, just to get food money. There are still plenty of people out there with needs. Married people with secret lives. Wade can be one of their secrets. Single people, alone and not liking it.

Or maybe it's time for Wade to go back east. He'll see what the New Year has to offer him.

Chapter 8:
The Condom Maker

"Will S." is a San Diego journalist and friend who'd been reading CHRONICLE *via computer from the beginning. It was his idea that I speak with a condom manufacturer because of the role of sexually transmitted body fluids in spreading the AIDS virus.*

I called the company that makes Trojans, *my "unaided brand recall" winner (the first brand name I thought of.) After many phone calls and a great deal of suspicion ("We're owned by Carter-Wallace, and we're not allowed to talk to the press") I gave up on them and found Schmid Laboratories, makers of RAMSES, Sheik, and other condom brands. They were cordial and readily agreed to the interview.*

I seldom drive. I always feel like an alien as I leave Planet Manhattan for the unknown suburban highways that every other driver seems to comprehend. However, despite a pouring rain, I follow meticulous instructions and soon am successfully in Little Falls, New Jersey.

Brent Gulick is the product manager of condoms for Schmid Laboratories. His prior experience was teaching high school social sciences before entering business. He's worked at Lehn and Fink, home of Lysol disinfectant and has been with Schmid for about a year. The company manufactures feminine hygiene products, deodorizers, and children's toothpaste in addition to condoms.

Brent and I relate to each other with immediate common ground because of my experience as a Lever Brothers product manager. I tell him I noticed that the A.C. Nielson company had signed into the lobby guest book. The Nielson people used to tell me if I'd gained or lost a tenth of a share point versus my competition at Proctor & Gamble and Colgate. What can Brent reveal about the market shares for condoms?

"Between Carter-Wallace and Schmid, we together have over 92% of the U.S. condom market," he says.

"What's the split between you?"

"They're about 45-50%," he says. "We're currently number two, at 40-45%." I ask him to tell me about his marketing of condoms.

"One problem with the category is that condoms are difficult to advertise. You can't advertise on TV, for example."

"There's a law?"

"There was until 1977. Then the Supreme Court overruled lower courts concerning the advertising and display of contraceptives. Perhaps you know that ten or twenty years ago, condoms were hidden in the pharmacist's back drawer. You had to ask for them specifically. Now you'll find them on the pegboard displays of drugstores."

I remember seeing small metal vending machines on the walls of gas station men's rooms. They were too high for me to reach, those tight little packages of Forbidden Adulthood.

"The law now says you can advertise, but networks generally refuse TV commercials."

"Why is that?"

"It's a concern about the sexual issue," he replies. "They seem to have an easier time with female contraceptives than male. So we decided to find a novel way to advertise, one that would also generate publicity about the fact that we've not been able to get television access. This summer in mid-July, we tested aerial banners over the beaches. Jones Beach, Coney Island, and the Jersey Shore. The region has four million people out on a summer weekend, so it was ideal for reach and frequency."

The statistics that measure the impact of advertising -- "reach" and "frequency" -- function identically whether a product is coffee, cough drops, or condoms. He shows me a photo of the banner the airplane displayed: "PLAN AHEAD WITH RAMSES." Press releases were sent to media people and distributors, with a small balsa wood airplane bearing the slogan.

"The plane flew Saturday and Sunday," he says. By the middle of the week, a story about our advertising had been featured on television, on a station that wouldn't normally accept condom commercials. The overall publicity was so favorable, in fact, that the program was expanded to cities like Chicago, Cleveland, Detroit, Los Angeles, Boston, and others. A company spokesman appeared on a number of TV talk shows.

"Here's a product that can help prevent the spread of a deadly virus," I say, "and yet it can't be advertised on television. Why do you think the networks are more cautious about male contraception than female?"

"I think part of it has to do with image," he says. Like any good product manager, he knows the history of his product.

Forty million couples use condoms worldwide, he tells me.

They're about as popular as the birth control pill. The earliest recorded description of the device was when an Italian scientist named Fallapio recommended a linen sheath moistened with lotion as a guard against venereal infection. That was four centuries ago in 1564.

By the 1700's, people realized that condoms were not only disease preventors, but also helped guard against pregnancy. Dr. Condom resided in the court of Charles II (1660-85) helped to popularize them. Condom shops appeared throughout England. Early condoms were made of sheep membrane and could be afforded only by the upper classes.

The vulcanization of rubber led to a synthetic replacement for the natural skin sheath. With rubber production, condoms became less expensive and were feasible for more people. The new latex process of the early 1930's made the product still cheaper and easier to manufacture. In one form or another, Schmid has been making condoms for almost a century.

"Despite the hundreds of years of human use of them," Brent says, "the fact is, they were hidden away and were almost an embarrassment to ask for, something to be ashamed of."

"So was the topic of sexuality in general," I say. I'm thinking of the questions I've been asking people lately, about attitudes toward sexual education in schools to help prevent the spread of AIDS. A cultural reluctance to be overt about discussing sexuality has a variety of implications, I realize.

"When you go to parties or other social functions," I ask him, "and people ask about your occupation, is there embarrassment when you tell them?"

"Yes," he says. "There's a lot of that."

"What is the discomfort about?"

"Condoms aren't often brought up in conversation," he says. "In some cases, people want finally to ask me questions they've been afraid afraid to ask anyone else."

"Like what? What are the most frequently asked questions?"

"Sometimes they ask questions about size. `Are there different sizes?' The answer is no, there don't need to be. The latex condom can expand to an enormous degree. Some products are contoured, but that's just different shaping, that doesn't have to do with size.

"Another question I get is, `can you really get condoms in colors?' The answer is, yes. Our 'Excita Fiesta' contains assorted colors. Green, red, different colors."

"Who buys those?" I ask.

"More likely it's someone who's experienced with condoms and ready to try something different, or else it's very young people who just like the colors."

"Color variations seem to me like straining for a product point of difference," I say to him. "I understand the points in your brochure about various other product forms -- the ribbed ones for female sensitivity, the ones that are specially lubricated to help a man who ejaculates too quickly. But I'm surprised there's a sufficient market for simple color differences -- 'Well, let's use the blue condom tonight.' What am I missing, Brent?"

"It's hard to know," he replies. "I don't really know what goes on between users."

"What are the trends in the market?"

"Lubricated products have been growing as a share of market for quite a few years. But the fastest growing segment is the condom with a spermicidal agent included. We introduced our first one in 1982."

"Brent, it seems to me all my adult life I've heard jokes about condoms . 'The condom broke and that's why my parents had me, ha, ha, ha.' That kind of thing. Is there not the technological possibility of a condom that just won't break?"

"Nothing for birth control is 100%, short of sterilization," he tells me. "Condoms are exceptionally strong. But they do break in a small percentage of cases, maybe one or two percent. They're tested individually, you know. Each and every condom you buy has been tested electronically."

"Are the thinner condoms more susceptible to breakage?"

"No. The difference in thinness is very, very slight. The reason some people are turning back to the natural skin condoms is not that they're thinner, but they conduct more heat for tactile sensation."

"What consciousness, as a product manager on condoms, do you have about AIDS?"

"I've been reading about it, not just as a product manager, but as a person."

"Part of the advice now given to people worried about AIDS is to use a condom," I say. "From a marketing point of view, that's good news for the condom, and not so good news for the forms of contraception that don't offer barriers to sperm transmission. Gay men are specifically being advised to use condoms for anal intercourse, and many did not previously use them at all. Do you see that as a marketing opportunity?"

"Well, certainly we're aware of the potential market implications. I won't get into details of our marketing plan, but you're bringing up things we've been thinking about ourselves. We have to be careful, as we offer information, not to be perceived as endorsing sex. 'PLAN AHEAD WITH RAMSES' is an example of our wanting to be discreet and not promote sex per se. We're simply ask people who make their own choices to at least be conscious of doing what they do with prudence and safety."

"What would you advise users of condoms? How can they be especially sure the product is working well to prevent disease transfer?"

"When and how you remove a condom can make a difference. Spillage obviously defeats the purpose of using one, and people who don't remove them properly can encounter that. They need to really hold the end of the condom against themselves until they are fully withdrawn, before pulling it off. When people don't do that, they can have spillage and therefore transfer of the fluids."

"How much research is being done on condoms and prevention of fluids transfer?" I ask him.

"It's ongoing," he says. "Plenty of research was done already on venereal disease, and condoms were in fact effective in blocking off the transfer. Not just my company's brands, but competition as well.

"My advice to your readers is very simple. I think, if someone is looking for a contraceptive product, condoms should be seriously considered. They are easy, safe to use, and effective. That's why they've been used for hundreds of years, after all. They can be used with other contraceptive products too. I think it'd make a difference, if more people were to use them."

We shake hands, and I head back to my car, protected from the rain by my leaky umbrella.

~ ~ ~ ~ ~

(December, 1985) - A news report notes that tests by Dr. Jay A. Levy, a virologist at the UC San Francisco medical school, show that the AIDS virus cannot penetrate the fine membranes of condoms. His study was commissioned by the San Francisco AIDS Foundation. Levy tested five kinds of commercially available condoms: three types made of latex, one kind of natural lamb skin and another made of synthetic skin. The condoms were filled with fluids containing a high concentration of virus and were then inserted into solutions of tissue cells which normally encourage viruses to culture. No virus particles leaked out of the condoms.

In another test, researchers examined condoms filled with fluid to see if the viral organisms would pass through them. Even after three weeks, there was no sign that any of the virus had passed through the condoms that were tested.

Chapter 9:
Dr. Grossman -
Late Summer's Night

In the middle of summer 1985, the entire cultural environment changed with the sudden announcement that Rock Hudson, world famous movie star, had AIDS. There began to be much more publicity about safe sex" guidelines: avoiding the exchange of body fluids. Meanwhile, Dr. Grossman's case load of patients with the disease continued to grow. I began to see his name listed more often as a speaker at public symposiums about AIDS.

Here is a summary of an update meeting I had with him near the end of summer, including a transcript of his comments on the difference between ARC and AIDS, and on the nature of epidemics in general.

It is a hot, oppressive night. I am just now installed into a nice, new apartment. The cardboard packing boxes are finally out of sight. I've got rocking chairs in the living room, and a few wicker stools to serve as tables. Otherwise, the room is still empty.

"How about dinner, at whatever time you're ready?" Dr. Grossman says yes. He agrees I can order from the Japanese restaurant nearby. At 9:00, I'm ravenous. I learn he is still returning phone calls. Finally at 9:45, the two of us are ensconced in the rocking chairs, like pilots in individual helicopters, coasting low above the carpet stretching out to the balcony.

"Lots has happened since we last talked," he says. "It works this particular way in our country, Michael. The recent media explosion seems to have triggered all kinds of things. All of us involved are now deluged with research proposals, requests for participants in all kinds of volunteer studies, requests to speak. It's accelerated at such a pace, I can't even measure it for you. I've got stacks of unanswerable stuff on the desk, and I'm only one person of so many."

We talk of Rock Hudson and the impact of his condition on the media and the public. "It seems pivotal, doesn't it? I'm sure someone from another country or another planet, observing the way we work, would be sure we're all madmen. But that's the way we work! Everything changes with one well-recognized and somewhat beloved figure. He's `Mr. Nice Guy,' right? At least two of my patients say they've dated him. They say it was really a kind of wonderful experience. Not hinting at the sexuality of it, just that he's a terrific person. He really is Mr. All American. Mr. Clean Cut. So with all this new attention, maybe Dr. Krim's two year scenario for a vaccine becomes more possible."

I ask him about the first chart he drew for me -- the curve of a virus. Where does he think we now are on that curve? The curve he drew, he tells me, was of people who are already infected and *will* get the disease. "We are still down on the low end of it," he says. "You ain't seen nothing yet; 12,000 cases now is nothing compared to the potential."

But is the progression inevitable? What hope is there?

"We are a real smart species," he says. "Just as we learned to fight disease in the general sense -- put on clothes, get a roof over your head, eat well, stay clean -- I think we're gonna master this guy too."

"So -- we'll INTERRUPT the growth curve?"

"I'm sorry, Michael. There's just no predicting with confidence where exactly we'll be on that curve, or when. It won't surprise you if I say that even if it takes ten years to reach saturation, and even if the total casualties are indeed a million, the number will still be nothing compared to the total population of this planet. One could argue, statistically, that AIDS will make no difference to the broad scheme of things.

"But I predict it will make a great deal of difference -- and have a devastating effect -- on politics and government and social structures. Many past epidemics have done exactly that. The slaughter houses didn't disappear just because they smelled: they spread cholera. This East Side area you live, Michael, had cholera while most of the West Side didn't." (He gestures out the window, to the United Nations building and the East River.) "The slaughter houses were right there, where the U.N. has taken their place. They're what fostered the epidemic. There'll be changes in our society just as sweeping as the change in this landscape, even if I can't pinpoint for you just what they'll be."

I serve coffee, and we talk about computers. Suddenly Ron says, "How is it possible for AIDS *not* to spread, Michael? Did I tell you about my gay patient who came to me and asked for the AIDS test? Because he and his wife want to have a baby. My face gave it all away. I didn't even know he had a wife.

"'Aren't you still promiscuous,' says I to him. He says, `yes.'

"I say, `Does it not bother you that you're still living that way?' He says, `well, that's why I want the test.'"

"Needless to say, his AIDS viral test is positive. That means he quite possibly has exposed his wife. If he wouldn't tell me about the wife, it probably means she's already pregnant. And who's SHE playing with, Michael? She's heterosexual. Who's SHE doing it with? Only with him?

"How does one halt a disease based on sexual transmission? It could be VERY slow. That's why I think it could be with us for a very long time. How do you halt it? Does `safe sex' mean anything whatsoever to this boy? No. His promiscuity is `no holds barred,' he admitted that to me. He says he just can't deal with less than his usual sexual habits.

We are silent.

I think about the man who gets sexually involved with other men and also wants to father a baby with his wife. I wonder for a moment, as I have at times before, about the many people out there past the edge of my balcony on a hot summer's night. Doing what they do behind a thousand darkened windows glistening back at me.

My mind stretches down 39th Street, where I can see New Jersey on the clearest of days. I imagine flying past the Hudson River, past the deep black windows in the Newark nighttime . . . to the faintly moving shadows behind the windows of Pittsburgh, Pa . . . flying on far beyond 39th Street, over to Fort Wayne, Indiana, continuing west.

While, unheard and unseen, is the occasional, quiet transfer of a virus from one person to another. A virus expanding its universe, as two people in Chicago share their passion in the heat of the night.

"When I reported the positive test to this man," Ron says, "he told me he wasn't surprised. And, no, they wouldn't be having a baby now."

"Well," I reply, "at least he knew enough, at least he was educated enough, to ask you for the test. I guess that's part of your point, Ron. What about the ones who don't ask?"

Again we are silent. Soon he leaves to visit a patient who had phoned here during dinner. It is almost midnight. Most of the windows are dark.

Transcript from a Dinner Conversation

"This is a disease with an enormously -- do you know the word `protean,' Michael, from the god Proteus who took many shapes? AIDS has enormously protean manifestations. There's apparently very little resemblance between the disease as seen in certain populations in Africa, and in our own country.

"Michael, I've got `ARC' patients who are sick . . . and `AIDS' patients who aren't!"

[I know by now that 'ARC' is Aids Related Complex, sometimes called `pre-AIDS.' ARC can be any of a variety of illnesses that are not officially defined by the Center for Disease Control as being AIDS.]

"We had a strong contrast the other day, an ARC patient who is consigned to home because of his diarrhea and weakness and fever and wasting. But he has none of the CDC stuff that would label him as an AIDS patient. The ARC patient -- today -- has evidence of exposure to the virus. He's got lymphadenopathy (that means lymph gland enlargement, Michael) weight loss, `thrush' (the mouth infection) . . . but he doesn't yet have the CDC's formal definition.

"The man who followed him was another patient I'm fond of, a young dancer. Three and three-quarters years now, he's had KS. Yet he's just been dancing in the European company of *CATS*. He's also my youngest patient. He was 21 when we diagnosed him. He has a difficult form of KS -- lymph nodes, mucous membranes. Now we are close to four years of his having had it. Because he has KS, he is officially an AIDS patient. Yet he has no restrictions at all on his life! He's just been invited to join a wonderful non-American ballet company. I'm so proud of this kid!"

[Ron Grossman grins, like a bragging parent.]

"But look at the irony. *He's* my patient with `AIDS' while the `ARC' patient is sick at home. That gives you a hint of the extraordinary, broad spectrum of this disease. Our arbitrary terminology in no way really describes the functional issues.

"Many of us would like to *expand* the CDC's definition of AIDS. Then a person with HTLV-III exposure, swollen glands, and so on -- a person with the ARC symptoms who, for example, also has TB -- would officially be counted as an `AIDS' patient. There was a beautiful piece of research done recently by the public health people at Columbia. They found a striking rise in ordinary TB in New York City, and it has CORRELATED almost perfectly with the geographical distribution of AIDS! Indeed, all of us who are in the field have seen this."

[I understand what he's telling me. AIDS, with its devastating effect on the body's immune system, makes people more susceptible to other terrible diseases like tuberculosis. Yet some of those patients with TB, acquired because of the AIDS virus, are not being counted in the CDC's AIDS statistics. I tell Dr. Grossman that, until this conversation, I've pictured a much wider separation between `ARC' patients and `AIDS' patients. What he's really telling me is that there are many more people with AIDS, for all practical purposes, than are actually being reported in the formal tabulations.]

"Michael, that doesn't even take into consideration the people who are *infected* but are showing nothing as of yet. They have no name, no eponym, no cute little abbreviation. They have no symptoms, but it's the same disease. The estimate is a half-million to two million people."

[But if they don't have any symptoms, I ask him, what's the difference?]

"Your question really strikes at the heart of my particular interest: the historical and evolutionary aspect of disease. You are describing just where AIDS was until 1981 -- hidden away within people. It was whereever its reservoir was . . . the heart of darkest Africa? Haiti? Who knows? Probably in countless individuals who were not sick, or not very sick.

"That is a clear picture that emerges from the study of prior epidemics. I saw in my own library, Michael, a book by a famous biologist. It's called *PLAGUES AND PEOPLES*. I'm just browsing through it, and I'm realizing, this is the story of the AIDS epidemic! But the book was actually published back in 1972. You can fill in the blanks, nonetheless. The AIDS epidemic is following a classic model!

"For example, AIDS is now the largest killer amongst *women* aged 30-34 in New York. Of course, most women at that age group don't die, so disease-wise there's no competition! That statistic was turned into 'scare' headlines a while ago. But I realized from reading about prior epidemics is that young adults are exactly the age group that ALL prior epidemics of recorded history most strike! That perspective goes very much against our image of flu striking helpless babies and old people in 1917. But it's statistically correct: young adults ARE the largest population group of distribution of any disease, and the ones most likely to die.

"Now the reasons for this are obscure. One could even argue, hypothetically, that sexual transmission may well apply to *every* epidemic. THAT would color AIDS a little differently, wouldn't it? That would change the whole flavor, the kind of moral overtone, that we've had with this disease from Day One, if AIDS weren't so unique in its sexual transmission.

"As I dug into that book, it changed the whole moral flavor of all this. What astonishes me is: we're nearly four years into AIDS. Have you read one word about classic epidemic patterns? This is a historical fact -- about young adults and epidemics -- this is not someone's speculation. The researcher pored over death certificates and vital statistics of even the cholera epidemic that struck right outside your window.

"Young adults are the age group most likely to get epidemic disease. Why? Maybe because babies are protected? Or because old people don't get around very much? I don't know. There's so much we still don't know about all of this."

84

Chapter 10:
Doris Williams and "Keoke"

Now we were hearing about AIDS hitting people other than Haitians, drug addicts, hemophiliacs, and homosexuals. "Normal people's" stories were beginning to receive more popular media attention. If this book -- computer readers were now telling me CHRONICLE was, indeed, a "book" -- were going to even approach an honest chronicle of the time, then I obviously needed to meet some of the "other" kinds of people affected by the disease.

I began to seek more diverse individuals whose lives were affected by AIDS. Amy Sloan in Indiana (separate chapter) was one such example. "Keoke," a five-year old child with AIDS, was another. What I discovered along the way were examples of courage and dignity I hadn't foreseen.

Like Doris Williams.

It is a perfect September day. A local TV news show feature interviews pet owners. We learn that their dogs really appreciate the crisp autumn air. An enormous bulldog face fills the screen: "He's like a pup again!"

Rejuvenation. People do seem walk more jauntily down the sidewalks. "Fall Preview" is on the magazine covers. "Back to School" is on store window banners. Angry parents are now picketing in Queens to have an anonymous child with AIDS removed from the classroom.

AIDS has been steady front page material this week. I'm following the *Post* each day as one breathless headline replaces another. Yesterday's Metro Edition featured: "S C H O O L   C O O K   D I E S   O F   A I D S, He chopped green beans and roast beef." Last night's front page offered: "T E E N   G E T S   A I D S   M A N'S   H E A R T, We had little choice: DOCS."

This morning, in a taxi headed for Newark, New Jersey, I see today's cover story, "Top doc's warning to schools, K E E P   A I D S

I am on the way to United Presbyterian Children's Hospital, to meet Doris Williams who cares for "Keoke" (a fictitious name) among a number of other children.   Keoke is five years old and has AIDS.   Her identical twin, "Kerina", does not.

When Doris answers the phone she always says "Praise the Lord" instead of "hello." She was ebullient when I talked to her at 7:20 this morning. "It's never too early to call!" she assured me. I had phoned to confirm our meeting at the hospital. Keoke receives treatment there every third week.

My taxi driver, Pierrot, is Haitian.   Another driver recently explained that so many Haitians now drive cabs in New York City because, "we are a very independent people; you are on your own in a cab."   Pierrot is lost for a while in Newark, but he spots another Haitian driver at a traffic light. They converse in French and we follow the other cab to the hospital.

When Pierrot learns I'll be interviewing someone with AIDS, he asks, "aren't you afraid?"

"Not at all," I reply. "AIDS is not so easy to catch."

"But will you be dressed like that?" I am wearing a suit and tie, fresh from a meeting with a prospective client. "Will they give you a mask?"

I explain: AIDS is not contagious that way. I will not be having sexual relations, and I won't be exchanging blood. I will be talking with a five-year old girl and her mother.

He is unconvinced. "I'm glad I'm married," he says. "Otherwise - - they could offer me the best-looking woman in the world, they could offer me a million dollars. I wouldn't touch her."

He tells me he's read a *Post* article about several young children with AIDS. They've been rejected by their families.   I have the article with me. I remember it especially because the newspaper's art director created a logo -- the "I" in "AIDS" is an upright hypodermic needle.

"It's terrible about those kids," Pierrot says as he lets me off at the hospital. It is 11:00. Doris Williams has had car trouble. She doesn't arrive until 2:00 in the afternoon.

~ ~ ~ ~ ~

At first I'm slightly nervous.   Anthony DePalma, a journalist whose work I've often read in the *New York Times* , is in the waiting room researching a new story. He's just published an interview with Doris Williams and Keoke in the September 3 *Woman's Day*.   As they chat together like two old friends, I feel unsure and awkward, uncertain when and how to begin my own relationship with Mrs. Williams.

"Did you see his article?" Doris asks me. No, I purposely didn't. I want to form my own impressions. Like friendly brown bumblebees, the twins are now buzzing all around me. I laugh at their uninhibited interest and feel more comfortable when I've removed my jacket.

The difference between the two girls is amazing: one would never take them for twins. Kerina is about SIX INCHES TALLER than Keoke. Tony had explained that the differences in their speech and mental development are apparently direct results of Keoke's AIDS.

The children are beautifully dressed. Kerina has three pigtails, each tied with a miniature painted clown's head and lavender gauze. Her dress is lavender as well.

Keoke, so short and meager, is as energetic as a monkey. She is flat-out adorable. Her crisp blue frock is trimmed with multiple levels of lace. She could be at the birthday party of a princess instead of waiting for gamma globulin.

For the first time I begin really to study Doris Williams. She is a large black woman and has a slight, arthritic limp. Her thick black hair is tangled and curly. She wears a simple white sweater and a black cotton skirt. It is obvious that she spends her attention and energy on the children.

Doris Williams is a foster mother. She is presently caring for seven chilren -- ages two through seven. I ask her to tell me about her background. She's a licensed practical nurse who's worked in day care centers and private duty nursing. Her own four children are all in their twenties. She confirms that I'm not the only person astonished at how young she looks.

Some years ago, Doris became ill and disabled and had to stop working. After a time she realized she could nonetheless be a foster parent. Because of her training as a nurse, the state tends to award "special" children to her care. I learn that this woman sitting next to me as we wait for the blood work to begin -- the woman who's made certain to bring cookies and Cherry Cokes for the twins -- has cared for eighteen children over the past seven years. Keoke and Kerina have been with her since they were only weeks old. Keoke's AIDS was diagnosed about two and a half years ago.

How did it happen? Both children had been victims of infantile botulism. Keoke was especially sick from the food poisoning, and for a while it wasn't certain she'd survive. In the process of being saved, she evidently received contaminated blood. That realization is, of course, in retrospect. Back then what was clear was only that Keoke was somehow constantly, routinely, unremittingly sick.

As we talk, I watch Keoke open a tiny alcohol sponge and rub it on Kerina's arm. They fiddle with the accoutrements of blood work the way they might play with dolls. Keoke, with her muffled pronunciation, announced to one of the nurses today that she is a doctor and her name is "Doris," just like her mother's. Now she hops around looking for "a needle." She finds the broken half of a tongue suppressor in the trash can.

"Which one gets the IV?!" Dr. Susan Morrison has entered the room as though about to award the most coveted of prizes. "YOU get it? `Doris'? YOU get it? Oh, boy!"

"Mommy!" Keoke cries. She is lifted up onto the table. First a blood sample needs to be drawn; then Keoke will be connected to a tall machine on wheels that holds the clear plastic sacks of gamma globulin. The blood serum component, Doris tells me, will bolster Keoke's immunity, helping her fight off normal diseases. Suddenly the machine emits a high-pitched whine, a signal it seems to give frequently, whenever something needs adjustment.

Kerina rolls noisily on a low stool. "Hey young lady!" Doris says sternly. Kerina looks longingly at my tape recorder, and stares up to her sister and Dr. Morrison. How does life seem to this alert young girl with two fingers in her mouth?   What ambivalent feelings must she have already as her sister receives the attention -- and the pain -- of a spotlight shared with AIDS.

Doris stands and swings her arm behind Keoke.   Dr. Morrison keeps a fast stream of lively patter directed at the girl, and tells her it'll be okay to cry, but she must STAY STILL. JUST STAYYY STILL. Up on the examining table, with the doctor in front of her and Doris standing tall to her side, Keoke looks fragile, her thin brown arms so helpless.

"What do you have to do?" asks Dr. Morrison. And they say it together. "STAYYY STILL." Dr. Morrison is looking for the right spot to enter the needle. I notice how tense I am, hardly breathing. The needle has been inserted now, and both women are repeatedly praising Keoke --

"My goodness,you are so grown up!"

"She said she was a doctor today!"

"I'm proud of you, I'm proud of you!"

The two of them sing an "I'm proud of you" song to Keoke.   The tube with gamma globulin is in for a while, but slips out. Keoke begins to cry. Kerina has moved to Doris's chair and looks up, frozen. Keoke's little shrieks are torn and wispy shreds of sound.   Doris is cooing in wonderful, rich tones as she holds the tiny girl, enfolding her from behind.

"It hurts," Keoke says faintly.   But she's controlling her tears, behaving remarkably I think. Dr. Morrison confirms it: the needle needs readjustment.   Time is passing slowly. From my chair in the corner of the room, I peer up at the table along with Kerina.   The two women and the girl are huddled together in front of me like the statue of marines I remember from childhood -- united around the flag, except it's a blood machine.

Before long, Keoke is back down to the floor, rolling the machine around with her, her arm now connected to a strand of clear tubing. Today Kerina and Doris must give blood samples, too. Keoke parks her serum dispenser next to a chair and waits restlessly. She stares at the red hearts hanging above our heads. The hearts hanging from the ceiling are made of pipe cleaners.

"Boy, Michael is gettin' some knowledge here!" Doris tells the children. She's being blatantly peppy as Dr. Morrison prepares Kerina's arm. "He's learning how to install IV's, and draw blood!" Kerina, who is terrified of the procedure, finds it difficult to celebrate my growing.

Dr. Morrison tells Kerina, "It's okay to cry" but she urges her to recite a rhyme, instead of thinking about the pain:

"One-Two, The cow says moo.
Three-Four, The lion roars.
Five-Six, The monkey does tricks.
Seven-Eight, Who's at the gate?
Nine-Ten, A big fat hen.
Eleven-Twelve, Start over again."

When it's Doris's turn to give blood, she sings out the jingle like a vaudeville pro. It's hard not to be moved by the energy she puts into making every minute tolerable for these two little girls.

Keoke scoots around the floor, hanging on to the tall, rolling serum dispenser attached to her arm -- a weird racing car and driver from another part of the universe. Occasionally (I wince to see it) she steps on the clear tube directing the fluid into her body.

"Seems that everybody's gotten so panicky," Doris says. "They heard about the disease five or six years ago. Now they're worried they'll catch it just by thinking about it! I've had five children since these girls were in the house. Three were born since these two were there. They grew up as infants in the same house. No one's `caught' it from Keoke.

Doris tells me that, after four years of carrying AIDS children along with others, a local transportation agency is refusing to let Keoke onto the bus. "They picked up some law they found way down in the whereabouts," she tells me. The law stipulates that a sick child cannot ride the vehicle unless the bus is sterilized on each occasion. The law was never enforced until AIDS.

Doris confers with Dr. Morrison who is now examining Keoke. The two of them discuss medications and symptoms -- foot pains, runny nose, Keoke's appetite. Doris's training as a nurse is evident in the familiarity with which she discusses one medication versus another.

I've been here now almost an hour. Doris could hardly have been more good-natured. I invite her to say something direct to you who are reading this now.

She speaks with extra clarity, as though enunciating on a radio microphone. "I'd like to say that this disease has been around for five years. It doesn't look like it's going anywhere in the very near future. We have to deal with it as best we can.

"Our end goal is the same as if an enemy invaded our country. We would all pick up arms, regardless of race, creed, nationality, or religion - - and FIGHT off the enemy. This is deadlier than any two-legged enemy we can have. We can't see it. We don't know where it's hiding, or where it will strike next. We just know the precautions the doctors have used for five to eight years to fight off the chance of spreading it. We must fight it together . . . not fight each other. If you run in a fire, everybody gets trampled. I think anyone with any common sense, and in any language, should realize: there but for the grace of the Good Lord, that could be you."

She pauses to pass out cookies and coke to the children. She pours the precious brown fluid -- as both girls watch intently -- as though transferring pure liquid nitrogen.

"All of a sudden," she reflects, "people began to realize that this wasn't just a gay man's disease. Like with all the children who acquired it. As soon as people started to realize that, they felt threatened. Even school employees and supervisors -- once Rock Hudson got it . . . . Now when you tell a teacher your child has AIDS, she can get crazy."

"CHERRY COKE!!!!" screams Kerina. She spills a bit of her drink on Keoke's beautiful dress. "OUTRAGEOUS!" she says, like the commercial she saw on TV.

"Where do you get the strength to do this?" I ask Doris. I am thinking how hard it would be for me to handle even one creature, no matter how sweet and loving, singing out the Cherry Coke commercial, and spilling it to boot -- let alone *seven* children -- let alone the hospital visits, injections, and worry.

I am not surprised by her answer. "I have to say: the Good Lord.

"Nobody said the road would be easy, ever. Somehow our society has forgotten all the teachings that we've had from the Bible, and from just plain common decency. Sometimes I can picture Job, and the trials he went through. Even his wife had gotten tired of it! But he just hung right in there. And that's the way I look at it: nobody promised that the road was going to be easy. When my husband died, I wondered . . . how am I going to make it? But you're gonna make it. You're just gonna keep going, and keep pushing."

I am preparing to leave now. It is late afternoon. As I stand, putting on my jacket, a nurse comes in with a letter. "This came in after the *Woman's Day* article," she says. "We've been saving it for you."

Doris takes the letter and, as I wait to say goodbye, starts to read it. She moves her lips very slightly. Keoke is hitting one hand against a chair, just for the fun of it. Kerina is tugging at Doris's arm, at her dress. I can see that Doris now is holding back tears.

"Are you laughing Mommy?" says Kerina.

Doris says nothing -- she hands me the letter. It's from a reader who does not sign her name. A few folded dollars are included with the crinkled paper. "You must be an angle" says the letter, meaning "angel." The author says how much she admires Doris's courage and spirit. She will pray for Doris. She blesses her.

I look at Doris who has still not spoken. She is a big, plain woman with a ready laugh and a clear head. She looks away from me, embarrassed by what the letter means to her. Doris Williams, R.N. is a woman with seven foster children, one of whom has AIDS. She is sitting under pipe cleaner hearts in a hospital and she will not allow herself tears from the praise of a stranger.

I do not know how to say goodbye to her. I do not know what to say as I leave her. So I quietly kiss her hand.

Chapter 11:
Two Addicts with AIDS

In 1985, New York City had a third of all the AIDS cases in America. East coast cities like New York and Newark began to see a shift in the direction of the disease: the percent of new AIDS cases occurring in homosexuals began to decrease, while the proportion of drug addicts -- many of whom were heterosexual -- increased.

Like most Americans, I have no direct knowledge of the lifestyle of a drug addict. I began to realize, however, that it was important to include into this AIDS chronicle the experience of such people with AIDS. Here are interviews with two heterosexual drug addicts. They added to my own growing awareness of how widely the AIDS net was spreading -- and could continue to spread.

Cheryl

AIDS has been swept off the front page of the *POST* today, replaced by Hurricane Gloria and a juicy "Singles bar murder." Inside is a report of a controversial Army study: are Berlin prostitutes giving AIDS to heterosexual GIs in Europe? Or, some have wondered, are the soldiers simply afraid to admit their homosexual and bisexual experiences?

With severe storm warnings and the rain already beginning, I've decided to hire a car service and have the driver wait during my interview. I'll have a definite ride home despite the hurricane.

I pass through the lobby of my apartment house to the car already waiting in the driveway. I hear a maintenance man joking with a UPS driver. The driver has gotten ink spots on the other man's hand. "Now look! I have AIDS!" They laugh together heartily. They cannot have seen this disease up close.

The rain is half-hearted. We've got hours before Hurricane Gloria arrives in full. In thirty minutes, we're in Flushing, a formerly industrial part of Queens that now is middle class residential . . . my Chinese driver tells me the neighborhood is Irish, Jewish, Chinese, and Black. He knows the area well and soon the car is in front of Cheryl's building.

It's a large, low apartment house, set far back from the road. Gray and maroon squares of slate create a varied patchwork sidewalk that leads the distance to the foyer. The squares are wet and astonishingly slippery. I almost take a bad fall, which unnerves me, and I step inside gingerly.

"That's dangerous!" I say to a tall black man. He stands in front of the locked door to the lobby. His pants and shirt are as gray as the slate; his belt almost matches the maroon. He seems to be blind.

He makes no reply, but extends his right arm slowly, pointing to dozens of doorbells on the wall. His gesture is stately, like an omen I don't understand. His eyes look past me and are distorted, off center. Have I suddenly stepped into an Ingmar Bergmann film?

I ring Cheryl's apartment and am buzzed in immediately. The man has vanished. The lighting in this building is harsh. Hard, white walls with decorative streaks of black under fluorescence. The elevator lining is Chinese red.

I arrive at Cheryl's door. She sounded peppy when we spoke on the phone. She has decided to give some interviews, a newspaper article said, to alleviate her isolation . . . alone all day and living with her mother now that Cheryl has AIDS. The newspaper photo showed a woman in her thirties with dramatic, even glamorous, lighting and makeup.

"I won't wear makeup when you visit," she had warned me.

I assured her that she didn't need to. "Don't worry, just because I used to work for Avon," I told her.

She laughed. "That's a good one!" I was surprised by her cheerfulness, and I enjoyed it.

Now, standing at her door in the stark and barren hallway, I feel a moment of apprehension. I know hardly anything about drug addiction. I am not sure what to expect. I ring the bell.

She's not as formal as her newspaper photograph. She is paler, and her features are more extreme. But she is certainly pleasant looking. Her short, reddish hair, despite its thinness, is like a pixie's. She's immediately easy to talk to. My quick reaction, in fact, is that she is fun and I like her.

The apartment is dim but comfortable. Two cats amble through the living room, and a small, black and white dog joins her in the arm chair. I set my tape recorder onto the table between our chairs, beside a stuffed toy dog staring down at the real one.

She tells me her father was a tailor and her mother is a statistical typist. Cheryl was an only child. At nineteen she moved to Manhattan, tired of her mother's complaints. Cheryl had been dancing in the disco's till five in the morning.

"I had a lot of gay friends and my mother didn't approve. In that day, there wasn't so much gay liberation. I'd come home late from the disco's, then turn around for work or go to beauty school. It was easier just to move into the City." She held a variety of jobs, eventually managing a boutique. As she talks about those years, it seems she once had enormous energy and capability, despite the drained, flat voice I hear now.

Ten years ago, at twenty-six, she'd begun to be unhappy with the noise and constant pressure of Manhattan. "I'd been on a fast pace for such a long time . . ." She wanted to get away. "I took a course in Spanish and moved to Puerto Rico," she says as though describing a change in nail polish. She traded places with a friend who wanted the "spotlight" of New York City. Cheryl was looking for quiet and peacefulness. Through her friend she was able to find another boutique to manage in Puerto Rico. She enjoyed the change.

"Now," I say, unsure how to launch into the topic. "You were an IV --"

"Yeah."

"Is it fair to say 'addict?' Is that accurate?"

"Yeah." She says it with a shrug.

"When did that happen to you?"

"In 1978." She had arrived in Puerto Rico in 1976. "I met Richard, my late husband. We fell in love." They were never formally married, but lived together in a "common law" relationship for seven years.

"Was he Puerto Rican?"

"Yeah. And I didn't know he used drugs. About a month or so after I met him, he drove us to this raunchy neighborhood and said, 'Listen, I'll be right back.' I could tell he was doing something because I had a drug history, myself. LSD, diet pills, and valium prior to Puerto Rico. But never heroin or anything like that. I got a feeling in my gut, you know? You say to yourself, 'Something is not right here.'

"Three days later, we go back to the same spot. He says, 'Listen, I owe this guy twenty dollars. Can you give it to me?' Then I was very suspicious. The third time, he said, 'Listen. I have to tell you my secret. Do you want to get high?'

"I said, 'Sure. Why not?'"

"Prior to your meeting Richard," I ask her, "did he have much drug experience?"

"Oh, for YEARS!" she says. "Yeah. He was a Vietnam vet, so that says it right there."

"He got the habit in Vietnam? That's where it happened to him?"

"Yeah. The opium. He was one of the many Puerto Ricans that

were drafted. He was living in Africa at the time, so he didn't have to go.

He went anyway, because he felt it was his duty. Over there, he got addicted to opium. There were no opium dens here when he returned, of course, so he went for the next best thing."

As I listen to Cheryl, I am boggled by the connections I'm encountering, the links to topics I haven't been thinking very much about. Vietnam is "over," isn't it?

I'd started out writing about AIDS as a kind of experiment, at first not expecting to be learning about drug addiction at all. Now, in the midst of really talking for the first time in my life with an addict, here is another major icon of the century, Vietnam. I'd read about these connections before, of course, but they were only distant concepts. Now I ponder more immediately the invisible tremors still occurring from Vietnam. How many newly created addicts came home with Richard? How many others have been sharing bloody needles? How many others will get AIDS or pass it on? Cheryl is matter-of-fact.

"What was his occupation?" I hear myself asking. "How did he pay for it?"

"He stole," she says gently. "He hustled. He conned. He'd do whatever he could."

"He didn't have a job, per se?"

"No. He was a hustler, he moved his ass. If he could get a job fixing something, he'd do that. If he had to stand on a street corner and ask for quarters, he'd do that too. He'd do whatever."

"When you met him, how long had he been back from Vietnam?"

"A long time. When I met him, he was thirty-one and I was twenty-eight. He'd come back from Viet Nam in 1969."

"So," I say. "He'd been back nine years before you met him. And during ALL NINE YEARS he had been on heroin?"

"Yeah." Nine years.

"I've always had this image, Cheryl, that heroine ravages you, it would tear you apart. That you couldn't survive nine years."

"Long as you've got money," she says, "you can survive." It's such a simple equation.

"All right. Richard had been on the habit, and it was entrenched, a solid part of his life. Then he met you and said to you one day, `Would you like to get high?' And you simply said, `sure?'"

"Yeah." She says it with another shrug. I laugh, I can't help it, at the casual way she acknowledges her decision in an instant and its overwhelming consequences on her life. "People find that hard to believe," she says, "I know. But it's true."

"Did you know it was heroin?" I hear myself trying to give her the benefit of some kind of doubt.

"Well . . ." she says heavily, "I knew he wasn't talking about smoking a joint!"

"Then what happened?"

"Well, see . . . the first time, he didn't want to get me in my vein. He didn't want to mainline."

"Why not?"

"He was afraid how I was going to react . . ."

"Is that a more intense way to take it?"

"Yes. If you just inject it -- what they call `skin popping' -- it doesn't go right into your bloodstream but the high isn't that intense. Nobody does that much. Everyone mainlines, direct into the vein."

"And -- what did it feel like?"

"Nothing very much at first, until I finally mainlined. Then you get an enormous rush, a sensation of euphoria. It's wonderful. I really liked it! That's why I was on it for so many years."

"How long does that feeling last?"

"A long time. Eight hours, twelve hours."

"And during that time, you could function?"

"Yeah. I was now an assistant clothes designer. I had a night job, too, in a discotheque. I found it easy to function on heroin."

"Do you think people could tell you were on it?"

"Well, you nod out a lot."

"You mean like this?" I drop my head onto my chest, as though incredibly fatigued.

"Yeah," she says. "That's what it means."

"Were you nodding out a lot?"

"Not so much at that point."

"And, while you were working, were you in a great mood?" She considers.

"No -- that's more of a cocaine high. Heroin's very mellow." She stretches out the word "mellow", saying it relaxedly, the way it might feel.

"So, you're doing your work, and you're feeling fine and mellow. During the course of a week, how often were you getting high?" I expect her to say, several times a week.

"Once a day."

"Every day? Sunday also?" She laughs at the quaintness of thinking she wouldn't need it on a weekend.

"Sunday, also. No day off for Sunday!"

"How much did it cost?"

"Well . . . in the beginning, it wasn't too bad. Maybe $20 or $40 a day. But then the drug started to overtake me. Once a day was not enough. The more you get, the more your body calls for. It's a physical need. You get sick. You get pain, intense pain, in your stomach. It's not like cocaine, you know. Cocaine is a mental habit. If you use cocaine, you use it because you like it and it's a great high. It's a rush, and it gives you a lot of energy. But with heroin, if you keep taking it and get the habit, then when you stop, you get sick!"

"Cheryl, $20 to $40 a day is $140 to $210 a week! How much money were you making at the time?"

"At that time, I wasn't paying rent. A place to live was part of my wages. I also had two jobs, so I was able to support the habit."

"Did you ever think about the future? Any question like that?"

"I was never a big future-thinker," she says, poking fun at herself. "I could get hit by a car . . . . It never came to that, though. I first turned on with Richard in early April '78. By May, the habit was completely out of hand." I shudder at the speed and force the drug must have had.

"But -- Richard was on it all those years. It didn't get out of hand for him for a long time, right?"

"Sure. But when you run out of money, that's out of hand. Then you have to start doing shit. You start selling your jewelry. You start using your credit card to buy booze, and re-sell it for money. You find any way you can think of to afford the habit."

"So -- after a couple of months, you were already into that mode?"

"YESSSSSS!" She says it huskily, again making fun of the captive she had become.

"You have a sense of humor, don't you?"

"Yes," she laughs. "People tell me that."

"Because, we are talking about stuff that could be very heavy, but the way you talk about it . . ."

"Listen," she says. "All that was light compared to THIS! That was light compared to AIDS." She tells me about the $2700 she had run up on her Master Charge account. And about Richard, the love of her life, working together with her at the disco -- until the boss started to notice her personality was changing and she was stealing.

"There were times I had to go to work sick, craving the drug, not feeling well. Not having the money, maybe, to get it that day. Not having the time, because you had to be prompt for work."

She talks about the people she bought from. "Sleaze balls. They don't take care of themselves. They make lots of money, but they all have habits too. So the money goes back into their veins."

She and Richard left Puerto Rico to avoid being busted. Ultimately they moved to the South Bronx, paying $15 a week for a room. The landlord was old, the tenants never paid, and he finally had given up and abandoned the building.

"Then the thieves came in," she says, "and took all the pipes. You can get nice money for copper pipes. They stripped the building -- no water, no electricity. Richard hooked up the room to Con Edison -- he was very intricate, he could do lots of things. So we had free electricity. We got a little refrigerator, and an electric stove. I went next door, to friends, to bathe and wash dishes. They gave me a key.

"I became a waitress. Richard hustled, fixed things, whatever. We were both on the drug daily. As a waitress, you have tips every day. After work, we'd get high."

I consider the agility of someone waiting on tables. Pleasantly remembering who got the fried chicken . . . Table 16 wants more water . . . the woman by the window wants her burger sent back to the chef.

"You keep telling yourself," she says, "'I've got to act like a waitress!' You try to smile even while you're thinking, `go fuck yourself, you'd better leave me a tip, I need a tip.'"

Cheryl tells me, step by step, of her unsuccessful efforts to get off heroin, including a hospital stay in November, 1981. She had wanted to "detoxify" -- no heroin, no methadon. She had intended to be "clean." Her plan was to wean herself away altogether, using lower and lower doses of methadon till she could tolerate the absence of the drug in her system. Heroin gave her a high she liked, but it was impossibly expensive. Methadon, the chemical various programs supplied to addicts to replace their heroin, had painful effects on her bowels.

So she'd entered a hospital. "They take you from 80 miligrams of methadon in two weeks down to nothing. Which is very fassssssst, let me tell you." Her voice is mournful. "It really leaves you sick. I got home from the hospital one day," she says. "The next day, I said, `Richard, listen, I can't stand it!' It was Thanksgiving."

"What had they said when you left the hospital? Did they think you were really `well'?"

"If they thought you could just go on with your life and be perfectly fine . . . they're out of their minds. Once I was completely clean, I felt horrible. My body was still craving the drug. So I went back on again. Back onto heroin."

Back and forth. She tried many times to kick the habit. Finally she and Richard went back to Puerto Rico with a plan to "chill out," to kick the habit. Yet on his family's farm, they still got high until they ran out of anything they could sell. Then they had no choice: they were forced to get off the drug. There was simply no heroin left to have.

"What did you experience?"

"Can't sleep. Can't eat. Pains, chills, hot . . . arrrrgh!" She stayed suffering in one room, Richard in another.

"So you both kicked it!"

"Yeah." For a moment the phrase sounds strong and definitive: kicked it! It was the second half of 1982, three years ago. Richard then went into a psychiatric hospital on a lawyer's advice; it was a method of increasing his Veteran's pension. He would get out on weekends, Cheryl tells me. "And, once a month we'd get high again."

Later, after this interview with Cheryl is completed and I listen again to the tape, I can hear a plaintive tone in my own voice: "But, Cheryl, you had just just kicked the habit!" As though addiction itself were not as overwhelming as AIDS. As though a happy ending to this story were more immediately possible

"Yeah," she replies with a shrug. "But we got it *controlled* at that point. That meant that, once in a while . . . ."

Richard died in May of1984. "Cirrhosis of the liver. He was also a drinker." Checkmate.

Cheryl came home to live with her mother on June 11, 1984. She got a job in the accounting firm that employed her mother. From June to November, she got high exactly three times. Three times only, she tells me, like a good little girl.

Then -- "weird things started happening to me. Rashes. Fevers. I wasn't feeling well, and it got worse. And then it got worse still. By Thanksgiving, I was very sick. The doctor diagnosed acute bronchitis. On December 2, I went to the hospital.

"They put me on oxygen. They put a line above my chest for intravenous feeding. And they told me, `We think you have AIDS.' I was so sick, and in so much pain, I could hardly react.

"Things kept going wrong. They didn't expect me to live. Respirators, biopsies -- snipping out a piece of the lung. I had pneumocystis carinii pneumonia, the pneumonia only associated with AIDS. It's powerful. It's much more powerful than regular pneumonia.

"I'm in Intensive Care. A fungus took over my whole body. It took over my ears; I could't hear. I couldn't talk. I had so much fluid around me, I had two cardiac arrests. They had to give me so much 100% oxygen to the brain, it usually leaves you brain damaged. It isn't healthy, but I was lucky.

"I had two collapsed lungs. Drainage in my lungs, that was incredible. I had a tracheostomy also." (I see the small, triangle-shaped scar on her throat.) "They told my mother, `If she lasts a night, it's going to be a miracle.' And I did. They tried different medications and somehow I got better.

"I left the hospital on Valentine's Day. I could hardly walk, came home by ambulance. I'd lost all my muscle tone after three months in the hospital."

That was six months ago. At first, while she was recuperating, she tried to deny she had AIDS. Then, she called the GMHC -- Gay Men's Health Crisis.

"They're a wonderful organization. They don't just help gay people. You know, I think the problem with this disease is, so many people are anti-homosexual that in the beginning they didn't allow for proper funding. GMHC helps *anybody* that has AIDS. They send people to your home. It's very important." She now has a volunteer who visits her regularly.

"I don't have much of a hope for a cure," she says. "I'm frightened of the way I'm going to die. Not of death itself -- Richard's waiting for me, and I know it. But I hear so many stories of lingering and suffering, of people getting to be a skeleton. That's my basic fear. My doctor is optimistic that I'll be able to last long enough till they come out with something."

"Suppose that happens. What would your attitude be toward getting high?"

"I don't know. Don't think I wouldn't like to! I have dreams about it. It haunts me in my dreams. In my dreams I say, 'I can't get high. I have AIDS.'"

I invite Cheryl to address you directly.

"What I really would like to say to them is, something about the disease. There is so much hysteria. I saw a woman on the news last night. I wish I had her here, I would strangle her. She was such a cold-hearted bitch.

"I want to tell the public to become more aware of the way the disease is transmitted and the way it's not. AIDS is a weak virus. It's very weak outside the body. It's not fair to people with AIDS that everyone's so panicked over nothing, over casual contact."

"If you were doing things over again, Cheryl, what would you do differently?"

"I WOULDN'T SHARE A NEEDLE WITH ANYBODY! And I wouldn't let Richard do it, either. But," she says anticipating my question, "the other part I wouldn't have changed."

"You would still get high?"

"Yeah."

"Why?"

"Because I liked it. I just liked it. I can't be a hypocrite. I liked it!"

"And if you could make public policy?"

"I'd legalize syringes. Everyone could have their own needle, and it would eliminate quite a bit of danger. People understand if you're gay. Some people even understand if you have AIDS. But once it gets to drugs, people are very prejudiced.

"I know lots of professional people who use drugs. A lot of

100

people get high on heroin. Owners of companies -- I know a president who lost his company. I knew a girl with a high position in a bank, and she was snorting heroin. It's not just people in ghettos. There's a lot of people doing it."

I thank Cheryl sincerely and say good bye.

The sky is darker outside, as the hurricane approaches. I'm glad the car is there to take me away. I walk to it carefully over the slippery stone path. The wide, wet slabs of rock are clearly dangerous. I realize just how easily I could fall.

Manuel Ortiz

When I arrive at Mt. Sinai, Dr. Chris Ritchlin takes me to Manuel's room. Dr. Ritchlin is Chief Resident, Department of Medicine. A heterosexual male with AIDS has agreed to be interviewed for *CHRONICLE*.

"At any moment in time," Dr. Ritchlin tells me, "we have from ten to twenty patients with AIDS here. Many of them are gay. Drug abuse patients, whether they have AIDS or something else, are not put onto an open ward unless they've been off drugs for at least thirty days. That's the case with Mr. Ortiz."

He escorts me to the bedside of Manuel Ortiz. The room is partitioned into four sections. The other three patients are Caucasian, older men. I don't know anything about their illnesses, but I hurriedly notice all three seem shrunken and deflated, like October pumpkins still outside in December sun.

Manuel is a handsome man. He lies flat on his back wearing only brown paisley pajama bottoms. An older woman in sombre clothing is saying goodbye. She blows kisses to him, over and over. She grasps at the edge of his hand, not wanting to leave. She helps, before she departs, to close the curtain that wraps Manuel and me in privacy. As the curtain is closing, I see her blowing more kisses at Manuel.

"*Hasta mañana*," I recognize in Spanish. Now, I see she is blowing kisses at me as well. Her expression is anguished and sad.

"Take your time," Manuel says softly as I plug in my tape recorder and settle into the chair beside his bed. His words contain small pauses. Each one seems to require a large amount of air.

"So -- your name is Manuel Ortiz," I say aloud for the tape. I sound like a Social Worker, I think. He doesn't know me, my personality, or what I know or feel about AIDS. He is gently submitting to my questions, just because.

I explain that I'm doing a book about AIDS, interviewing all kinds of people. "The only requirement," I say, "is that you tell the truth." I offer him the chance to use a cover name. He feels fine, he says, both about telling the truth and being Manuel Ortiz.

He is forty-two and was born in Puerto Rico. When he was eight years old his mother, who moved to Brooklyn "to get a better life," sent for him.

"What did your family do for a living?" I ask.

"In Puerto Rico? Oh man!" I smile at the romantic, dreamy gusto with which he remembers. "We were fisherman. That was our only way. We had a farm. We produced all kinds of foods. Mainly we ate off the fat of the land. We lived in a little hut, real shabby-like. But that's where it started."

The necessary slowness with which he speaks gives a stately quality to his description, like the formal beginning of an adventure. I am struck once again at the special opportunity this project is providing me to talk intimately with people I would normally never know.

He'd been living with his grandparents. His mother had told him his father was dead. "For twenty-one years, I believed he was dead. Back in 1962, I went back to Puerto Rico. I was already a grown man. I was taking my life over, I was working down there, and I was engaged for a while to a girl in Puerto Rico. Her name was Pilar. We was going to get married, but I didn't have my last name -- my father's name -- and it was required.

"I went to my grandmother and explained my problem. She said, `Look. Your father's not dead. Go to these places, and ask these different people, and they'll tell you where he lives.'

"And I did that. When I met him, I thought he was, perhaps, the most gentle human being I've ever met in my life. Such a gentle person. And he knew he had a son, somewhere. He knew his son would eventually, one day, pop up. Which I did."

Manuel learned then his father had been a construction foreman, and was supervising work on a bridge, away from his home. He met Manuel's mother on that trip and at first he didn't tell her he was married. "It was a mistake," Manuel says simply. He pauses. "You have to 'scuse me, 'cause I'm gettin' out of breath a little bit."

"Yes," I say, as he waits to recover. I hear coughing on the other side of the curtain. It's like a faded shower curtain. Dingy manila with thin vertical stripes. While I wait, I examine the stripes. Blue-yellow-green-orange. For about twenty seconds, I find it interesting to stare at them. They could get to feel like bars, though, after a few days.

Manuel wears an oxygen tube clipped into both of his nostrils. His arm is receiving liquid from the clear plastic pouch above our heads. A black metal TV is suspended above him; the channel controller, a black lump on a cord, rests on his chest.

102

On the small table next to me is a plant and an arrangement of flowers. A card reads, "All my love, may god be with you, Mom." I see an Avon Care Deeply Lip Balm, some Butterscotch lifesavers, and an inch-high plastic Jack-O-Lantern holding a few lollipops.

"I started using drugs in Brooklyn in 1956," he says. "About thirteen or fourteen. Then I used drugs all of my life -- heroin, cocaine -- until I graduated from a program a few years ago and finally got clean. I became a drug counselor myself, helping other addicts."

"How did you get started on drugs?"

"Well, you know. Living in Brooklyn in the 1950's was pretty rough. A bunch of us would get together, mainly guys who didn't have a father. We just wanted to hang out. We started, I remember, with a $2.00 bag. Gradually, that's how I really got into it. There was nothing else to do in our neighborhood. That was it. It was only drugs, prostitutes, you name it."

"From thirteen to about thirty-seven, then, you were on drugs. Twenty-five years? How could you afford it?"

"Well, I was a thief," he says. He laughs at his simple admission. His breath comes so hard, it's a slice of a laugh. "And a con man. I never hurt nobody to get it, though."

"What kind of -- what kind of stealing?"

"The first things I used to steal was cars. Then I learned how to open doors, with `els.' They're master locks." Ultimately, I understand that els are something like bobby pins. "You pick the lock with that little el. One end goes in, the other one, you fix it up. You just gotta hear the sound, one by one. Bup, bup, bup. But then I have to give that up. I got beat up a couple times when they caught me in the act."

"So you were stealing cars and breaking into apartments. And then what did you go on to?"

"Well I went into sales."

"To what?" He's like a college graduate discussing insurance.

"Selling dope. I was in my twenties when I started that, and I did it for many years. But I got caught and got convicted a couple of times. It was on and off. Out of twenty-five years, I'd say I spent about six years behind bars."

"Was that very hard?" I say, embarrassed by the foolishness of my question. Of course!

"Not really," he says. "You live in the streets, you come from the ghetto, you don't have time to think about what's good or bad, you've gotta survive. If you can survive in the streets, you learn how to survive in prison.

"It wasn't all that bad for me. I knew how to keep people away from me. I would carry a knife with me at all times. It didn't bother me. Or any one who was black or Hispanic. The identification was mainly the Caucasians who would come in. They were the minority."

He is talking about homosexual rape, he explains. His pure brown eyes look up at my green ones. "That happens a lot. It's a sad thing, but it happens a lot. It happens mostly to Caucasians."

"When I was in jail, I got into my little cell with my roommate, my cellmate. You learn to keep to yourself. You learn not to be in people's way. Not to be in people's business. You survive, you know. Nobody bothers you. Most of the time, I knew people in jail anyway. When I got there, there was people doing time and they would take care of me."

Briefly, he strokes his black beard. It has a few white hairs. He is pausing for breath. Now I notice an open bible behind the plants.

"How did you get to carry a knife?" I ask him. "How could they let you?"

"I made it," he says. It's obvious to him.

"But what did you make it from?"

"There's a shop called `M & M.'  Every penitentiary's got it. It's for work in metals, big machines. `Metal Maintenance,' maybe. I would be working there, and I would take something like this -- " His hand rises to trace across the black metal bar on the bottom of the TV. "I would cut it on the machine. I would file it down on one of the grinders. I would file it down, real fine, till I had it like a knife. And I would go -- there's a process -- I would make the piece and I would take it to another guy, and give him a couple of cartons of cigarettes. He would put the handle on it. So it was all a process that we had."

"How did you get the cigarettes to barter with?"

"My mother was always in my corner. She was always able to send me money. You accumulate. You gamble. You sell sandwiches in the tiers. It's a hustle."

"Sandwiches?"

"My job was mainly working in the kitchen. I would take a bucket. The guard and I got pretty close. I would take a bucket of twenty-five or thirty sandwiches. Steak, pork chop, egg sandwiches. I would go sell 'em through the tiers."

"How could you get out to sell them?"

"Once you got in good with the officer, the officer really didn't care. Give him a couple of dollars. You don't get locked up in your cell twenty-four hours a day, anyway. They would open the doors at certain times, so you coult take a shower, things like that. Then I would come in from the kitchen. I would know what time they open.

"If you wanted steak, it cost you two packs of cigarettes. You wanted pork chops, two packs. You wanted egg sandwich, one pack." He laughs -- a subdued, wheezing imitation of a normal laugh -- he laughs at the lower status of egg salad.

"The penitentiary didn't have that bad a food. It's just the way it was made. We made it to sell. We put extra care into it. We made it good, on toast or rye, whatever they wanted. It was like a treat. That's how we survived."

The phone rings. "It's probably my girlfriend," he says. I hand him the receiver. "Hey!" I recognize words. *"Trabajo"* -- work. *"Yo tengo una `interview' ahora, Carmen."*

As he speaks, I read the sign above his bed:

ENTERIC PRECAUTIONS

BLOOD/BODY FLUID PRECAUTIONS
Wash hands before leaving area.

I notice an instruction for the "transporter" in case Manuel has to be moved: "no isolation garments necessary." I replace the receiver for him.

"So . . . how did you get off drugs?" I ask.

"It was a funny thing," he says. I am still not used to the subdued, breathless moan of his conversation.

"I went inside of a bank in '81, to rob this lady, you know?"

"Behind the counter?"

"No. I had been following this lady, because I knew that she had a lot of money. So when she gets the money, I'll snatch the pocketbook." I hear a horrible cough again on the other side of the striped curtain.

"By this time, I was so far gone, that I didn't really think about nobody or nothin'. So when I snatched tahe purse in the bank, what happened was that -- " He laughs ruefully. "About ten people jumped me. They caught me on the spot. Once again, they took me to jail. By this time you know, I was pretty tired. Tired of roaming the streets and using drugs. So I told the lawyer I realized what I'd done. And that what I needed was some help, because I was an addict. So the judge thought about it.

"He said, `You been convicted for sales. You been convicted for robbery. And now this. So what's gonna guarantee me that if I let you out to a program you're not gonna go back?'

"I said, `Well, that's the chance we have to take. But I don't need jail, because I been there. All it does is get me more bitter, and I come out here and the same thing happens. Maybe if I go to a program, I change my life.' And I did!"

"What program was it?"

"Project Return."

"What's the main thing they did to get you off drugs?"

"The main thing they do is they teach. They give you information about what drugs do to a person. It's a longterm thing. A twenty-four month program. A `therapeutic community' they call it. The first year you're there, you work in the house. They teach you how to be responsible. How to feel good about yourself.

"Most addicts lack that. Most of us don't really feel good about ourselves, because we have this stigma. `Once an addict, always an addict,' and `they're just no good.' It's extremely difficult for a guy coming out of jail, trying to get his life together, having all this pressure around him.

"Years ago, they didn't have any kind of programs. They had mental institutions and jail. You want to kick the habit? You gotta go to jail. There were times I would do something crazy just to get ninety days in jail. Just to have a chance to get off drugs. Just to be in a place where I could kick the habit. That was the only `rehab' they had."

"What would you do?"

"If I felt like I wanted to do ninety days to get my health back, I'd let a cop come by and drop some syringes out in front of him. That way he'd have to lock me up for ninety days." His chuckle is too weak to contain any mirth.

"So you changed your life, and you got clean. You were earning a living."

"Yes. I was happy, not an addict any more."

"Then, what about AIDS?"

"I was working with homosexuals in the drug program. I was a counselor for them and a few of them had AIDS. They told me you could shoot up today, get the virus today, and not know about it for even five years later. When I started to get sick in June, I had a feeling -- I knew it was AIDS." He means to tap his heart to signify his intuition, but his hand can only limply reach the TV controller on his chest.

"First symptoms was, short of breath. Extremely hard to breathe. Around July, I was weak and was losing appetitite." I see two cans of ENSURE Liquid Nutrition, Vanilla, on a tray near the foot of his bed.

"One day I woke up with a rash in my nose. I had seen a special about AIDS on TV. They had a guy with the same symptoms and I said, 'Oh, my God!' Everything was going well, you know. I was clean. I was working. Carmen was happy. I love my children. I have three children from this girlfriend I got now, Carmen. I love them."

"So you'd gotten involved with Carmen while you were on drugs, and then you came clean?"

106

"Yes."

"Do you ever worry that you may have given her AIDS?"

"Yes I have. She had a test. We're still waiting for the results. Carmen and I got to get married, we have to legalize before -- you know. When I die, I want to be able to leave them something, the social security benefits. We got legal aspects to take care of before I die, and I'm hoping God will give me enough time."

"Are you religious?"

"You know something? Most drug addicts are religious. That's the only place we got where we don't have to prove anything. God is the only one to really help you. Most drug addicts are religious." I see that what I'd thought was a length of cord taped to the edge of his bed frame is actually a cross. It is an inch and a half tall, made of pieces of twig and bark, a gift from his mother.

"If you were living your life over again, what would you do different?"

"Oh, boy." It is the most mournful reading of those words I've ever heard. "With the wisdom that I have now? Boy, I would do a lot of things different. A lot of things. I always wanted to be an actor. That was the only dream I ever had. I wanted to be a great artist."

He is a handsome man. In my fantasy I imagine him without the oxygen tube. I can picture him as a screen heartthrob if not a theatrical artist.

"What do you think could have been done? How could you have headed in a better direction?"

"I'll tell you," he grunts. "Back in the 1950's, there was a stigma of blacks and Hispanics. We were the bad guys. We were the junkies, the drug addicts. Caucasian people were not aware of the fact that drugs were spreading all over. So when a guy wanted to kick his habit, or he wanted to stop, they would send him to jail or a mental institution. They would just think he was crazy.

"But now in the middle `60's, white kids started using drugs. Then it became a problem for suburban people. Finally, they started doing programs for it. Before then, they didn't care, because of our stigma.

"If they had cared earlier, if they started drug programs earlier to help us get off it. That's the only thing I regret. They didn't pay much attention and now we all pay a price, including them.

"I used to think, why do I have to leave jail and go back out to the same conditions. Nobody to help you much. They'd give you fifty dollars and set you out on the streets. Before long, you're back on drugs."

"And that's how you got AIDS?"

"Sure. Intravenous drugs."

"Did you used to share needles with other people?"

"Oh man! One person . . . a million. I used to have what they call a `shooting gallery.'"

"Tell me what that is, Manuel."

"OK. Basically it's an abandoned building, or semi-abandoned." He is offering me a recipe. Most people when they get their drugs, they want to shoot right away. I had this room for them, it was my shooting gallery. They would pay me two or three dollars. It was another way to make money. Sometimes they'd give me half of the drugs they had.

"Were you providing the needles, or would they bring their own?"

"I would provide 'em."

"Is it a dangerous thing to be in a shooting gallery? Do they ever rob you?"

"Not if they know you." He means it as reassurance. "If they don't know you. Well, it's always dangerous, but not that bad. You get a hundred people coming in every day."

"So, you've used needles that lots of other people have used?"

"Yeah! That's how I got AIDS."

A phone has begun ringing elsewhere in the room. I try to ignore it, but I can hear someone struggling, and the grunt of someone failing to reach it.

"What do you think should be done about AIDS?"

The phone continues to ring. I hear the night table jiggling, but the phone just isn't reachable.

"Let me -- "

"He get it, he get it." I imagine Manuel doesn't want to lose our focus, but the struggle I'm hearing is too insistent.

"I'll be right back." I step out of the color-barred curtains and find the patient diagonally across from Manuel. I'm moving as fast as I can. A gaunt man, shrivelled, is reaching his hand out, barely off the pillow. I hand him the phone.

"Thank you," he says hoarsely. I return to Manuel.

"What do you think should be done about AIDS?"

"It's just like the drug stigma. They didn't pay attention at first. They don't realize it's going to spread. They should better do something NOW! This nation is so hung up on politics, they don't really see what's coming. If they get stuck in the stigma of who has it now, it's gonna bite them back, themselves. They don't see that. Anybody can catch it."

Between a crack in the curtains, I see two visitors looking in at us. A man and a woman. The woman is wearing a gauze face mask. Instinctively, I feel offended on Manuel's behalf. She doesn't need that, I hear myself thinking. I stare hard back at her, mentally trying to impress her awareness with the fact that I'm here, inside the curtain tent with Manuel, and I am comfortably not wearing a mask.

"I'll be finished in just a minute," I say to them. They nod and hover backward.

"Is there anything else you would like to tell readers who now know your story?"

"Well, I'll tell you. Whoever reads this, right? My immediate advice is not to mess around with drugs. You never know what's out there. Stay away from drugs."

I thank him, and pull back the curtain. As I leave, the couple moves forward to the front of his bed. The woman has removed her mask.

Chapter 12:
Hugh Cunningham –
After Jerry's Death

Hugh Cunningham's lover died of AIDS. He was one more person who made me realize how valuable the Gay Men's Health Crisis has been in helping people deal with the consequences of the disease. As simply one example of the sorrow AIDS leaves in its wake, Hugh is part of this chronicle.

He's a funky-Irish Kris Kristoffersen: reddish-brown scraggly hair and beard, wide spaced teeth, denim jacket exposing bare chest, his complexion lined and ruddy from the sun. He is thirty-nine years old. Hugh Cunningham is a contractor. He builds, paints, fixes . . . cabinets, bureaus, stage sets, rooms, and houses. He is authentic "blue collar." If you believe gay people fit a stereotype, you would probably not easily guess Hugh is gay.

He left his family in the Bronx at the age of seventeen. First he lived in the City with Richard, "a man that I met." The arrangement lasted three years. At twenty-one, he lived with a woman, Nadia. That lasted five years.

"I was in advertising at that time, as an art director. I hadn't told anyone I was gay. I was at a party with my friend Nick. He met this girl, Bonnie, and her girl friend was Nadia. We both started making out. Before I knew it -- I was living with Nadia."

"As simple and fast as that?"

"Very simple, yeah." I hear a shuddering whisper of a chuckle.

How many men are there, attracted to other males, who hide their sexual interests and live with women by default? How many never leave, and how many have children? Which of them secretly hire male prostitutes for sexual contact with a man . . . or slip away to bars, just as Hugh did while living with Nadia.

"I was living a lie," he says. "That's exactly what it was. And turmoil. I finally told her I was gay."

After various other encounters, Hugh met Jerry in 1980. They were lovers until Jerry died in May of 1984. Hugh had actually been attracted to his own gender at the earliest age he can remember. His first sexual experience with other boys was at six or seven.

"I still feel a bit guilty," he says about his sexual preference for men. He says he never became active in "gay politics" and never went to the consciousness-raising groups in the 1970's to develop more self-acceptance. Until Jerry got AIDS, Hugh never had peer relationships with gay men unless they were sexually oriented. Because of Jerry's illness, he joined a "Care Partners" group through the Gay Men's Health Crisis. For the first time, he began to feel close to other males based simply on friendship without a sexual component.

Jerry was a scenic artist for New York movie productions. If a director wanted fingerprints, fake marble, or cobwebs, Jerry could create it beautifully. Hugh mentions some of the films Jerry has worked on: any serious moviegoer has seen his work many times.

Near the end of the summer of 1983, Jerry left for a TV series filmed in North Carolina. "He was Head Art Director," Hugh tells me. "Jerry was just finishing up the movie, and I flew down to meet him. When I saw him at the airport, he looked terrific. But there was something totally different about him. Just something I sensed.

"We went out to Block Island." Jerry and Hugh owned a house on the rustic retreat, about 179 miles from New York City. They were restoring it together, as though working on a stage set. "When we got there, he wasn't feeling well, he was tired. The next week he felt even worse. Diarrhea. Stomach aches. We came back to the City to a doctor on the East Side who did amoeba testing. She took a blood test.

"I went with him that first day, but not the next one. It was early in the morning. Jerry came home and woke me up. He started crying. He said the doctor told him he had `a little case of AIDS.'" Hugh's laugh is dry and wispy, just the husk remaining from a joke that had long ago withered`

"`That's impossible,' I told him. `They can't say you have AIDS from just one blood test.' I spent the next three or four days checking with everyone I knew. We got an appointment with another doctor and he said, `All you have is colitis. You've been overdiagnosed.'

"At some point that summer, we went to a priest in Worcester, Massachussetts. He does healings once a month in this big auditorium in Worcester. It was an unbelievable experience. He talked about God, how God doesn't want people to be sick. He was very charismatic, for about six or eight hours. He goes around touching people, and they often pass out. While he's doing that, we're singing `Jesus, We Love You,' over and over.

"When we left, Jerry said, `Oh, I'm so glad I don't have AIDS!' He felt better for about a week or two.

"We went back out to Block Island. But now Jerry was getting sicker again. We were working on a lot of the house, so it was opened up, some of the walls down. It was getting colder. Jerry was crazy about that house, and he tried to work with me on it. He'd work in the mornings, but he was weak. He'd go to bed at noon and sleep a lot."

"That must have been very upsetting," I say. I imagine wanting to believe one's friend does not have the dreadful disease, wanting to believe he'll get better . . . but watching him set the hammer down weakly, seeing him head for bed in the middle of the day.

"I had put the whole AIDS thing out of my mind. It was `colitis.' I suppose somewhere I really knew it was AIDS, but -- " He shakes his head. "By mid-October, Jerry was getting worse still. We decided to go back to New York. Fevers were 103, 104. A friend suggested another doctor who'd been working with AIDS.

"This doctor has a tiny waiting room. It was jammed, and everyone in the room seemed to have AIDS. I was terrified. I sang it to myself again. `Jesus, We Love You. Jesus, We Love You.' There was a black man across from me, I guess he had pneumonia, coughing like crazy. Three or four other people, all of them looking so terrible. It was frightening. I sang the song over and over to myself like a mantra."

Once again, I hear the jittery exhalation that is this unhappy man's laugh at himself.

"By early November, it was clear Jerry had to go into the hospital. But the doctor didn't have admitting privileges, so the protologist had to admit him. It was horrible. I took Jerry to the Emergency Room at 7:00 in the morning, but then I had to go to work. That night, I had messages on my machine from the Emergency nurse -- `Come over right away, your friend Jerry is very upset.'

"I got there about 8 o'clock that night. Jerry was still in a cubicle and had not yet been admitted. In fact, he wasn't allowed in till the next day. They needed a private room, they said, I guess because it was AIDS. Nobody admitted that officially, but they put him into quarantine. When he tried to go to the bathroom, this janitor who was cleaning it told him, `GET OUT OF HERE! You have AIDS!'

"It was so hard to comfort even myself, but I tried to be good with Jerry, to do whatever I could. I just pushed away my feelings. I stayed with him that night. Finally a nurse gave him valium and he went to sleep there in the Emergency Room.

"One intern, a woman who did antigen tests on his arm -- they inject tuberculosis and bacteria to see what your immunity is -- she was cocky and said, `these tests are a waste of time. You've got AIDS.'

"He was finally diagnosed as having `CMV Colitis.' CMV is some minor virus that people normally can handle, but with AIDS your immunity can't fight back. He was allowed to leave the hospital, but it was clear he needed someone to care fo him. I decided I had to move in. We had separate apartments, and I was still paying the rent on mine. We had no money now but I moved in. Nothing gotbetter.

"He lost weight, so much weight. The diarrhea wouldn't stop. They were still saying it was colitis. I went out and got a nutritionist. I started a whole macrobiotic thing. It became a special occupation. You go to 14th street to get the Miso bean curd, you go someplace else to get brown rice, you go someplace else to get the special vegetables.

"I was trying to work and take care of Jerry too. Get up, make breakfast, go off to do a construction job on a big kitchen, come home to make lunch, go back to the construction. More and more it became clear to me, whether I wanted to believe it or not: it was AIDS. It really was."

In January, Jerry was moved back to the hospital. A month later, Hugh joined an AIDS support group at the GMHC, despite his initial apprehension. "Eventually, I became relaxed with the idea of going there," he says. "It was an emotional help while I had this, like, full time job. I was living at the hospital. Just cleaning the diarrhea. . . ."

"Tell me," I ask. "Do you always laugh like you just did now? Just in the middle of whatever you're saying?"

"Yes," he says. Again I hear the fluttering whisper-chuckle I'm getting used to. "When I'm nervous."

"And, can you tell me, what's making you nervous right now?"

"Just talking about these things," he says. "Instead of crying, I laugh. This was all extremely painful." After a sip of coffee, he says, "You know, I think I used to be funny. I've lost a lot of my humor now."

Jerry was "a big guy" when Hugh had met him, but went from 210 pounds to less than 50 when he died. I make Hugh repeat the figure to be sure I've heard it correctly: less than FIFTY pounds.

"Yes," says Hugh. "He was already down to 110 when he re-entered the hospital in January. By that time, I 'd called his family. They live down South. I thought he could die and I wondered, could his family sue me somehow? I was scared, and I didn't know what to do.

"Had Jerry's family known about you all along?" I ask him.

"No. I'd never met them. I saw them for the first time when they came here. I called and said, `I'm a friend of Jerry's, and I'm taking care of him. He's really sick.'

"I went to the airport to meet them. I was so nervous, I went to a bar and started drinking. I actually just missed them. When I realized what time it was, they'd already taken a cab into the city to their hotel!" He grins at me, embarrassed.

"Did Jerry tell his family about you, about your relationship?"

"No, I don't think formally. But I'm sure they knew. I remember, in the waiting room, his mother asked me --" (he imitates a thick Southern accent) "`What's wro-ong with Jaairry?'

"I said, `Jerry has no immune system left.'

"And she said, `What does that me-an?'

"I said, `Jerry has AIDS.' She turned to one of her other sons and said, `Well, ah do declare . . . ah had no ideah Jaairry had that lifestyle. Ah think we should go to lunch.' She's a very proper Southern lady. A tough cookie, but proper."

"So they did put it together and understand your relationship with Jerry?"

"I'm sure they did. They stayed at my apartment, even. Went home, then came back for a few more times in April. Then, you know, we finally decided we'd let Jerry die. We'd stop, we'd stop everything. They put him on morphine and, you know, just let him die."

His voice has dropped. There is no more nervous laughter. His eyes are filled with tears, and his words are interrupted as he pauses to wipe his eyes and swallow.

"So . . . I think the doctor . . . the doctor just . . . called his family. They said he'd die in a couple of days. The mother and a younger brother came up. But Jerry wasn't dying. It took about two or three weeks for him to die. His mother left for a dentist appointment."

"For a dentist appointment?"

"`Mah bridgework'. She left a slice of pizza and a note by his bed, saying, `I love you and I have to go. Good bye.'"

"She came up again after he died. We got into fights about money. The mother got into cahoots with the night nurse to get power of attorney. Then, after he died, we fought over the coffin and the funeral. They wanted to send his body back South in a cardboard box because it was cheaper. You know, `Why fly a coffin all that way when you can save a few hundred pounds of weight?'

"I said, 'well, I want to have a service in the City here.' She'd say, `Jerry wanted this,' and `Jerry would want that.' I had wanted to bury him on Block Island; she wanted to bury him with her husband. It was difficult."

"That was May, '84," I say. "Almost a year and a half ago. Tell me about the time since."

"I'm just now beginning to feel a little better," he says. "You know, the last couple of weeks with Jerry, I was there twenty-four hours a day. I was really sick of it, of the hospital, of the ward.

"I'm seeing a psychiatrist now. I was sweating all during one night while Jerry was sick, and that's when I started therapy. I'm seeing the therapist at least every other week. Sometimes I don't want to go, because I don't want to cry. But I'm working it through, living with AIDS every day. I went to a funeral last week of a twenty-five year old kid from my group. I've been to about ten funerals already this year, about once a month.

"Looking back on the last couple of weeks with Jerry, it was like a high. I had such love, it was unbelievable. The things you can do when you have to -- it made you feel you were Superman, you could do anything. Whatever it took.

"That last week, even the doctors wouldn't come into his room. He looked unbelievable. There was black stuff . . . it was like he was actually shitting out his insides. It was like his stomach was just coming out. They started the morphine. They gave him a huge dose. I was afraid it would kill him right there."

"How was your communication with him at the end?" I ask.

"Well Jerry was always talking about Block Island, Block Island. He wanted to go back. Once they started the morphine -- the last thing Jerry said to me was, `You're killing me.' And he spit at me."

We are silent for a long while.

"That was our last communication," he mumbles softly. "I felt horrible. I loved him a lot. I helped him die." The burly construction worker across the table from me now wipes his tears away and sniffs.

"People tell you 'you're going to feel horrible' afterwards. But they all make it sound like you're only going to feel horrible for a day or two, you know? I mean, really! But in a couple of days, I started having panic attacks -- you feel like you're going to die. The psychiatrist put me on medication. And I went to my support group. I needed that.

"The most difficult thing was having nobody intimate to share this with. If it had been my wife or something, society would have been, there'd be more people who would understand the bereavement, that this is someone you truly loved who has died. I don't think my family really understood. Some friends would say, `don't be depressed, let's go out, or go do this, whatever.' But I really needed that GMHC group where I could just express my feelings.

"May 10th was a year exactly that Jerry died. I sat around, waiting. My shrink said I was waiting for him to come back." He is sobbing very softly, then he composes himself.

"What about you socially? What are you doing?"

"Well, I started going to Dignity after Jerry died. That's a group of gay Catholics."

"Is it a club of some kind?"

"They have services every Saturday, the Eucharist, and a social afterwards. I've made some friends there. I now feel it's mostly okay to be gay. I have a whole group of friends that I met at Dignity. We go out for dinner afterward -- nice, interesting people.

"A couple of weeks ago, nine or ten of us went out to dinner. And I had the greatest time. I like being with men as friends now. A lot of things have really changed. I guess at least some good has come out of this."

"As you look ahead, Hugh, what do you imagine?"

"I think about death all the time," he says. "I never did before. Now I imagine I might have a heart attack or something."

I ask him if there's anything he'd like to say directly to people who have now read his story. Here is what he says:

"People do not choose their sexuality. I found out, we all need to be intimate, we all need to be loved and to love. That is, totally, the bottom line. I'm just beginning to understand, that I need to touch, and I needto be touched. We may not always understand that. It's not about getting your rocks off. It really is about being a human being.

"People should understand, too, that there are human beings, just like themselves, who are dying the most horrendous deaths possible. I mean I've seen things now . . . I don't ever want to see them again, but I have seen them again.

"Out of this whole thing, what I did as one human being for another was totally an extraordinary experience. Never mind that it was someone I loved. Just the fact that I was looking at someone with his spine coming out of his stomach, and would share with him, and clean his ass, and bury him, and stand there with him. I think people should realize, that's what's going on.

"If any of your readers have ever buried their wives, or their children, it's no different. Those are the feelings going on now for a great many people who are really alone. The amount of pain is unbearable.

"What gay people are doing, people should know. 1200 people each day pass through the Gay Men's Health Crisis. 1200 volunteers every day -- shopping, cleaning, going to hospitals. You don't hear much about that on the news, or read it in the papers."

He is crying. I am glad he's letting himself cry, I decide, so he can eventually get back to laughing.

When something is funny.

Chapter 13:
GMHC – Training

I'd been hearing consistent high praise for the Gay Men's Health Crisis, the leading support organization in New York for people with AIDS and their friends and families. Because of its reputation for positive impact on the multiple human problems of AIDS, I decided to learn about them up close. I obtained permission to audit a day of the longer training program given to GMHC volunteers. This chapter is my report to you of that experience.

This observer was so impressed with what GMHC is accomplishing that a portion of royalties from this book is being donated to the organization. If you wish to contribute, you can mail a check to GMHC, Box 274, 132 West 24th Street, New York, New York, 10011.

(Saturday morning, 11:00). I am in a church gym-auditorium with several hundred volunteers to the Gay Men's Health Crisis. About 15% are women. On my right is Mrs. Evelyn Arcudi, a heterosexual woman, age sixty-five, who volunteered at GMHC after seeing the play *AS IS* and "crying through most of it." On my left is a gay man who's lost ten friends and acquaintances to AIDS. Now he has two friends with ARC. He decided "it's time" that he do something to make a difference.

I am observing the Saturday Volunteer Training session -- the first of several days' preparation these people will receive -- from 11:00 this morning to 7:00 tonight. The session is convened by Diego Lopez, Clinical Director of GMHC. He is a tall, slim man, wearing white cotton pants, and a red and gray sweatshirt. He has a big, warm smile.

Diego tells us that GMHC began with only thirteen volunteer workers. "Unfortunately business is booming," he says. From about a dozen client referrals originally, GMHC now gets upwards of 110 new people asking for help each month. 60-65% of these requests are from people with AIDS. The rest are spouses, lovers, friends -- people who want to be better caregivers for a friend or relative.

GMHC is experiencing about thirty deaths a month. The number of new AIDS cases being diagnosed is greatly outnumbering the death rate, so resources are being strained. The organization is looking for a new location, three or four times the size of the present one.

GMHC volunteers sometimes exhibit "magical thinking," Diego tells us. As though, "if we just get involved in volunteering, maybe we'll avoid getting the disease." Now, however, "some volunteers are becoming our clients."

He introduces Dr. Nathaniel Pier, a young general practitioner with a private practice in New York City. Dr. Pier sits on a blue folding chair in the large semi-circle of our training group. He shares his memories of the early days of discovering AIDS . . . the early cases of KS and pneumocystis pneumonia . . . the eventual correlation of the disease with intravenous drug use. Our chairs fan out across the auditorium, with Dr. Pier at the center. We are gathered around his campfire, listening to a now-familiar horror story.

He tells us about the "single agent" theory of AIDS causation versus the 'multiple agent' theory. Single agent proponents are concentrating mostly on the HTLV-III retrovirus. But there are potential "monkey wrenches" in that theory, he says.

EXAMPLE: many, many more people have been exposed to the AIDS virus than have actually contracted the disease. Why do some exposed people get it, while others do not? Probable implication: other factors make the difference.

EXAMPLE: 80% of gay male subjects in a 1982 study had signs of immunosuppression, but only 20% had HTLV-III. In another study of 150 sexually active gay men, many were immune-suppresed, but only three had the AIDS virus. There is some possibility that one needs to be immune-suppressed *before* getting the virus.

EXAMPLE: There are many people in Africa and South America who have been exposed to HTLV-III, but who have not gotten the disease we now know as AIDS. Why not? Are there co-factors in the U.S. that don't exist in those countries?

EXAMPLE: There is additional co-factor evidence in some studies of hemophiliacs. The effects of the AIDS virus *may* not be as severe if it is contracted from blood transfusions instead of other means. Why?

The less that a "single agent" theory might explain the cause of AIDS, the less a social solution like quarantining becomes practical even to fantasize, he says. Instead, it is public education that becomes the near term approach to take.

43% of recent New York AIDS cases, in the latest Department of Health statistics, have occurred in heterosexuals. The majority are IV drug users. Over half are minorities -- black and Hispanic men. In general, however, the heterosexual population may be in the same situation now that the gay male population was in 1981-82. Education and resulting lifestyle changes now, wherever appropriate, can make a dramatic difference on the future.

There is in fact some indication that if already exposed people change their lifestyles -- to safe sex only, and drug elimination -- their ability to handle AIDS is statistically improved. More conservative living won't eliminate the disease, but its progression may be slowed. For people with ARC, he tells us, the evidence shows that avoiding "unsafe" sex and drug "co-factors" will definitely prolong health.

There is also evidence that the change of sexual lifestyles among gay men in 1982-83 is beginning to result in a diminishing rate of AIDS growth among this risk group. What about testing currently healthy people for exposure? Unfortunately, current test technology is still "extremely limited." False positives and false negatives are too easy to obtain. The most common false positive group is women who have been pregnant; there could be as many as 30% false positives for that group.

Dr. Pier emphasizes that HTLV-III is not an easy virus to catch. It's "nearly impossible for a healthy person to pick it up like other viruses." It is not casually transmitted, even among people with close daily contact. It is not transferred by mosquitos, because the virus (unlike malaria) does not have a life cycle within the mosquito.

Dr. Pier makes a special point of noting that there are now 10,000 deaths a year from hepatitis-B. He would recommend that anyone in the high risk AIDS groups to have the hepatitis-B vaccine. There is even some evidence that receiving this vaccine helps reduce the risk of AIDS, though researchers are not sure why.

As for the safe sex guidelines, he says, one of the brilliant things about them is they not only protect against the AIDS virus, but also against AIDS co-factors.

"What kind of safety is there in using condoms?" asks a woman in the audience. Speaking speculatively, he says, rather than 100% definitively -- they offer "incredibly good" protection. Especially if used with a water soluble lubricant containing spermicide, which also helps kill other venereal disease germs.

We don't really know about oral sex, he says. Interestingly, researchers have NOT been able to induce the AIDS virus in chimpanzees by only the oral route.

Diego asks Dr. Pier to comment on the safety issues of hospital apparel -- the need for wearing gowns and masks, the safety of touching people with KS lesions, etc. Clothing precautions are "absolutely not necessary!" Dr. Pier replies. If you handle bodily fluids, you should take some precautions like wearing gloves or washing your hands.

"I don't take special precautions when I draw blood," he tells us. But he recommends that an AIDS patient use his own razor, toothbrush, and hair brush. "The vast majority of people seriously ill with AIDS no longer even have the virus," he says. "They're probably among the safest people around -- the virus inside them has been depleted."

Dr. Pier stands and leaves the circle, receiving strong and lasting applause. This crop of GMHC volunteers has received its first bit of training.

~ ~ ~ ~ ~

It's quite a project, as I now consider it, taking such a varied group of volunteer citizens and equipping them for the demands AIDS will make on them. I've heard stories of "burnt out" buddies, exhausted by the process of getting close to People With AIDS who, one after another, have died in excruciating ways.

It is a system born of necessity. Gay men, at the beginning, were forced to care for their own in the jaws of a mysterious monster that many professionals wouldn't approach. As they gained experience, they quickly expanded to the teaching of others, again of necessity. A diverse but willing group of volunteers was thus established to care for people who were just as diverse and in urgent need.

Each of us in today's volunteer training session receives a packet of information -- flyers, newsletters, article reprints. There's an order form for taped cassettes on topics like "Nursing Protocols for People with AIDS in the Hospital" and "Preventive Health Programs for Gay Adolescents".

There is a hefty training manual:

> GMHC Volunteer Guidelines
> Diagnosis of AIDS
> GMHC Services
> Outside Resources
> GMHC Referral Procedures
> Legal Aspects of AIDS
> Financial Advocacy Program
> Psychological Issues (Overview)
> A Brief Summary of Death and Dying
> Working with Depressed, Physically Ill People
> Bereavement/Mourning

It's all organized so neatly on the cover page, the journey these people sitting around me have enrolled for. Like documents for visiting a difficult foreign country, there are reports and forms attached. An organizational chart, a bibliography, a Hospital Release Form, a Buddy Support Report, and many more. With a "Pledge of Confidentiality" that must be signed and returned to GMHC.

There are times during this day when I'm merely absorbing information. But there are moments I'm in awe of the process I'm observing. And of the hundreds of people on hundreds of blue folding chairs, learning what they can do to make a difference for over eleven hundred clients.

Diego stands at a podium now, frequently pacing out in front of it, and describes the various types of volunteer work available. One of the more well-known positions is being a "buddy." This can be highly stressful, he warns us. Volunteers work on teams to share experiences and give mutual support. There are now forty teams, and eighty-three various team leaders.

Financial Aid Counselors help clients through the bureaucratic paperwork of social security, health insurance, food stamps, Medicaid, etc. This job may not be "glamorous," Diego says -- in fact it's tedious -- but it's the most urgent need GMHC has. This assistance offers the most practical benefit to PWA's.

Having financial issues handled will do a lot to relieve stress for your client, he says. "All you need is, be able to write and read. We'll teach you the rest! You can be a disco dancer, a topless dancer, a bottomless dancer -- you can still learn to help PWA's handle their paperwork. You can help them know where the money is coming from."

"Many of our patients who are hospitalized for a long time end up losing their apartments and homes," he says. "Gay or straight, many are evicted." He tells us that legal assistance is another important kind of support given to clients. Thirty-five lawyers volunteer their time and knowledge to GMHC.

Diego reviews the "psycho-social needs assessment" done for each new referral coming into the organization. That's an evaluation and historical summary of the person's lifestyle, present condition, and needs.

He tells us it's okay, as new volunteers, to feel anxiety and even to admit it. Before seeing your first client, he says, you may feel terrified. "What will I wear?!" (The group laughs in nervous recognition.) "What shall I bring. Will my client like me?"

"Don't present yourself as a cure-all," Diego says. "Present yourself as real as possible. And don't expect them to open their heart to you. Don't ask --" (he imitates the question with exaggerated drama) "'How do you FEEL?' Don't! Just deal with the concrete tasks. If they really tell you how they feel, you'll be overwhelmed! It takes time to build a relationship."

"Don't go to bed with your clients, don't shoot up with your clients." He catalogs the rules very clearly, to occasional jittery laughter.

"We don't chose our clients by their sexual preference," he says. "We accept them because of AIDS. We are an AIDS organization. Our clients are everyone. We don't charge our clients a fee, and if you ever give them a bill, I will personally kill you! We are not there to get their money. We are there to offer assistance. If they want to make a contribution, refer them to Administration.

"Don't be surprised when you're dealing with straight men and women with AIDS. Especially the IV community tells us, `I want someone gay. Send me a gay counselor.' They figure we've been doing it for four and a half years and we have experience. They also know we have a lot more at stake, that we'll be advocates.

"You may wind up with a client you can't stand. Someone horrendous. A hideous `queen!' You may feel you hate this person." (laughter) "I'm telling you: some of them are not easy! And you know what? You're not there to tolerate abuse. It's a partnership. They have to do some things as your partner, and you have to do your share.

"You don't have to like the person. You could say, `Listen. I don't like your calling me at 3:30 in the morning, just beause you want to talk.' Draw the boundaries. It's a a real relationship you're getting involved with. Just because they're sick doesn't absolve them from responsibility.

"And get ready to be manipulated. What you're basically talking about is intimacy. We all have to draw our boundaries. It's a business relationship. We're in the business of helping people."

He tells us that when a person's life is ending, we need to be ready for that client to withdraw. There'll come a point when "they're not wanting to be bothered with the outside world, or with you. A point when they're letting go."

He talks about group therapy, anywhere from eight to twelve people. But he also stresses the importance of "recreation therapy" as a means of providing support. Some GMHC volunteers will be recreation therapists, hosting recreation of various kinds for PWA's. Like a movie and dinner with a group, where no one is asked to leave a restaurant because of that strange brown mark on his cheek.

Diego talks, amusing some, about the knitting workshop on Wednesday and the real value it provides. "A bunch of queens knitting, clacking gum, chattering -- but you'd better believe, lots of psychodynamics too!"

Everything around GMHC recreation deals with food. "Sometimes it's the only time our clients eat," he says. "Some can't stand the smell of food. Some can't cook. Some can't afford food. So whether it's fruit, cookies, whatever -- we always try to provide food with the recreation."

"You will NOT give medical advice, however," he says. "Say,

`Why don't you discuss that question with your doctor? I'll write it down for you so you won't forget.' Your job is referral. It's all too easy to get sucked into `doing for,' especially if you're a Nurturer, and you've got fourteen tits, and you're into nurturing everyone around you." (Hearty laughter.)

"I'm one of those Nurturers," says Mrs. Arcudi, when she hands me a mint during the break.

Diego answers a question about the demographics of GMHC clients: Staten Island, for example, brings referrals who are mostly heterosexual men and women and who apparently got AIDS from their own drug habits, or from sexual contact with someone who was an IV drug user. Similar clients come from New Jersey and Connecticut, but it's difficult to service clients that far away. "We'd need a recruiting process out there, but actually they need their own organizations."

Brooklyn, Queens, the Bronx, Staten Island -- they have all kinds of clients. "We have a six-month old baby in the Bronx. We have one heterosexual married couple with three kids, all of whom are sick." I imagine what it must be like for that family, and I shudder as he continues. "You need to be really clear about your feelings of working with a junkie. Your personal feelings can't get in the way of doing quality work and service. Our purpose is not to change values. Our purpose is to deliver a service. Period. I give two fly shits about your values . . . I don't care.

"I guess that's why we're good. That's why heterosexual families are flipping out over the fact that they got the most incredible service from a place called the `Gay Men's Health Crisis.' That's why they give incredible donations, so we can continue this work. We're into quality service delivery. Period. That's the agenda."

We hear now from several different specialists.

~ ~ ~ ~ ~

Financial Advocacy: an overview of financial alternatives. How do you negotiate rules, procedures, and stipulations to obtain "bare bones" money for a client who's lost his job because he has AIDS? We hear about N.Y. State Disability, Social Security Disability, "SSI" (the supplementary Social Security Income), and other options.

John Mocricky, who covers this section, is a precise man with wire rim glasses and a neat, gray-brown moustache. It is clear, as he talks, that he thoroughly knows his material. One patient's medical bill, he mentions, was $220,000.

GMHC is able to make one-time grants of $400 (last year this was only $200.) That's not much, he admits, but it can stave off desperation

123

while you wait for an agency to process paperwork. Or it can help bury your client with dignity. He mentions negotiations with several insurance companies who want to deny health benefits to PWA's, saying the disease may have been a "pre-existing condition" and may thus be ineligible for reimbursement.

~ ~ ~ ~ ~

HNS is a company founded in 1980 for patients requiring "parenteral nutrition," meaning feeding or nurturance through means other than the digestive tract -- tubes, catheters, injections, etc. This outside resource can often cut medical costs and make a patient feel better by being at home. Families can sometimes be taught to give treatment. Allyson Faist, R.N., who gives the presentation tells us that often no one could be better than a properly trained parent to give intravenous treatment to a child.

90% of AIDS patients will receive antibiotics, she tells us, and for much longer periods than do non-AIDS patients. In most of us, she says, our immune systems "kick in" to help an antibiotic work. That help can't be offered by an AIDS patient's body. An AIDS patient might need intravenous antibiotics for as long as six weeks. That very need may be the only reason the patient is in a hospital -- it can often be handled at home.

Insurance companies quickly realize the benefits of home treatment. Maybe it's the difference between $7,000 for care at home and $35,000 in the hospital. But the approach is relatively new. GMHC volunteers can help patients realize home care might be an option.

~ ~ ~ ~ ~

We next meet the GMHC Ombudsman: Bob Cecchi. He is gaunt and unshaven -- intense, wiry, and Italian. He shakes a little at the podium. "I didn't really prepare," he says. "I'm more nervous than usual." He proceeds to give a presentation that stuns and moves many of us, as we stare up in silence.

Singlehandedly, Bob Cecchi is a go-between, helping volunteers deal with state, city, or private services when extra help seems needed. "I'm in overwhelm," he admits. He works twelve hours a day in his paid, full time position. "I try to get the service provider to give the same service to a PWA they'd give anyone else."

While everyone should ideally have a private physician, he says, many of the people who come to GMHC don't have one. A person can feel sick on a Friday, go to an emergency room on a Sunday, and be

124

diagnosed with "PCP" pneumonia on Monday. Emergency rooms probably diagnose more AIDS cases than anyone in the City.

He tells us stories of people waiting thirty-six hours in an emergency room. Sometimes there are psychiatric issues. One patient was literally tied down in an emergency room, waiting for admission -- but because of the staff's fear of AIDS, no one on staff was willing to help the patient urinate, defecate, or eat.

He explains how it happens, depending on hospital procedure, that a patient can have a headache but receive not even an aspirin until twenty-four hours later. If the hospital requires special goggles, masks, or gowns for dealing with AIDS patients, a nurse who has finally suited up to visit him might not want to get undressed again to get a Tylenol, then suit back up to deliver it.

Sometimes, the houskeeping staffs avoid the rooms of AIDS patients. Medical wrapping papers, old bandages, tissues, spilled urine, even defecation can remain on the floor for weeks. Bob handles ten or fifteen really serious grievances a day, and he isn't always confident he's tackling each one the best way. There are "politics" to be aware of -- state agencies versus city. Sometimes the patient or care partner is inaccurate in reporting a problem.

Some staff members are simply "homophobic" or terrified of AIDS. Volunteers have walked into a care partner's room and found two days' worth of old meal trays, all still wrapped under cellophane. The patient was too weak to reach them, and no one stopped in to feed him or remove the food.

One AIDS patient hadn't bathed in three weeks because one doctor said he could use the public bathroom, but another said, "You've got PCP, you can't go in there!" The patient was too weak and confused to sort through the confusion. The staff avoided him.

One woman was denied assistance by an ambulance. Later, she had a gynecologist refuse to touch her.

Another patient with kidney failure had a hospital refuse to give him the blood dialysis he needed. First they said a nurse was on vacation. Then it was "nursing burnout." The next week they excused the neglect with "lack of funding." A social worker who couldn't speak on the record told Bob, "call me at home," and discussed the staff's intense fear of AIDS.

Bob can report that he's had some encouraging successes. The only way a hospital can correct a situation is by knowing it exists. He tells us of about the responsive and caring administrators he's encountered. Lately, he's been trying to send "praise notes" when he hears of a particularly compassionate or dedicated hospital worker.

More than anything, he says, hospitals probably need more staff.

125

Some studies show that the typical hospital patient needs three and a half hours of care, but the AIDS patient needs seven and a half. Bellevue is becoming the first hospital in New York City to have a special ward for PWA's, which should help improve care.

GMHC care partners -- volunteers like the ones in training today -- have made strong, positive impressions on hospital staffs, he tells us. That's because volunteers roll up their sleeves and help: if the patient's behind needs wiping after days of neglect by the staff, then the volunteer wipes. Some staff members became embarrassed. "If these unpaid volunteers aren't afraid, maybe I shouldn't be."

Sometimes the reaction to gay male volunteers is, "We used to think they were faggots; now we see they're loving human beings."

I seldom go in accusing," Bob says. "That approach can backfire in my face." As the tired-looking man leaves the podium, he is thundrously applauded.

~ ~ ~ ~ ~

Director of Legal Services: Mark Senak. He tells us about the legal services offered to clients -- wills, powers of attorney, insurance, discrimination. Insurance issues are growing rapidly, and discriminiation problems are "going through the ceiling."

The issue with wills is that people have a "strong system of denial," he says. They imagine that signing a will is "like signing your own death warrant." Yet without one, the relationship between two men or women living together -- no matter how long and no matter how loving -- is not recognized by the state. The only way to legitimize "gay families" for transfer of property, he says, is with a will.

He tells stories of parents or blood relations, after the death of a person with AIDS, leaving the surviving gay partner with "only the shirt on his back and his grief." Because there was no will.

Powers of attorney are also important because they can elevate the status of a partner so that a hospital will allow visiting priorities. A medical power of attorney allows a partner to make decisions if the patient is incapacitated.

Recently, insurance companies have been denying benefits to PWA's because of `pre-existing condition' clauses. Mark is getting good cooperation from the City of New York to prosecute cases where the refusal of benefits seems unjustified.

Discrimination is now the fastest growing area of need, he tells us. People with AIDS are being denied service in restaurants, by doctors, lawyers, psychiatrists, dentists, ambulance drivers, even funeral directors. He says it is illegal to discriminate on the basis of a disability, or the

126

perception of a disability. AIDS is a recognized disability. Sometimes a PWA can regain his or her job, or receive a cash settlement.

He notes that some employers have gotten panicky and are firing people *without* AIDS. Of the nine job termination complaints Mark received last week, only three were PWA's. Six were from women who were perceived as having CONTACT with someone with AIDS . . . a boyfriend, for example. Three children were asked to leave school when their mother's boyfriend got AIDS. Another woman was forcibly dragged from her desk; her lover had died of AIDS.

Fortunately, he says with a grin, many companies are being "blatantly stupid" in their termination policies. They're not saying (he imitates a personnel official) "uh, let's just look back over your performance reviews and attendance records, Mr. Foster." Instead it's (he screams in fright): "ARRRRGH! You have AIDS. You're fired!" Once they do that, he says, "you've got 'em. That's discrimination."

There are landlord-tenant issues as well. In one building, neighbors tried to evict a PWA's dog -- they claimed the dog had AIDS. (much laughter). Mark was able to help the dog stay at home.

The New York State Division for Human Rights has been given "strong direction from Governor Cuomo." They now send a delegate to GMHC once a week to catalog discrimination cases against which they move aggressively.

To date, GMHC and its volunteer lawyers have helped 700 clients. He asks the volunteers around me to please be supportive of settling legal matters early. "Don't wait till your buddy is on a respirator to have a will," he asks. Once he had to visit a hospital and hold the pen for a patient who took six minutes to sign his name. Mark had to wake him four times during the process. That's not the best way to have an uncontested will, he says.

~ ~ ~ ~ ~

Diego now covers "psycho-social" issues. We discuss what a person with AIDS is likely to feel, from beginning to end. How varied the reactions can be. How important it is that a volunteer maintains giving support. Do not taking certain reactions -- anger, withdrawal -- too personally. Don't be that grandiose. AIDS is bigger than you are.

He leads us in an eyes-closed exercise:

We are each to imagine sitting, waiting, in our own physician's office. Picture the furniture. Picture your doctor. (I picture Dr. Grossman.)

Now you are given the news. "Michael. You have AIDS."

"What are you feeling?" Diego asks.

I am "there" in the office and he has just told me. I'm in the green, stuffed leather chair across from his desk and suddenly notice: I hate that chair, I always have. The way it sucks you down in its puffy fullness. I notice my arms are quivering, as my doctor discusses details.

By now, I think to myself, I am informed, I am `sophisticated.' I know about AIDS, and I feel doomed. Can a vaccine be ready in time? "Hello, Dr. Krim, hi! How's that research coming along?"

How much time will I have? How weak will I get? Will I be able to work? Will I be able to write? What about my bills, what about my bills? I imagine my doctor's difficulty in breaking the news to me. He doesn't want to. He wishes the results weren't true. Ruefully, I see myself making it easier. I am polite, I am gentle. I am not going to let myself cry. I will not be a "difficult" patient.

I pull myself out of the chair, this leather executioner's chair I acknowledge contempt for. I reach to shake his hand. He gives me a hug.

Okay, so I cry a little.

I compose myself and head down the corridor. The lights, these flourescent lights, they're too bright.

"Now you are heading home," Diego tells us. "Notice what you feel. You are entering your home or apartment. What do you do?"

In my fantasy, I drop onto the bed. I don't fold down the quilt; I collapse, right on top of it. I watch the sky and the room get darker.

Darker. I do not reach for the lamp. I am still and silent. I do not eat dinner. I lie frozen in my fear, listening to the street sounds. At last I stop avoiding them, the thoughts of the people I love.

"Open your eyes."

I look at us all -- we've each just experienced the news. Every one of us seems altered, in a different dimension.

"Let's talk about it," Diego says.

Some felt anger. One woman decided to get her vodka and her valium and check into the Plaza Hotel. An architect made arrangements to move his clothing and his piano back to Africa. A man with a beard wondered how to tell his mother, "Mom, I'm going to die in two years."

One by one, we share what we felt. Isolation. Despair. Relief: "I don't have to worry about getting it any more." Hopelessness. Fear of pity. "I'll go it alone." Confusion. Denial. "I'll just go to work." "I'm vacationing in France." "I see myself in a casket."

We are drawn together, I can feel it. We're no longer 200 separate chairs.

A robust, attractive man in his late 30's, has entered the room. He sits outside the circle, to the left. He is a PWA and he will speak to us.

~ ~ ~ ~ ~

I won't describe him. He's made it very clear to us that, as a school teacher with AIDS, he'd be in jeopardy if his identity were known. I'll simply tell you, he looks really healthy. I'll call him "Amos."

He's just come from the GMHC "800 Men" experiment, which is also happening this weekend. That's a research project, a kind of pilot that could become a model for later efforts with heterosexuals. Its purpose is to change attitudes and boost an interest in safe sex. The 800 gay men are being exposed to various kinds of education -- film, reading material, lectures, and group discussion. All of it encouraging safe sex.

When Amos steps up to the podium, I feel an ambiguous tension in myself. Why? Ah, I realize my own awareness of the contrast between this man's outward, almost radiant appearance and the disease he carries in his body. I'm also aware that he's been listening to our discussions of progressive psychological stages for people with AIDS. How has he felt, auditing our discussion? I hear my own voice in reply: if I were he, I'd want to know EVERYTHING I could about my condition and what's likely to happen.

He has a bright smile. With guilty cynicism, I wonder it it's genuine.

"I would like to have spent the entire day here with you," he says. "I went through the training as a GMHC Crisis Worker in January, 1984." So he is a volunteer, himself.

He talks about his early feelings as a Crisis Worker -- he was scared, nervous, excited. His first PWA assignment was only two weeks after the training. "Why couldn't I get someone closer to my own neighborhood?" he'd wondered at the time. "Why couldn't I have gotten a man in better shape, as my first client?" The client died a few months later.

"You're doing a wonderful thing," he tells us, "in being willing to volunteer." But he cautions volunteers to stay alert to their own limits, to be willing to admit the truth when a situation has gotten too difficult.

Amos himself decided in the spring of '85 that he wanted to do something else for GMHC. He'd had enough of Crisis Work's intensity, and he acknowledged it. Now he would handle intake interviews instead.

"As luck would have it," he says, "I got diagnosed as having AIDS myself. It was June, the next to last day of school." He reports this to us evenly, conversationally, exactly as he has talked about his earlier experiences.

"Nothing changed," he said. "I did my first intake last Tuesday night. I'd been trained. I felt really good. I feel I'm making my contribution. So what I'm telling YOU is `trust yourself.' Don't feel you have to be that perfect volunteer, the person who gets the perfect score. Be true to yourself.

"What I tell my students is what I'll also tell you: `Do your personal best.' That's all we can do as human beings. Our personal best. Feel good about whatever that is. What I realized myself was that if I'd continued as a Crisis Worker, I wouldn't be able to do my personal best."

He is speaking to us as a coach, irrespective of his own diagnosis. I'm wondering if anyone else feels the nagging tension I feel. But maybe that's precisely the point, I think. Am I so quick to want box him into his sick-person "role?" Am I so quick to set aside all his previous experience because he now has AIDS?

It's as though he's tracking with me. "Something I also do want to share with you," he says, "are the new sensitivities I have, now that I'm a PWA. For example, every time I read about that boycott madness of parents about the seven year old girl with AIDS -- and whether she should be allowed to attend school -- I keep thinking, `what would they do if they knew I had AIDS?'

"You see the thing is, I don't feel sick. In fact, I'm not sick. I have AIDS, but I'm not sick. You've probably heard a whole lot of stuff today about `denial.' Or maybe that's in your sessions next week. Maybe you're sitting there thinking, `oh, listen to this one. He's all steeped in denial.'" He smiles, a big smile. And he is right: I'm wondering about him just that way.

"But the point is: I'm not sick till I'm sick! Nothing in my life has diminished in terms of energy level or activities. Except for the fact that there are three spots on my body you can't see. At this point.

"That may change. And if it changes, my self-evaluation may change. My point is for you to be aware of all these trips going on inside someone's head. When you read about jobs, housing, those kinds of issues in the paper, when you hear about them in a training course like this one, they may not seem so real to you. Those issues are real for a person with AIDS.

"And if I had a KS lesion on the tip of my nose" -- he points to his nose, and I imagine a spot there instantly -- "it would be a different story. People would ask, `what's that?' and I might answer `a busted blood vessel,' something like that. Depending on how honest I was feeling with that person. Someday, I may have all those spots but right now, I don't, and I'm feeling fine."

He tells us about a therapy group he's in -- six people with AIDS. The group got into a discussion last week about how each member feels. Three were feeling healthy, three were feeling sick and depressed. One of the men feeling sick got angry at the ones feeling positive.

"I think it's important for you to be able to ENCOURAGE this well feeling, if someone feels well," he tells us.

I think back to my own fantasy during Diego's exercise,

imagining myself limp and without hope on the bed. I discover that -- if I had the strength -- yes, I*would* like to continue living, to do positive things, even to smile if I feel like smiling. If others could believe in my wellness, or at least my FEELING of wellness, then I would like them to. Yes, that's definite: I wouldn't want anyone so hastily mourning me, in the way I was just ready to do to Amos.

He tells us he wishes he could speak publicly as a PWA. But as a teacher, he can't. Even though he knows he's not contagious, he would immediately be viewed that way.

He congratulates our group again on the willingness to volunteer. "Who knows?" he says. "If I ever need a Crisis Worker, that person could be sitting here now.   But maybe it'll be the other way around."

He asks for questions.

"How often do you think about dying?"

"Every day," he replies, as evenly as before. "Every morning. When I go to bed.   Much more on weekends, they're the hardest."

"What did you think when you got the news?"

"I thought, `Why me?' I've been pretty good. Why me? And why now?"

I decide to ask him a question, the question I often ask.

"If you could speak to the public," I say. "If you didn't have to worry about your job, and you could send a message direct to the world . . . what would it be?"

He thinks about it. Again, that smile.

"I'd say, `Don't be afraid of me.   I pose no threat to you. You don't realize, when I walk into a classroom, I'm exposing myself to the sneezing and coughing of twenty-nine children. I'm the one taking the risk.

"Don't be afraid of me."

Chapter 14:
GMHC – People

Here is another way to perceive the character and contribution of the Gay Men's Health Crisis : several of its people. Diego Lopez created the Training Program that had so impressed me. Dixie Beckham is a social worker who has led many groups for GMHC. And Paul Popham was one of the original founders of the organization and its first president.

Diego Lopez

He is tall, thin, and angular. His thick black eyebrows point sharply upward as do the peaks of bare skin on either side of his forehead. His ears are tapered, too. And even his moustache, like the top of a triangle. All those angles . . . and the way his long limbs swing out into space when he gestures . . . give you the impression of something piercing. A man who can be intrusive.

Indeed, he has that perception of himself: a guy who won't roll over to quietly take abuse from "the system." A man who has helped awaken decent and caring hospital workers to the particular mistreatments of people with AIDS. He designed the GMHC Volunteer Training program to be intrusive as well, to have an impact on each volunteer.

Only seconds after meeting Diego Lopez, however, the sharpness of his features is old news. You feel his warmth. You enjoy his humor. You notice the large brown eyes and their softness. While he could play the part of Satan at forty, you quickly sense his caring. You feel the power he has and uses on behalf of whatever moves him.

He is the Clinical Director of GMHC. We sit at his desk on the second floor of the organization's cramped headquarters. I climbed the same gray-carpeted stairway a television news crew avoided, lest they catch AIDS from the air in the offices. Today he wears a light blue shirt and a dark gray suit, for an NBC discussion taped early this morning (in the safety of their studio.) His necktie is gray, with a pattern of sharp red diamonds.

"I'm a social worker by profession," he says. "In 1981, this disease was called 'GRID', Gay Related Immune Deficiency. Very few people knew anything about it."

A good friend had moved away from New York City. Only later did Diego learn that Joey had left to die at a distance. Diego left his job as a counselor at Hunter College, and joined this new organization, GMHC. He earns $35,000 a year, less than if he'd stayed at Hunter.

Like other individuals across the country now, Diego Lopez devotes himself with single-minded passion to the cause of doing something positive about AIDS. How does a person become so urgently committed? What in his life and background has brought him to a cluttered office in the middle of the AIDS-care war zone?

He grew up in the South Bronx, in conditions that were clear-cut poverty. He is Puerto Rican. His father was a laborer for the airlines. All available money was put into schooling for the five children.

"To be quite honest with you, I think I was a unique, beautiful human being back in the South Bronx, but back then I didn't know that and couldn't feel that good about myself. I just didn't believe I was a good person because everything around me said: you're not."

Diego was sent to parochial school, for which he still has anger. "I rebelled at fifteen," he says. "I simply let myself fail everything. Everything. That was the only way I could get out. I thought the treatment was cruel and inhumane. Most of the Dominican nuns -- I thought most of them were sado-masochistic."

"Do you really mean that?" I ask.

"Oh yeah, yeah. They were evil. In the sixth grade -- " He laughs, a skittish laugh. "I'm glad I've gone through therapy for all this now! They would punish me all the time. The only way I knew to get back was to fail a test. That would make them crazy, 'cause they knew I could do better. I was fighting for my life, my own autonomy.

"It was a difficult environment anyway. The Italian and Irish kids at school used to make fun of me as a Puerto Rican. Unfortunately, my parents hadn't prepared me for that. All they understood was `good grades.' They didn't realize, maybe, what I'd experience.

"During this period, the nuns would bring my brother into the school room. He was a few years ahead of me. They would stand him up in front of me. `Look at him! He's got A's. He's a success. Look at you!' It was cruel to pit my brother and me against each other. Cruel and insensitive.

"I remember being in Church one Sunday. In the middle of services, after I'd received Holy Communion, Sister Hildegarde leaned over and whispered, `you've got a red, white, and blue report card!' The paper itself was white, the blue was normal grades, the red was failing. I was sitting there in Church while she was taunting me. `I guess you're glad to know this, eh, Diego? You're a failure, Diego.' The services were going on around us, I was kneeling in the pew, and she was jeering at me."

"Do you think she's still there?" I ask. I consider my own childhood in South Carolina. What a polite and good little boy I was, and how unhappy and unsure as I got my good grades. Here was Diego, on another planet altogether.

"When I came back many years later, after college, I went back to taunt her."

"You did?" I withdraw automatically at the thought. Diego didn't receive the Southern Gentleman training I did.

"I had to. I looked for her and got her. I had Honorable Discharge papers from the Marine Corps, from Vietnam. I said to myself, `Boy, wait till Sister Hildegarde sees this shit! I'm gonna really twist her head around!'" I can't help laughing at the thought of it, and at his satisfied gusto as he relives it.

"I did, I did. She was a very old lady then. But there was something that drove me to do this, and I'm glad I did. `I survived!' I told her. `I'm not a junkie!' I was screaming at her, and she just looked at me. She didn't know what to do, she was surprised and shocked. Confused, I think. Very old. But I had to do it. When I walked away, I was in heaven.

"At that point, my kid sister was being terrorized by a nun. Now it was in the East Bronx. My family had graduated up to lower middle class. I heard how my sister was being treated, and I saw my mom was not going to do anything.

"So I went to the school and I told the nun: 'I know exactly what's going on. I'm gonna kick your ass. I'm gonna lay you out physically if you ever touch my sister again.' My sister had been beaten.

"Then I went to the principal and told him exactly what I'd said. I told him I would press charges if my sister were ever touched again. The nun was totally mortified. Most of the time when I confront people in those situations, people just can't say much. I converge on someone. If I feel I'm in danger, or if someone I care about's in danger, I have to do something. Even today, if I see a patient neglected.

"Back then, as a child, I was also fighting for my own sexuality. I can remember being attracted to my uncles and cousins when I was four years old. It wasn't until I was thirteen that I started to realize, `it's not okay for you to be this way, Diego.'

"Eventually I repressed the feelings. I knew I wasn't like everyone else. In the marines, in Vietnam, I avoided taking a shower when some of the other men would mess around. There were plenty of marines around me who were screwing each other, but I was repressed by then.

134

"Maybe only 5% of the men were doing it, but I was aware of it all the time. Myself, and two other guys, we used to stick together like GLUE to avoid it! `Let's shower together when that stuff isn't happening.'

"I remember one day, I went to shower after coming back from the field. I was filthy and exhausted, full of mud. It was monsoon season. I felt like an animal. I went to my tent, then I went to the shower. And there was this guy -- he was a terror in the whole headquarters battalion, Mr. Macho, a sergeant. He'd come into the shower too. And as I was showering, he turns around and says, `You know, Lopez? You got a niiiiice looking back! Oooooh, look at that back, and look at that ass. You look GOOD!'

"I said to myself, `Holy Shit, let me get out of here!' All I cared about was surviving Vietnam. I'd made it out of the South Bronx, I wanted to make it out of there too. Forget about sex! Today, I dare someone like that to approach me -- they're in trouble!" He is practically giggling at how much he's changed. "Then, I was terrified. I never finished that shower!

"Maybe, actually, I was prepared for the whole Vietnam thing by having been so poor. For poor people, Mike, death is part of living. It's not unusual for people in a poor community not to get adequate health care, or medical care, and to die. Poor people are more used to losing the people they love. When I was growing up, friends were dying of rheumatic fever. They couldn't get good health care.

"As a poor, Hispanic person, you're not protected from death. Everyone experiences it. All of us go to the wake, the funeral. The children too. The children were shown the corpses. It's part of the culture. That prepared me, in a way, for Vietnam. I'd lived through a neighborhood of junkies, and gang wars, and killings, and illness. That made me ready.

"After Vietnam, I went to Iowa." (He laughs at the picture of himself in Middle America.) "I went into the service as a Chubby, weighing 250 pounds. I came back at 141. I was a totally different person, and I was angry.

"Vietnam was when I started to wake up to my own consciousness. I was angry watching so many men die in a futile, futile war. I was angry that my parents hadn't prepared me for the bigotry I experienced. The marine corps was a racist organization. I was a Puerto Rican kid from the Bronx in a white Southern platoon. The only reason I was treated a little better than the blacks, is that I'm light skinned. Puerto Ricans are a rainbow people, and I just happen to be on the white side.

"At a party welcoming me back from Vietnam, a friend told me about a school in Fairfield Iowa. I went there with $300 in my pocket and the G.I. bill. Nothing else. I worked three different jobs in Iowa while I was studying. I maintained honors, with years of 4.0 grades.

"I was president of the student body. I led demonstrations against the Minute Men in Fairfield, Iowa who were racist and bigoted. I developed a political consciousness. I was a history major, and that really did it to me!

"I was still ambivalent about my own sexuality. I'd met a really sweet girl. She turned out to be the daughter of the Chairman of the French department. Six days before the wedding, five days before graduation -- my family was out there, staying at her parents' home -- my fraternity had a big bash. A huge party. I went back to my room, and got 'twisted' with booze and beer.

"I was seduced by a fraternity brother. I woke up the following day. I think he should have stayed to talk with me. He didn't. He'd gone already, back to Connecticut. But what I knew was: I had enjoyed it too much. I was twenty-six. And . . . I broke off the engagement. It wouldn't have been right to go through with it. I didn't admit the reason to any of them.

"It was a very hard thing to do, because I knew I wasn't telling the whole truth. I loved Jeanine. She was a wonderful woman. But there was something important missing.

"I was thrown by what I'd done. I hid out in South Bend, Indiana for three months, on the verge of suicide. Ultimately, I came back to New York and called a kid who'd gone to school with me. He was openly gay. I said, `I've got to talk with someone.' I was lucky. I went to N.Y.U. and got my Master's degree. I met loving, good people. That helped. And I got into therapy.

"When I left Hunter College to do this work, it was like a whole inner me was coming out. An advocate. The work of taking care of those that can't. It was a perfect thing for me to get into. There'd been times when I needed help but no one was there. This was my chance to be there for somebody else.

"I'd been one of the first thirteen Crisis Workers here. I'd been at Hunter for ten years. The Gay Men's Health Crisis started as purely a volunteer organization. People were concerned about the disease. They decided to do something about it since no one else was. These offices, being able to have them -- we've only been here a year and already the space is too small -- all of our capability began with community donations.

"Nobody wanted to bury these men. We had to do everything. Feed them, wash them, fight with the hospitals. I'd walk into a hospital and terrorize the shit out of them. I almost got myself arrested. We had fights over the fact that a patient was in a hospital bed for three days without being fed. If the person was too weak to get to the door where the tray was left, too bad.

"He or she could be lying in feces. Not just gay AIDS patients, you know, but straight ones. From the very beginning, AIDS was not just a `gay disease.' But people acted like it was, and as though treatment didn't matter. That's what plugged me in. That made this cause seem important. An injustice like ethnic racism. It was another form of bigotry, only this lack of medical attention was based on sexual orientation.

"It was natural, when people heard about us, that others began to call us for help. One of the first things we did was set up a hotline. My job now is to supervise a variety of services. I developed the crisis intervention program, for example. This year, for the first time, the New York State AIDS Institute is paying for our clinical services department.

"We reach people in all kinds of ways, one on one and in groups. At the bathhouses, even, we reach people who've amazingly not understood about body fluids. People from small towns, only visiting New York City. We reach everyone we can about having sex safely. There are 200 heterosexual sex clubs in this City, you know. Only ten gay baths.

"All this stuff is becoming visible. Until Rock Hudson, this was a disease of the disenfranchised. There had been 7,000 faces buried with it. But they were unknown faces, invisible. Now people see that even a man with money and influence had to leave this country, flew to Paris to try to save his life.

"But who cared about black and Hispanic babies with AIDS? That was happening three years ago. Who cared about gay men? We're not so visible to the world. We can hide too easily.

"We certainly have white, heterosexual clients, too. We're the advocates of anyone with AIDS. And we don't want any of our clients to be buried in mass graves. We want to help them be memorialized. For a lot of clients, we just pay their funerals. They've got no one else. If you don't have anybody to pay for your funeral, you're put in a mass grave."

I still don't fully get it. Later, I realize what I've learned to take for granted -- a social security number, a telephone, a television, and a grave with at least a little square of concrete as a marker. Your own space.

"What do you really mean?" I ask him.

"Like at one of the cathedrals here. They have these graves where they just take your body, they put it in a plastic bag, and they throw it into the ground with others. There's no headstone. It's for the people who don't have enough money for an appropriate burial."

He is upset. He has been talking fast, in a high-pitched voice. I'm only vaguely aware of an image in my mind that I do not want to see: a face peering out through the heavy duty plastic, an arm, a torso, a body wrapped around itself. `They're probably not transparent,' a practical voice inside me murmurs. `The bags are probably opaque, like Hefty Bags.'

What a privileged little prince I am, I think. Worrying about my income tax, wondering about the Master-Charge bill, and taking things for granted that aren't.

"I'm sorry, Diego. I didn't realize. What do they have above ground?"

"An open plot," he says. "A designation that it's a public burial ground."

I can't resist. The practical side of me wants to know: "Then they have to wait? Till they can fill up the space in the ground with a sufficient number of bags?"

"Yeah. Yeah." At first I'm not sure he is really listening to me, he is speaking so softly. "That's all very real," he says. "We deal with that at GMHC. We're supposed to be a civilized society. People who lose people need to express something, need to do something. Some cultures burn bodies. That may seem barbaric to us, but it's important to them. A memorialization of some kind helps people deal with grief. We help make that happen."

I shift in my chair. He stretches.

"Diego. What are you getting out of doing this job?"

"Satisfaction. This is my memorial to Joey. Creativity. Selfish reasons too: I've published work here. The opportunity to buck the system. Change. To wage peace.

"AIDS is a metaphor for a lot of other illnesses and a rotten health care system. AIDS may be the tool to make a big improvement in health care. How can we tolerate one social worker in a hospital having 500 AIDS cases, inpatient and outpatient? What kind of attention can one person give to that many? We've got to improve our health care capabilities. And I'm trying to help." He leans back and stares up at his bookshelf.

"Some good things are coming out of all this. A closer-knit gay community I can be proud of, one that's visible finally. We are different kinds of people with different backgrounds. We're not an abomination.

"We've always been loved. Lesbians and gay men have always been loved by the American nuclear family. We are part of its legacy, we always will be. My family loves me. They're heterosexual, you understand. But they have always loved a gay man! Now that fact is much more visible.

"One of our people with AIDS is a seventy-year old Holocaust survivor. His wife doesn't know he's been bisexual all his life. She hasn't even known he has AIDS. He was afraid of being expelled from his own community -- again. But I think, if he finally tells her, his wife won't leave him. She's been married to him all these years. She's his first wife. She'll stick it out. I think she loves him."

"There are people in all kinds of situations who are dealing with AIDS. I get calls from Sweden, from France, from everywhere. `I had an experience with a man one time, and now I have a terrible cold. I feel panicked. Should I tell my wife?' There's uncertainty all the time now. Ed, my lover, and I just completed our wills. Because who knows what's going to happen.

"My mother says, `I don't know how you're doing it. You've lost more friends than I have and you're only forty, while I'm sixty-five.'

I'm feeling tired. He lives this every day. I'm ready to go.

"Diego -- what would you tell readers directly?"

He stares at the tape recorder, and then at me. "We still have an opportunity to be Christian, to be moral human beings. That means responding to a cry for help. Responding to someone who is sick. It doesn't matter what color you are, what sex you are, what your gender identification is. To legitimize homophobia, or racism, is a sin. What matters is, we all are human beings. As human beings, we have an obligation to each other. An obligation."

Dixie Beckham

She has an M.S.W. degree and works as a social worker and therapist. She's employed at a leading New York hospital, and she specializes in AIDS patients. Dixie has also been a volunteer at GMHC, supervising other GMHC volunteers and leading groups of PWA's with Kaposi's sarcoma. I'm curious to learn what she's experienced in that volunteer role -- what do GMHC volunteers most need from a support group? What about people with KS?

We meet in her Chelsea apartment on a chilly autumn Sunday. She isn't eager to be interviewed, but she readily talks about her AIDS experiences. AIDS is now a steady part of her life.

She was born in west Texas and came to New York twenty years ago. For a while her life fit a typical pattern: she became a Pan Am stewardess, got married, had a son. She and her husband, an advertising copywriter, lived in well-to-do Connecticut suburbs.

But the marriage didn't last. She moved back into the City ten years ago. Only then did she discover that she really identifies herself as gay. ("I think of myself as 'gay,' not 'lesbian.') Now her household consists of a teenage son, her lover Nan, and herself.

"I don't mind telling you one of the reasons I got involved with AIDS is the loss of important men in my life. My brother died in the Navy in a skin-diving accident. Somehow, as I work with people struck in the prime of their lives, I feel I'm doing something for my brother. Also, my ex-husband died of heart failure, at the age of just thirty-six. That's another connection for me, another man removed at a young age."

"What do GMHC volunteers most need from you when you run a group?" I ask her. "What do you most try to accomplish?"

"I try to thank them," she says. "I want them to know, more than anything else, they're doing just fine. Simply being there with someone who has AIDS is important. Sometimes they freak out in a difficult situation -- `what do I say when someone tells me they want to die?'

"I let them know, if they don't know what to say, don't worry about it. It's okay *not* to have all the answers. People with AIDS, like when they're first diagnosed, often feel deserted by both family and friends. Some people leave their lives forever. So part of the job for a Buddy is simply not being afraid to be there -- no matter what wisdom the volunteer has or doesn't have. I try to help them realize the real benefit they offer -- caring enough to even hear the person's question."

"When you lead a group of people with KS," I ask her, "what is your focus then?"

There are usually eight people in a group, she says, with different degrees of visibility of their lesions. "The first issue they bring up is usually treatment: what protocols are available from different doctors and research programs? That part is informational. Then, as people get to know each other better, they develop trust. Then issues about feelings can be discussed -- about disfigurement, for example. Body image. Feelings of shame. Feelings that they caused the disease because of their lifestyle.

"I always hold back and let the group do the work. It's better that way. But if no one else says it, I will: `It's a virus that causes this disease, not your lifestyle.' It is moving into the heterosexual population, and the virus impacts those human beings in just the same way.

"Disfigurement is a painful issue. If the lesions are small, people can cover them up. But that can get increasingly difficult. One person in the group was approached in the gym; the other clients were worried that the lesions on his arm were contagious. Could they get it by using the same gym equipment? People still don't know it isn't spread that way.

"Too often politicians and public health officials cover themselves: it *seems* to be spreading this way,' 'it *appears*,' 'it is *unlikely* that.' There is so much research on the basic causes of transfer, but they keep being guarded. No wonder the public stays worried unnecessarily. I had a hairdresser in one KS group. He was asked by the salon not to come back because people didn't want him doing their hair."

"That must have been a devastating thing for him."

"Sure. It was. When people are fighting off a major and often terminal illness, they need all the energy they can get. To have to handle the added stress of fighting for your job back -- often they just don't have the energy."

As she talks, I'm still thinking about the hairdresser. I can picture his arms, his hands, his sleeves rolled up. I imagine him shampooing, his hands dotted with purple-brown lesions amidst the bubbles. How would I feel, myself? Would it be so easy, no matter what I 've now learned and realize,to let him wash my hair?

"Dixie, let me be honest. I'm sitting here, just getting in touch with my own feelings. Rationally, I can say to myself, `just because he has KS marks on his hands, big deal.' But what I realized just now was that my intellect says, 'Fine,' when I pictured him washing my hair, I felt funny about it. Can you relate to what I'm saying?"

"Sure."

"Well that concern I noticed in myself, it's like superstition. It doesn't make sense from what I know, but I felt it anyway."

"I do understand the feelings," she says. "But I think there's a difference in the responsibility of politicians and health officials, in they way their obliged to deal with how *they* feel, too. They're supposed to be leading the public at large. If a politician is too empathetic . . . in other words, Mike, I can feel empathetic to how you feel, but I can also say: `Mike, that doesn't mean we're going to fire this man when we really don't need to, just because you feel a little uneasy. Can't we educate you so you don't feel so worried? Maybe if you read -- instead of just once -- if you read a HUNDRED times that this disease is not spread by another man washing your hair, or by touching equipment he has touched . . . .'"

"Or even by touching his spots," I say.

"Yes. Or even by touching his lesions."

"Well, then I went on to imagine . . . I know he shouldn't have to wear gloves, Dixie, because that's not how it spreads. But I fantasized, what if he does wear gloves? I wondered, as a kind of compromise, might I, as Average Citizen in the barber chair, might I feel better and let him get to the point of washing my hair? If he wore gloves, even if they're not needed, I might feel more comfortable, Dixie, just psychologically."

"Sure. That's a reasonable middle ground if it lets him keep his job."

"And THEN . . . you know, right, that I make my living not as a writer but a marketing consultant? I can't help myself from seeing the marketing angle of things. Well the fact is, despite the discomfort I realized I was feeling, the fact is I would like to get over it. I don't want someone to lose his job when he's not really doing harm to people. So I began to wonder, what if there were a barber shop, a hair salon, actually STAFFED by people with KS. Maybe I'd actually seek it out, as a personal opportunity to be doing some good. I need a hair cut anyway, right? I could give my business to someone who doesn't need to be cast away. I haven't yet worked out the ad campaign, you know, but do you see what I mean?"

"Someone's actually starting an organization like that," she says. "The PWA Coalition. A group of people with AIDS who got together at GMHC, maybe they even meet there. They're starting an employment agency for people with AIDS.

"This business about not wanting to touch them," she adds. "There's a lot of anger people with AIDS have about that. Like a man in the group whose mother said she didn't want to touch him, didn't want to hug him, didn't want to hold him. She said, `don't touch me.' That was hard. And they have anger at dying, too. A lot of rage at dying."

"Dixie, I hear you lost three AIDS patients one Wednesday. Tell me, you came into this work partly because you lost some people at a young age. Now you're in a situation where you're continuing to lose young people. How are you feeling about that?"

"It was very difficult when I first started," she replies. "It becomes less difficult with experience. We build up defenses to help us do the work; without them, I couldn't do it. If you're too open, if you sit there crying when patients are in pain, you're not going to help them really. The focus would become you, your pain, your empathy. So you learn to build up a perspective."

"So, on that Wednesday, how did you cope with losing three people at once, three people you'd been working with?"

"You know . . . I just don't remember, because that isn't unusual for me now. Every day brings loss. What I hope for is not to have to do this work much longer. That there'll be a cure. That there'll be really good treatments."

"What would you most want the public to know?"

"I've said it: this disease is not transmitted by casual contact."

Paul Popham

He is the picture of conservatism in his dark gray suit and brown silk tie, with his gray and brown moustache to match. He's a member of corporate management for a large business publisher. As soon as he opens the door to his Greenwich Village apartment, I can see that he fits the professional role.

Except -- there is a subtle disturbance of pink-brown splotches on his face. They could, I suppose, be considered just a skin irritation.

I arrange my tape recorder in his living room, amid soft spotlights striking porcelain, brass, and crystal. I notice books on a nearby shelf -- *The Drawings of Henri Matisse, The Complete Visitor's Guide to Mesoamerican Ruins.* The fireplace is swept impeccably clean. A dozen candles in different holders create a neat and controlled array on a glass table in front of the couch.

"I hear you're a very private person," I say. "I'm going to encourage you to be just as open with me as you can tolerate."

"You're right," he says in a mumble. "I'm not a public person. I'm not crazy about having my name in print. But I'm willing to have it happen when necessary, if it does some good."

"You're one of the founders of GMHC?"

"One of six people."

"And you're the President?"

"Yes. From the beginning."

He tells me he grew up in Idaho and Oregon. His father owned a construction company, and his mother worked at a hospital. He has one brother and two sisters and was the youngest child in the family. He studied political science at an Oregon college and spent five years in the Army, becoming a Major. He entered the training program of a New York bank and stayed in banking for ten years.

He's thought of himself as a gay man since his final year in college, when he had his first sexual experience with another man. "It just happened," he says. He is now forty-four. For most of his fifteen years in New York, while he's not been totally monogamous, he's "always had a boyfriend. The only problem I've had is that being gay affects how you deal with your family."

"Tell me about that."

"Because if you haven't come to the point where you can talk to them about it, it creates a situation where you're not being yourself. So your family doesn't see you as yourself. There's always a shield that affects you with your own family. It's something that was always a problem until — well, now my family all know.

"But until that happened . . . well, then, I didn't even *want* to go home in some ways. Or you go home and you only want to stay two days and get out of there, because you want to relax and be yourself as opposed to being this other person you think they expect you to be. That's the only problem I've had being gay."

"You first realized you were gay as a senior in college," I say, "at twenty-two?"

"About that."

"And many years passed, then, before you told your family, 'This is who I really am.'"

"Yes. AIDS actually brought it about. Living so far away from them, it wasn't something that needed discussing. But my best friend was the first AIDS case treated in N.Y.U. My mother knew him, and they communicated. So of course I told her what he had. She checked around -- she was still working at the hospital -- to see what she could learn about that particular cancer. It wasn't long, of course, till it became obvious what kind of cancer it was, so that gave us the reason to talk about being gay."

"Until then, for more than twenty years, your own sexuality was something you held in."

"That's right." His voice is flat. "Looking back, that was probably a mistake. I'd probably have been more comfortable if I'd told them long ago. But that is hindsight."

"What was it like for you, being gay in the Army?" I ask.

"Mostly it was not being gay. Once in a while I would go to Atlanta or Washington for a weekend. But I spent two and a half years overseas, one in Vietnam and one in Thailand. And I spent another six months in Okinawa. I was in training -- Special Forces training, Psychological Operations training, Airborne School. In short, not that much time or opportunity to be gay. I finally left. The military just wasn't for me."

"What about in business? Has your sexual preference ever been an issue there?"

"Not that I'm aware of," he says.

"My perception of you," I say, "is that you are one of those gay people whom others would never imagine is gay. Can you see why I say that?"

"Mm, I suppose." In fact he reminds me of my cautious, married accounting professor in graduate school, the one who always made us each sit in the same chair at every class. What a foolish stereotype, I think to myself. As though a cautious, married accounting expert can't also be gay. But Paul is the opposite of the popular conception -- of a certain type of hair dresser, decorator, or dancer.

"So you're one of the `invisible' people?" He tells me of a corporate meeting, when in the middle of a discussion about high oil prices and economic problems, his boss interjected, "Well it didn't keep those fuckin' faggots from marching in the Gay Pride parade."

"From out of nowhere," Paul says. "He just created an opportunity for a snide remark. But at this particular company, that group has also made remarks about Puerto Ricans and blacks. They had no women on staff at that time, so women took their share of abuse as well. They had no Jewish people, either; they used to make jokes about how Orthodox Jews have sex.

They didn't know they had a gay man on their staff. They were just a group of executives, so insecure they needed someone to look down on."

"Outside of business, how politically active were you, before AIDS?"

"Not at all. It's just that, all of a sudden there was a problem and no one was doing anything about it. Within nine months, three of my closest friends had died of AIDS. It was July of '81 that we first started to do something. We tried to raise money on Fire Island and got a negative response. There were forty cases or so back then. We went to disco's, lots of places, trying to get money. People just didn't think they needed to worry back then.

"But some of us knew. There was a cocktail party that summer, and somehow we raised about $12,000. We gave it to NYU for research. Gradually we began to get more volunteers than just the six of us."

"How did you get the name, 'Gay Men's Health Crisis?'" I ask.

"We were kicking it around, and someone just said the phrase. That was it. Personally, I'm sorry that's the name."

"Why?"

"I think it's limited our ability to reach out and educate the non-gay public. We always have to explain to people, `this is not a gay illness,' and they say, `well why do you call yourselves what you do?'

He interrupts himself with a strong, sharp cough.

"But -- there's a lot of other people on the other side of the argument. I can understand it. GMHC was the first gay organization that was ever able to be financially responsible to this degree. It's done a lot to help mobilize gay people across the country. And it brought a respectability to gay organizations we didn't have before. GMHC does a lot of service for people who aren't gay, you realize that, too.

"Back then we didn't foresee how much the need would continue to grow. We were simply doing what had to be done, raising money with parties or however we could. Who would foresee AIDS would be so totally consuming? Eventually we realized we needed more than a mailing list. We needed headquarters. We needed to educate. We needed financial help to do it."

"All of you were doing the work in your spare time?"

"Right. But it began to be every day, every day. At work, at night, on weekends. My boyfriend, Richard, was involved then in working with me." His use of the word, "boyfriend," seems quaint as a description of the man I'd caught a glimpse of at the door. Now, all of a sudden, I realize who Paul reminds me of: my uncle Melvin. Twenty years older and of another generation. My uncle is a CPA, in fact, and has a precision similar to Paul's. Nothing zippy, nothing flashy. But you can trust him with your life.

"It was very, very hard," he says. "I wish the Mayor, long ago, would have provided money for public education, or done it himself through the City Health Department. If we could have educated people sooner, there'd be fewer people with AIDS today. The City could have avoided some of those hospital expenses. But they just didn't see the seriousness of the problem."

He coughs, and we sit in silence for a minute. I have a particular topic to raise with him, but I feel cautious and delicate about it.

"Paul, how many people with AIDS have you known personally?"

"I don't know. LOTS."

"Now. Let's talk about you. Tell me about you." I pause. He is staring at me, quietly. I see how intense and sharp are his blue eyes. "About AIDS," I add.

"What do you mean?" he says. No expression.

"Tell me about . . . about your health," I say. "And how long have you had any sense of, of yourself being involved."

He looks at the empty fireplace, then back at me. "How do you know that?"

I can only shrug. More than one person has told me already: the president of GMHC has AIDS.

"I've known since, actually, March of 1985."

"How did you know?"

"'Cause I'd had had a spot." He says it in almost a whisper, but in the same, controlled and level tones as before. "I knew what it was. I just wasn't ready to have a biopsy done. I knew what the doctors would recommend."

"What would they recommend?"

"Nothing. Just see what happens. And hope that the progression -- I mean, when you know the disease as well as I do . . . ." He coughs again.

"Were you shocked? Stunned? Afraid?"

"No. Because I knew my blood was positive back in 1982."

"You'd had yourself tested?"

"I particpated in a study. It was one of the first things GMHC funded. They had samples of blood. And I knew. Also, to have had a former lover die of AIDS, I wasn't surprised. I've always thought it was a possibility."

"And then in March of '85?"

"That's when I had the biopsy."

"Because you were seeing more lesions?"

"Yes."

"And -- then what happened, in terms of your feelings?"

"It became something else I was dealing with."

"Do you have any other symptoms, any weakness, anything else besides the spots themselves?"

"I have a cough," he says. "For about three months now."

"When you were officially diagnosed," I say, "did anyone in the organization know of it?"

"No. Not until recently. Richard knew."

"And -- when did you tell your parents?"

"I haven't."

That stops me for a second.

"So. They learned about your being gay when a friend died, but they don't know that you have the disease?"

"No. They know I'm involved with working on it. But they don't know I have it myself. My mother's not in good health, and she's also a worrier. I just can't see, at this point, telling her. She couldn't do anything about it. I know her. I know how she'd worry."

"How did you come to tell the organization?"

"A couple of people had figured it out and they started to talk. So I met with them and reminded them of how strongly we're committed to confidentiality. They agreed.

"I didn't want to be the subject of gossip. Now people are calling who haven't called in years. They call and say how sorry they are. It's AWFUL. I think there are a few people in the gay community for whom this whole thing is something to talk about. They gossip about who's sick, people they don't even know, just to have something to talk about.

"Now some of the people who phone are people I'm not even friendly with. A friend from L.A. told me he'd heard from another friend in Sante Fe, New Mexico . . . someone I haven't seen in eight years. I guess it's because I've been so visible for so long."

"When people call you like that, how do you handle it?"

"I just try to get off of the phone," he says. I can feel his discomfort. "I say thanks, I appreciate your call, but I can't really talk now."

"How knowledgeable are you about research on AIDS?"

"I'm pretty knowledgeable. I know that if you don't get 'PCP' --." He's referring to the pneumonia. "And if you have a healthy blood count. Then, even with KS, you can do very well. I have a good white count. I haven't had anything else, nothing other than the cough."

"Do people at work know?" He shakes his head, no. "So is your strategy in general to contain the knowledge of it?"

"Yeah." He tells me someone told a reporter for *NEWSDAY*. Paul urged the reporter, please not to mention his condition. The writer couldn't promise, he said. Finally -- after a fight between reporter and editor -- the story omitted the mention that Paul Popham has AIDS.

"I'm sure you see the irony and poignancy, yes? The president of an organization, devoted to helping people fight this disease, turns out to get it himself."

"In a community like this one," he replies, "what's so surprising? It's not strange for one of the people involved with AIDS from the very beginning. In fact, there's another one of the original Board who has AIDS. He was actually diagnosed before I was. I just don't find it so strange." There is classical music in the background, soft and steady. As steady as Paul.

"What are your hopes for the organization?" I ask him.

"I don't see anybody but the government being able to solve this," he says. "Both in education and research. Some of the cities like Cleveland and Cincinnati, they don't have much of an organization to work with AIDS. They're underfunded. The biggest failure so far is not enough education of the mass population. Media coverage has tended to be sensationalist, with not enough responsiblity for level-headed education.

"The number one thing I wish the public understood is that it isn't casually transmitted. I wish they'd realize that gays didn't create it. I wish they could know how responsible we've been in dealing with it, while the government was doing nothing. Four years ago, we were the only ones who cared, the only ones out doing something."

"Do worry a lot about yourself?" I ask.

"No."

"Truly?"

"Truly. Recently I read some book that said, people who get angry seem to do better. I thought, oh God -- I'm not that type. It's not in my personality. How do I make myself angry? The biggest worry is how to get accurate information to decide what to do about myself. I mean, should I take a drug prophylactically to prevent PCP? Ask five different doctors, and you'll get five different answers."

"Suppose a book comes out called *CHRONICLE*," I say. "With a portrait of GMHC and of you as well. What would you say to its readers?"

"AIDS is a tragic disease," he replies, "that by accident has hit primarily disenfranchised communities. But those communities are people's children and, in some cases, also their parents. I think a country that's supposedly compassionate and caring should be trying to have more understanding and acceptance. I'm a political conservative. I'm not a believer, necessarily, in big government. But I would wish for Americans to realize we can be more caring."

As an afterthought, I ask him about the marks on his face.

"KS" he says.

"And at the office?"

"I'm sure they've noticed. Nobody's asked me. People are not aware," he says. "Unless you've been involved with AIDS directly, people don't know. They'll just think I have something wrong with my skin."

I wonder.

"About a year ago someone sent a GMHC flyer to my boss. He phoned me to see if I was the same Paul Popham. I said I was. He asked what we do at GMHC. I told him. A few days later, he came down to visit and closed the door. He told me that what I do on my own time is my own business." Paul is gruff as he imitates the man, but I'm thinking that the boss didn't have to give Paul the reassurance he actually did.

As I pack my things, I wonder about the formal man standing beside me, a man who works steadily and keeps his feelings to himself. Might Paul actually be perceived with more clarity at work than he knows? Might there be more support, even affection for him, than he realizes?

I suggest, and Paul agrees, that I will not send these words out to computer readers. His story will simply not appear until the book itself is published.

That way, he'll have more private time to tell his mother.

Chapter 15:
"Ralph" –
Chat With a Funeral Director

Talking with Diego Lopez at the Gay Men's Health Crisis made me curious to know more about a disease so powerful that it was frightening even after death -- at least to funeral directors who reject the bereaved families of someone with AIDS. Through personal networking, I found a member of the profession who assured me, despite some nervous concern that he not be revealed, that he would talk with me frankly.

As I wait for him to arrive, I have no idea what to expect. I have never directly had dealings with a funeral director. As a marketing consultant, I can analyze the consumer image I have of the profession: it is not wonderful. But I'm the first to acknowledge that "image" and "fact" are not always the same.

As I wait for "Ralph" (he's coming to my apartment after work), I realize that I'm expecting an unctious smoothie I will neither trust nor like. I'm surprised when I open the door and find a chunky red-head, five and a half feet tall, who could be a peppy, middle-aged model for a peanut butter commercial. He is not oily, just friendly.

He asks me again not to mention his name, nor the funeral home where he works. He is concerned because the industry is still "touchy" from Jessica Mitford's book, *The American Way of Death.*.

"The public doesn't have an accurate impression of some of us," he says. I ask what beverage he'd like. "Wine. I talk better with wine." I open a bottle of beaujolais. Normally I drink Classic Coke, Perrier, or orange juice. A little wine with me goes a long way. But I decide it will put him more at ease if I have some wine too.

"1983," he says. "It's best to drink beaujolais only a year to a year and a half later."

"We'd better hurry, then," I reply, "if you're telling me this wine is already too old. It's been on the shelf a long time." He sits in the rocking chair I'd planned for him, facing away from the window to minimize his distractions. "Cheers," I say, having rejected "Happy Days" and "To Your Health" as potentially ironic.

He is from Detroit, from a poor family. His father had no education beyond high school. Ralph was the only son, and was expected to achieve more. ("To go beyond . . . " my mind says, like Boris Karloff. An intrinsic image problem of this industry is that I think of death every instant I talk to this man.) Ralph's father felt it very important that his son find a career with "no layoffs."

He talks with hesitation and his hands hardly move, as though strapped within the rocking chair. "I've never been interviewed," he says, when I ask if he's comfortable. "I guess I'm still nervous." I realize I've forgotten to bring the wine bottle in from the kitchen, so I retrieve it.

"Good!" He laughs. He has a jolly, happy laugh. "I function very well on wine! It gets me mellow."

"If that helps the interview . . ." I set it on the tray beside him.

"So from high school I went an extra year to mortuary school. I wasn't academically minded, so I didn't have many choices. A State of Michigan guidance counselor helped me pick it. She'd given me a test where I picked different occupation cards. I picked 'Archaeologist' as one of the jobs. Little did I know you have to speak four or five different languages, go to college, and all this other stuff. I also picked 'Music Conductor.' I like the idea of creating something out of nothing. And, I picked 'Funeral Director.'

"She said, `Why don't you pursue this funeral thing. You seem to have a lot of social skills, which is very important in that type of work. Will working with blood bother you?'"

"I said, `I never thought about it.' She said, `human blood?' I said, `blood is blood.' I looked at it as something positive. Nothing gory. It didn't terrify me.

"So I looked around to be an apprentice. Nobody would take me. I didn't understand it at the time, but what they were looking for someone to sleep in and be a slave. They didn't want anyone from the same area, because they were afraid a local apprentice would later steal away business.

"How a nineteen-year-old apprentice would steal away customers from an established, 100-year old business, I don't know. But that is the caliber of people in the field. They are so afraid of somebody getting something on them that they want slave labor.

"It turned out, for family reasons, a sick uncle, that I had to move east. That helped because I wasn't 'local' out here. I got an apprenticeship in Queens through a lucky situation. I was making $75 a week. I was given a night job living over a church, like a caretaker, and a day job at the funeral home.

"I'm a Licensed Funeral Director. I have one year of apprenticeship and another year of Mortuary School. I've been working for my present employer twenty-five years."

I pour us both some more wine. "Are there multiple funeral directors at your location?"

"Right."

"And how does it happen -- how do they decide who gets which job?"

"You always try to match the people up. One person might be good in an area of -- like, if we have an Italian funeral director, we'll try to give him an Italian funeral. If he's Irish, we'll match him with an Irish one. Episcopals have low key funerals. Hispanics are more flamboyant. If the director has a lot of patience, we'll give him the Chinese funerals, or anyone else you need patience with."

"Why do you need patience at a Chinese funeral?" It sounds like a set-up to a joke. Why does the chicken cross the road?

"You have to have patience with them because, traditionally, time is meaningless to them. You take your watch and throw it away. Usually it's all done very slowly and very delicately. They don't like schedules."

"You mean their funerals actually take more time?"

"Yes."

"As a purely business problem -- thinking about pricing now -- if it were my funeral home, I might wonder about charging more to the Chinese if they took up a lot more time." Are my words coming out thick? I am already feeling the wine. That's fine, I conclude. Ralph's hands are now on the sides of the arm chair, not nested inside. We're having a nice visit.

"In theory, yes, you're right. But my specific place charges everyone the same. We know how many Chinese we get in a typical year, and we just amortize it."

"What do you typically do? I mean the basic services."

"Well we're now in the Period of Itemization." He says it like the reign of an emperor. "Under New York State law and the Federal Trade Commission, we list all different types of services in which the family may partake, from A to Z. Whether they will have any service at all, a graveside service, a chapel service, a room service for a gathering of people. We can offer home preparation -- that's home embalming. We can have the remains embalmed at home if so desired. We can ship remains all over the world. And we're nonsectarian."

"What is the least expensive funeral people can buy?"

"Terminology is very important. 'Funeral' meaning disposition? We have a direct cremation service. Is that what you meant?"

"I guess." I'm slouched into my chair now. The wine makes it seem very cozy, chatting about these various matters.

"`Funeral' usually means a formal-type service," he says. "Having the corpse present."

"Oh. Then I think I'm asking what's the least expensive funeral AND the least expensive 'disposition.'"

"Well I don't have the prices in front of me, and I can only give you approximations. I wouldn't want anyone taking these prices literally."

"Okay," I assure him, on behalf of readers everywhere. "They won't."

"I'd say, for a direct cremation in the industry, it could be anywhere from $250 up to $1600 or $2000."

"That's a terrific range!"

"Yes. Prices can vary with factors like the prestige of the funeral home's address and their overhead. Some of the Manhattan funeral homes, their buildings are worth $18 million, so you can imagine what their real estate taxes are each year."

"And what about the basic funeral with a service? What's the price range there?"

"Everything is itemized," he reminds me. "There's a special overhead factor. Caskets can go from a particle board casket -- that's an 'ultimate container' used for direct cremation, it's made of sawdust glued together. That's just a few hundred dollars at some places. But you can go up to $34,000 at some of the fancy homes truly special caskets."

"How special could it be for $34,000? It's hard to imagine what it does!"

"It's seamless bronze. It's all one unit, made from a mold. There are no ways for air to get in, or water. There are not many made. It could be a status thing. Or some people want something that will preserve them for the longest possible time -- something thicker, more durable, heavier."

"Now -- something I've never quite understood . . . " I pour us both more wine. More in his glass, a token in my own. We're getting along fine. "Tell me about embalming."

"Embalming is the temporary preservation, restoration, and cosmetics to a lifelike appearance. It brings the body to a natural state as best as possible."

"Then it's not mandatory that someone be embalmed?"

"Under New York State law, no."

"So if a person wanted to just be buried, and don't do anything to me, don't touch me, NOTHING -- that can be done?"

"Sure. That's if the burial is the same day or the next day. If the

153

remains need to be kept for a week, then you're going to get natural decomposition, and some form of preservation would be mandatory. People don't realize that there is decomposition, there are changes."

"What percent of people who have funerals opt for embalming?"

"People are embalmed more than unbalmed. More than half."

"Now, Ralph, let's talk about AIDS, all right?"

I can feel it. Both of us change when I mention AIDS. I believe I'm actually breathing less so as not to make him nervous. He is holding the wine glass against his chest, both hands protecting it against a negative public image.

"As someone in the business, Ralph, what do you see as the issues with AIDS and funeral homes?"

"Well . . . ." I feel impatient with his hesitation, but I hold myself back from prodding him. The wine helps me tolerate his caution.

"I guess I'd have to say that, in the greater metropolitan area . . . in the beginning . . . most funeral homes did not want to handle AIDS victims at all. They didn't want to be contaminated by the virus.

"It was the same fear that made some people wear masks and gloves in courtrooms when a person with AIDS was present. The same fear that made nurses refuse to feed their own AIDS patients, or doctors not treat them. Or had people being chased out of their apartments. It wasn't just us in the funeral profession.

"It was the unknown. And also the stigma attached to the disease. The disease of the homosexuals." He says nothing for a while. I wait as long as I can stand it.

"But Ralph. Funeral homes have been treating homosexuals forever."

"Right."

"Knowingly."

"Right."

"So that only became an issue when someone had AIDS."

"And only to some funeral homes," he says carefully. It's as though he's in a courtroom: very precise. That's fair; being accurate is appropriate.

"Yes. Only to some funeral homes. When did this first become an issue?"

"Right when the epidemic started among the gay community. Around 1981."

"Did your funeral home have a discussion about what to do?"

"Not at first. The whole thing happened overnight. Suddenly here was a body. Nobody knew about AIDS except from scary newspaper articles, reports from San Francisco, a two minute blip on television. But here was this body that had come in the door and nobody knew what really had made it die -- or if it was contagious. You realize, we're licensed by the State of New York. But even our manual on contagious, infectious disease doesn't have AIDS listed yet. Which proves there's still a lot of research to be done on that.

"None of us knew how it was spreading, and of course we didn't want to get it. You can understand that. What if you had a family and children, like I do. You don't want to take the disease home, right?"

Now it's my turn to answer, "right." Of course I can understand being afraid of mystery and death. That doesn't make the rejection less poignant, when you phone, sick with grief, and are turned away. But, yes, I can in truth understand.

Someone had told me today, a novelist doing research on plagues, that Napoleon lost 200,000 men to the typhus epidemic. The population was terrified, and fearful public riots were a side effect of the medical problem. Fear of an epidemic is certainly not new.

"In our case," Ralph continues, "we decided it would be in the best interests of the people we serve -- and of ourselves -- to have special systems for AIDS patients. We'd heard theories of sexuality, of dirty needles -- but did the virus float around in the air? Could you get it if you breathed it? Was it still alive in a dead body?

"To protect ourselves -- we wrote away to various places for opinions. The general consensus was, treat it like Hepatitis B. That was a guess. Use the thickest rubber gloves, wear protective garments and masks."

"Then, your company did serve people with AIDS?"

"Yes. We may not have been the first to start the policy, but it didn't take us long to decide it was right. Partly we felt it was a moral duty to try. Partly we made a judgement: we could be safe. And partly, I admit, we knew it was illegal to discriminate in New York State. I'm not a lawyer, and I'm not the owner of our funeral home. But I'm pretty sure it's illegal to discriminate against someone with a disability and, even in death, AIDS is a disability. We wouldn't want to lose our license. If the state wanted to, it could be making it tough right now, I think, on all those funeral homes that didn't decide to handle things like we did. Because some homes are still turning them away.

"We're trained so we can smell an AIDS case, you know. There are some hospitals where they cluster, first of all: Memorial Sloan-Kettering, Bellevue, Mount Sinai, St. Vincent's, Beth Israel . . ."

Here he imitates the thick, syrupy voice I'd been dreading. He sets the wine glass down on the table and suddenly is an actor, with extravagant gestures that mock his solicitous tone of voice:

"Oh, nooooo. How sad. You lost your dear friend? Ohhhhh. And, ummmmm, what did he die of? Ahhhhhh. Pneumonia? Or a skin cancer? Mmmmmm. And how old did you say he was, sir? Ohhhhh. Only thirty-four. Tsk, tsk. That's tragic at such a young age. And -- what was YOUR relationship to the deceased? `Close friend?' Well . . . ." His voice becomes hard and cold. "I'm sorry, but we don't take AIDS here. You'll have to go someplace else. Good bye."

Playing that role has loosened him up. For the first time he seems really comfortable in the rocking chair. We're both rocking gently now, as he talks.

"Personally, I'm glad to work for a funeral home that doesn't reject them. It just doesn't seem right. I'm praying it's not necessary, that we're doing the right thing. But it seems we are.

"We had a policeman's family come to us, it was all hush-hush. They were embarrassed that this cop got AIDS. Several homes had turned them down. I felt sorry for them, for the strain it was putting on the family. But you know, people are so grateful when they find we accept them, they don't have the strength or the will to press charges against a home that said no.

"I went to a local funeral home one day in New York City. I told him who I was, and the home I worked for. I asked him for his policy on AIDS victims. I was just curious.

"`We don't handle them,' he said.

"`Oh,' I said. `Can I ask why?'

"`We're a family-owned business,' he said. `My sons work for me. We don't feel we should be subjected to the unknown. In fact we sent a client down to you two or three weeks ago.' He proceeded to tell me about the client.

"`Oh, yes.' I remembered the case actually. I had directed that funeral, and everything came back. I told him what they purchased, and after I told him, his face dropped, as if to say, `I should have kept them. That was a good one.'

"I respected his answer and his feelings. But if I owned a place, I would not do it. There must be fifty major funeral homes in New York City, and many little `store fronts.' A fair percentage of them, I'm not sure how much, say no to people with AIDS. One of the tragedies of this disease is rejection, including from the certain members of my profession." I pour him still more wine. We're a pair of birds, rocking on a lawn.

"I'll tell you something you may not realize, Mike. There are many more cases of AIDS than are really reported. It all depends on what's put on the death certificate. There are plenty of doctors who do NOT put 'AIDS' there. For various reasons, they might, let's say, not emphasize the disease."

I think about the official tallies I see in the newspapers each week.

"Is that what the CDC statistics are based on? From death certificates?"

"Sure. I would estimate -- only from what I see, I can't speak for the country or the rest of New York -- but I would estimate there are almost two and a half times more cases of AIDS than are officially reported at my funeral home."

A disease so awesome, even its name can't be mentioned on a death certificate. What is the political effect of the reported statistics being lower than the truth? Would the disease have been more alarming to people sooner if every death had been counted? Would research on its mysteries have been funded sooner?

"Most families of people with AIDS don't want much made of it. Most of the deceased are emaciated. The families have been through something torturous. A few families, unfortunately, reject their own. In one case, the lover did everything, and the family had nothing to do with it. From what I could tell, the father was a minister and was just too embarrassed. Some of these companions, especially of gay men with AIDS -- they're like saints, what they go through."

We rock in silence. Finally I invite Ralph to address you.

"My profession has always been portrayed as ghouls. As leeches on society. Some of us are. Some of us are not. I'd like the public not to think of us all the same way. We are individuals. Some of us really do care about providing a service, and in a sensitive way, when fellow human beings are suffering grief.

"I'd like to say: there are a lot of loving and caring funeral directors. You'll know us by what we do. We're really out here."

Chapter 16:
Dr. Grossman, After Hours
And Jan Kostrobala

Dr. Grossman, in allowing me contact with his patients, has always taken pains to protect their confidentiality. So have I. Often that necessity meant disguising the details of a patient's identity while being faithful to the experience.

This chapter contains a description of Dr. Grossman's phone conversation with "Franklin," an AIDS patient with pneumocystis pneumonia. It is reprinted here just as I transmitted it over the computer wires. My subsequent interview with the patient himself, Jan Kostrobala, follows thereafter.

Dr. Grossman, After Hours

He calls at 8:00 to say he can't join me for dinner. A patient who phoned him earlier today is arriving back from Italy tonight and probably needs hospital admission on arrival. Dr. Grossman must wait for the call.

"Then let's have dinner at your office! Can I bring you a sandwich?" Anything. I get tuna salad and chicken: let him have his choice. A slice of cherry pie, and one of blueberry, two cups of coffee. By the time I enter his office, it's 9:00. He sits where I've seen him before, alone behind the receptionist's glass shield. We move to his consultation room where I set up the tape recorder on his large wooden desk. He doesn't care which sandwich he has; he doesn't care which slice of pie.

I place two bundles in front of him; they stay housed in wax paper while he writes into patients' folders. I unwrap whatever fate has given me: chicken. Secretly I'd hoped for the tuna, now nestled in amongst his charts. I am certainly not going to switch them.

"This disease exposes every day the incredible diversity of jobs gay people have," he says. He tells me about "Franklin," the patient coming in from Italy. He is a world-class wedding gown designer; people sometimes pay many thousands of dollars for his artistry and talent.

The phone rings. "It's YOU! Thank God they let you off the airplane. Tell me in twenty-five words or less what happened . . . when did you start getting sick?" He switches the intercom on so I can hear Franklin's answer.

"I was taking very, very shallow breaths," says a young man's voice. It is faint. There are fast and subtle pauses between words. His voice has no weight at all -- it is the sound of mere air, forming words out of clouds.

"When did it start?"

"As soon as I got there."

"Got to Italy? You got there on Tuesday or Wednesday."

"Yeah. I took the medicine you gave me, but nothing happened. I had high fever, and sweats, and chills, and -- I can't stand up!" I hear the panic in his fragile voice.

"Okay, listen to me."

"I feel my guts are coming out."

"Listen to me. You probably have pneumocystis. First: relax. Calm. You're going to be in good hands. Howard, and the Emergency Room infectious disease specialists are standing by and waiting for you." Franklin does not want admission to the hospital Ron was able to arrange; his lover, "Gustav", died of AIDS there.

"It was a year ago this week," says Franklin. "This week he died RIGHT THERE!" Ron explains that it *has* to be this hospital. Franklin's oncology specialist is there, for example. Franklin ultimately agrees. A friend has arranged a taxi, and it's waiting. Ron promises to visit after Franklin has been admitted.

"That shortness of breath," he says afterward. "That is the voice of pneumocystis. You can't get" (he demonstrates for me) "enough -- breath -- to -- talk." He replicates the struggle. "And there's a cough that goes with it, too. When you've heard it enough, there's no doubt about it. They cough --." He coughs with a kind of sharp conclusion. It's as though the cough ends with a click.

"They're not really coughing," he says. "The reason is, their lungs are so filled with this disease,the organisms occupying the lung space, there's no breath available to complete the cough. That's why it sounds that way.

"I'll never forget the first time I saw it. It was in February or March of 1982, so I had only seen one AIDS case before that. It was very cold. A patient who had been with me for many years -- he had a high position in City government, surviving Mayor after Mayor. He came to me complaining of an odd kind of cough and some extreme discomfort -- you heard what Franklin just said -- extreme discomfort in the chest and upper abdomen.

"So what did I do? I pursued a gastro-intestinal workup. We did a G.I. series, this and that, couldn't find it. The cough got worse and worse and worse. Mind you, we'd done a chest X-ray which showed nothing. A week later in a chest X-ray, the lungs had turned white!

"He was admitted to the hospital, the same one as Franklin. He was gone in five days. Three New York mayors came to his funeral. What contrasts! His death was consistent with our track record back then, when 80% died from the first pass of pneumocystis. Today 80% survive."

"Survive pneumocystis?" He nods. "Why? What's changed?"

"Rapid identification of it and rapid treatment. Separate in your mind, Michael, the difference between treating AIDS -- for which there is still nothing acceptable -- and the complications of AIDS. Treated rapidly and appropriately, and on the first pass, pneumocystis can often now be turned around."

"Cherry or blueberry pie?" I ask him. I can't help it, I say to myself -- I am ravenous. But I wonder if this moment's passion for the pie is an avoidance of a sad little fantasy on the edge of my mind, of what Franklin's own meal must have been like tonight. Hardly able to breathe on the long flight over the ocean. Watching TWA meal carts trundle past as he tries to hold his guts in. Remembering the lover who died exactly a year ago . . . of the disease that's now stealing his breath.

"I haven't even touched the sandwich," Dr. Grossman tells me. "I will make my decision later." The pie decision. The process sounds so formal. I think of all the decisions a doctor must make in a day. Especially a doctor under seige. I learned with surprise tonight that Ron Grossman, personally, has thus far treated 1% of all the AIDS patients in the country.

"Ah -- you want your pie now, Michael. Pick whatever you want." Cherry pie compensates for the absence of tuna, and I chide myself for caring about the sandwich I didn't get.

"Franklin's designs are sought after everywhere," Ron is telling me. "I picture him chained to a drawing board. To give you an idea of how much this kid is loved -- his boss fronted the entire money for a lovely co-op. Not a big deal, maybe -- a small, one-bedroom co-op near Gramercy Park. But he fronted the entire nut in lieu of a raise, because a raise wouldn't really have done it. His designs are evidently extraordinary." He sets down his pen and looks at me, worried.

"Michael, that voice on the phone is the voice of someone who is going in the next 48 hours, unless he can rally right. He's got to get treated and he's got to RESPOND. By the way, he's allergic to the main drug that treats pneumocystis; we know that upfront."

He exhales -- a full, deep exhalation in contrast to the patient's voice on the speaker. "The fact is, I'm . . . torn to pieces inside."

He changes subjects. He talks about "fear mongering" in some of the press instead of education. We talk about women and AIDS, and sexual transmission. He points to a headline, "DREAMS OF LOVE TURNED TO FEAR BY KILLER IN OUR MIDST."

"Today," he says, "a lady I see only once a year because she lives in Europe came back to tell me -- so thrilled -- she wants her annual female exam, and her breast exam, and so forth. She's met a guy, an American she met in Spain where she's living. They've fallen in love. She's going to wind up her business over there and return to the U.S. and marry this guy.

"There's only one catch -- after they fell in love, and after they'd been sleeping together, she found out he's a hemophiliac. It's that very newspaper headline, `dreams of love turned to fear.' Here's a heterosexual woman, whose own promiscuity I know nothing about, who has fallen in love with a hemophiliac, whose sexual habits I know nothing about. Now she is tasting that fear."

"Hemophilia is a rare disease, isn't it?"

"What would you guess," he says. "How many in the U.S.?"

"A tenth of one per cent?"

"One per cent would be 250,000," he said. "A tenth of one percent is 25,000. You're close to the mark. There are actually only between seventeen and twenty-one thousand cases in the U.S. It's not a common disease. What brings it to the forefront is that these people are absolutely dependent for their lives on blood and blood products from the moment the disease is identified, right until they die. It's not exact, but something like 80% of all hemophiliacs now show the antibody in tests for the virus.

"Do you understand that the threat to hemophiliacs is not that they bleed to death?" he asks me. "Not at all. In the first place, they're too smart for that! No hemophiliac sticks himself with a knife, if he can help it."

"Right," I say. "But the way I've pictured it is, he might accidentally get cut."

"Absolutely," he replies. "But what kind of cut do you get accidentally?"

"Like, a kitchen knife."

"EVEN a hemophiliac, if he presses the cut together long enough, will clot. They don't have zero clotting, just slow clotting. No -- what hemophiliacs get is . . . suppose you're an enthusiastic, seven-year old hemophiliac, on your way to play baseball with the boys. You take a slide into third base, and you turn your knee. Two minutes later your knee is the size of a pumpkin and getting bigger.

"If you don't get that knee drained of blood -- which now contains about a tenth of the blood in your body! -- and get the transfusions to clot immediately, you may or may not bleed to death into your own knee. But without those transfusions, you WILL NOT have a knee. That's a key issue in hemophiliacs. They do give themselves blood products regularly. An adult learns to inject himself."

The stacks of done and undone charts on the desk are now almost level with each other. "Would you like to see the Face of ARC?" he asks me.

"Yes." He covers the patient's name and shows me the bottom half of a lab report. It's a computer printout showing the test results compared to norms.

"This boy is in his third year of fairly severe AIDS-related complex," he tells me. "Without focusing on the specific test, flip to the second sheet. It's called `find the normals.'

"I mean, when I call Michael Greenly, I tell him, `Michael, congratulations, everything's okay except your cholesterol's too high, lose some weight.' Find me this man's normal test." The column for exceptions from the norm is filled with numbers indicating extremes.

"This is the slow, relentless progression to full-blown AIDS. Although this kid has staved it off something remarkable. By the way, he's in the test of Isoprinosine we're part of." He sets the patient's chart into the completed stack, after writing something in it. "I won't know the test results until we break the code."

He talks about the progress still needed in AIDS research. For example, moving beyond a test for the AIDS antibody -- with its inherent imperfections -- to a test for the virus itself. That's still "experimental," he says. "Still being worked out. The test today takes between six and ten weeks to complete. The actual cost is between six and eight hundred dollars, although I can get it for three-fifty with a friend. The test is fraught with technical problems, so a negative test has to be repeated, over and over again. It's by no means a routine."

How difficult, to even try to fight a disease early on when it's still so difficult to know if someone has it in the bloodstream. Dr. Grossman explains to me that it's always been difficult to isolate a virus. Viruses have to live in cells, which they end up destroying. So if you want to study a virus, you have to keep providing it new cells to live in. As it finishes wrecking what you've given it -- a mouse cell, a chicken cell, whatever -- you have to "pass" it into a new one. "Sometimes the passage must happen hour by hour," he says. "From one tube of nutrient cells to another."

So dealing with any virus at all is a difficult feat. "Recall too, Michael, that the AIDS virus is unique among human viruses. He is a retro-virus. He takes the genetic heart of the cell, called DNA, and makes a mirror image of it. . . which he then incorporates into himself." I notice that Dr. Grossman personifies this disease, the way I sometimes do to understand it. A microscopic speck is a "he" to him.

"That process," he tells me, "lets him duplicate -- replicate -- and explode out of the cell. And now there are a hundred of him! To add to the aggravation, the AIDS virus is capable of replicating at ONE THOUSAND TIMES the rate of any other known virus! He is a most formidable little opponent. Yet the same virus -- sprinkle a little dilute clorox on him, and he's dead. A one to ten clorox solution will kill him." Scant comfort to know it can kill an AIDS virus on your hand. If only we could put Clorox in our bloodstreams. (Immediately I imagine the product manager working on that laundry brand.)

"I've got to get on with these charts," Dr. Grossman says. "And I need to visit Franklin tonight."

I say good night. It is almost eleven. Only as I leave, is he finally unwrapping the tuna fish. How does he avoid getting sick himself, I wonder. And what would he have eaten if I hadn't brought the sandwich?

Jan Richard Kostrobala (alias "Franklin")

Has October been this beautiful all along? I am forty-one years old and I realize, waiting for a traffic light, October scintillates. All these years, how unconscious have I been? First pursuing studies, then a successful career. The crisp of this air, the gold of this sun, the clear of this sky . . . is October like this every year? Or does it suddenly poignant as I encounter people dealing with death, with illness, with pain.

I cross the street and enter the luxury apartment house of a man expected to die of AIDS in just a few months. I appreciate the beauty of October.

He is "Franklin." That's the pseudonym I'd given him when he called Dr. Grossman, arriving from Spain. I'd said Italy, to further disguise him. I'd consulted with Dr. Grossman on whether to switch Franklin's profession as I've done with other interviews, but it seemed things were fine to leave as is.

"Actually, I'd like you to use my real name, Mike," he says when we're seated in his livingroom. "Gay people live in disguises all the time. I don't want to. I haven't for years. If my story can be of use to someone else, I'd like them to know who I am."

Jan Richard Kostrobala has worked at a successful bridal house, Mori Lee in New York, for fourteen years. He is thirty-eight years old. Bridal buyers come from around the world to see the wedding collections he designs and to bring them back home to their bridal shops. One of his more popular designs has graced more than 250,000 brides.

Now he sits on the white linen couch in front of me. His burgundy bathrobe and blue checked pajamas set off pale, ashen skin. Blotches of red color, like spilt drops of wine, dot his face and his neck. He wears several rings, a thin gold bracelet, and a fashionable red plastic wrist watch.

The apartment is splendid. The mirrored panels that cover the east wall give me the illusion of looking out the window behind me, at the New York skyline. Red gladiolas rise from a large glass coffee table. My tape recorder is next to an autumn arrangement of pumpkin and corn sheaves on the table. Everywhere I look, I see more fresh flowers. Two chairs in a window terrace bask in the sunlight not far from a palm tree.

"I have a Polish background," he says. "I grew up on the lower east side and have mostly been in the City. I lived in Queens for ten years with a lover. Then I moved back into the City -- I love the whole New York thing."

"How did you get into designing wedding gowns?"

"Everybody asks that!" he says, smiling at himself. "I have always -- always, always -- been fascinated by weddings. The whole mysteriousness behind it, the preparation, not seeing the bride, the special clothing, all the flowers and the schmaltz. The emotion. I'm an emotional slob. I cry at the drop of a pin.

"I find something so incredibly emotional about a wedding. I think it's just the beauty of it . . . people being so in love. Most people, when they get married, are starry-eyed. It's creating such a special day -- the tuxedos, `Here Comes the Bride,' all of it."

"I'll never forget the first wedding dress I ever did. The girl, my friend, said, 'I really trust you. I have faith in you.' I'd never done a wedding gown in my life. I just knew I had the feel for it. My nickname is `yards and yards' because whenever I made a veil, I always made it so much longer than it needed to be.

"That first dress, I did it all by hand. The entire inside was covered with spots of blood where I pricked my fingers! In Bridal, you have to take tiny stitches around the lace, to make it look like it's just been glued on. With a very fine needle, like a couturier. In a store, 80% of the dresses girls buy have had all the lace and beading glued on. If you're buying a dress you've paid two and three thousand dollars for, you're not going to get any glue. They'll be all hand-stitched."

"Jan, wedding gowns are not typically ever worn again, right? All the effort is made just for a day?"

"Exactly. That's the fabulous thing about it. All the money, all of it, for one special day. I have planned so many weddings, I could do it backwards and forewards. So when I found out I have AIDS -- and I know what the outcome of all this is going to be . . . I'm realistic and I know

I'm going to die -- I said, `I've planned so many weddings, I'm going to plan my own funeral.' My funeral is written down already. Exactly. The music, what I'd like people to wear, everything. Why should someone else plan it? It's the last thing I can do that people can remember me by, something I've created myself."

(Pause.) "My lover was a romantic like I am. He just passed away a year ago."

"AIDS?"

"Yes." Jan explains that he and Joey were lovers for ten years. They actually had their own wedding ceremony. "We wore caftans. We had a wedding cake. We used a friend's brownstone, with stained glass windows, for the ceremony. People were crying as we exchanged our vows. They still talk about it, `Jan and Joey's wedding.'"

They separated in the mid-seventies as Jan's career became his dominant pursuit. Jan found it hard to get involved with someone new.

"I was going to the bars, trying to be very social, dating every night. I got so wrapped up in the whole singles thing, wanting to meet somebody. I think part of my problem was I still loved Joey." I notice he still refers to him as "my lover," even though they'd been living apart for a decade.

"Joey died just a year ago," he says again. "He'd been sick for almost two years, but at first they didn't know it was AIDS. He was an incredibly healthy man. He worked out at the gym, ate health food, everything."

Jan is sure he got AIDS from sexual contact. "I used to go to 'Charlie's' every other night. That bar was conveniently just down the street, and I was a star. I was young and pretty. I played the game."

"How long ago was this?" I ask. He sighs.

"Mike, I was even young and pretty three weeks ago. That's how fast this thing is, that's what it's doing to me. I feel like plaster on a wall, peeling away. That's what I used to look like." He points to a photograph on the wall behind me. I walk over to it, a closeup portrait of a sprightly blond man with a blond moustache -- not the muddy, sandy-gray hair I see on Jan now. The man in the photo is almost shining in his exuberance. I would guess he is thirty years old.

"How long ago was this taken?"

"April." He says it flat, no emotion allowed.

"April of '85," I repeat. I am stalling. I cannot imagine what to say to someone who, less than six months ago, looked twenty years younger.

"And --" he says, "If I showed you pictures from only three *weeks* ago, you wouldn't believe it. This all happened in three weeks, with the trip to Spain. What a shock that was.

Jan tells me that, except for a slight cough, he felt fine as he left for Spain to visit an old friend. "I know I'm dying. I want to make my peace and finish my business. Like saying good-bye to my friend."

I am still not used to hearing a thirty-eight year-old man talk this way about his own death. After just a few days, Jan says, he got very sick: coughing, gagging, breathing only with difficulty. He was too weak to walk and was gasping for air. He knew he had to get home right away.

"I had an examination before they'd even let me on the plane. Thank God I bluffed it. I said it was the food I ate, the climate, I must be coming down with the flu. I had long sleeves on, so they didn't see my lesions. If they had, they wouldn't have let me on the plane even though they're not contagious.

"I've had the KS lesions since February. At first I didn't think they were really KS. It's incredible how they creep up on you. Now my body is covered with them. This afternoon I really looked at myself. There are so many new ones, I got really depressed." He readjusts his position on the couch, as he remembers the flight home from Spain. As though squirming in his seat.

"I took a tranquilizer to try to sleep through it. But when we landed, I didn't have strength any more. When I stood up, I blacked out. I told them, `there's an ambulance waiting for me.' But the plan had changed, and there wasn't. The staff began to think I was trying to hijack the plane or something.

"I heard my girlfriend on the walkie-talkie: `Is he alive? Is he alive?' They wouldn't give her information, so she thought I was dead!

"I asked them, please, to let me speak with her. I could hear her voice. I asked them to let me tell her I was alive. `You can't talk with her,' one of them told me. `This is an official police radio.' The next thing I know, there are five policemen around me. Officials in Iberia Airlines suits. Customs agents. And they're asking me questions about my passport. This one cop kept yelling from three seats over: "DO YOU HAVE AIDS? YOU HAVE AIDS, DON'T YOU!"

"I told him no. If he'd been a doctor, I would have admitted it. But I thought it was none of this screaming man's business. I asked them if they could just help me down the staircase. I couldn't stand up, because I kept blacking out.

"But I'd pushed my sleeves up. One of the customs agents saw the KS on my arm and thought I was a junkie. He asked if I was on narcotics. Because they do look like track marks."

Jan slides up the sleeves of his bathrobe and pajamas to show me his lesions. The marks are brown, unlike the crimson splotches on his face. It's as though his arms are covered with old burns, from a political torture with molten dimes.

"`I have Kaposi's sarcoma,' I told them. The entire cabin emptied out in two seconds flat, including the doctor! The only one remaining was the nurse. They came back with a white, plastic sheet. A large bib they made me put on. This time they couldn't wait to get me off the plane. They couldn't whizz me off of there fast enough! But still nobody would touch me. They finally let my girlfriend into the cabin. She was a mess. She was gray, because she thought I was dead.

"They got a police ambulance for me, but they treated me like garbage. Not even a pillow for my head. They just threw me into the ambulance. They wouldn't even give me a blanket. They wouldn't take me to the hospital. Instead, they dumped me off at a medical facility in Queens. But they wouldn't let me lie down while I waited for a cab.

"`It's a private office,' they said. 'There are no facilities.'"

"`All I want to do is lie down,' I told them. `Let me rest on the floor! Please! Because I just can't breathe sitting up.' But they wouldn't let me out of the wheelchair. It was an absolute nightmare.

"Finally I got to the hospital where Joey had died. I was admitted on the anniversary of the day he went into a coma. I was placed in his same ward. I went once for a test -- and ended exactly face-to-face with the room he'd passed away in. It was horrendous. I had roaches crawling all over my bed. At night, and during the day. But people were wonderful. Half the staff has agreed to take care of AIDS patients, and half will not. So at least you're not handled by someone who hates being with you.

"So, Mike -- that was my trip to Spain!" Now we laugh at the end of his vacation travelogue.

"Okay, Jan. Now you've been home from the hospital for a while. What is your state of mind?"

"They'd wanted to do more tests on me. But I told them no. I said, `I know what I've got. I know what's going to happen to me. Now I want QUALITY life. Even if it's just three days. My family has been nursing me -- not just physically. They've been making me get out of bed and do things for myself.

"There are times I go through deep depression. I just try to let myself experience it. My life is coming to an end. So if I feel like crying, I go ahead and cry. And if I reflect on my sadness at losing my friends, then okay, I feel sad.

"I do look back. For a year, I was able to pull it off -- not letting people know I was sick. Now I can't hide it anymore, not from them, not from me. As soon as I knew I had AIDS, my sex life ended. Sometimes I would jerk off with a videotape.

"I went to bed with one person -- having safe sex, just jerking off and rubbing. But it was awful, I was so nervous. I hate that occasion being my last memory of sex with another man.

"I've known too many people with AIDS, Mike.   A lot of people I went to bed with. I must have been one of the unlucky ones, part of a circle where it travelled. For a long time, I was like Scarlett O'Hara: `I'm not going to think about it today, because it hasn't happened to *me* yet.'

"Most of the people I knew with AIDS were people I'd had sex with, five or six years ago when I first became single. I was never one to sleep with someone more than once or twice. I was afraid of getting involved emotionally, and getting hurt.

"For a while I was a big `tea room Queen.' I never went to the baths in my life, and I guess I never will now. But I did go to subway men's rooms, to get a blow job, or give one. I found that scary but exciting. It was a release, even though it was dangerous. You're always afraid someone will come in. Now the bathrooms are locked down there, so people end up having to piss all over the subway station.

"Tell me about the future, Jan. How are you planning to spend your time?"

"With as much quality as I can. Every year, I have a Christmas party where my friends, this group who's been together so long, we get together. We sing Christmas carols and it's really schmaltzy. I've been doing it for the last ten years, and everybody looks forward to it.

"Each time it's a different theme.   I've always wanted to have a formal one, with tuxedo and gowns -- last year I finally did that. I think it was a premonition. I accomplished what I'd wanted to.

"I honestly don't think I'll make it to this Christmas. They're giving me till January. But one doctor told my brother they don't think I'll make it much beyond that. So I'm planning this year's Christmas party, yes. But I think last year was my swan song."

The skyline reflected on the mirrors in front of me is softer, as the afternoon light recedes. "What would you like to say to readers, Jan?"   I see him swallow. He leans forward, like a bird, his eyes locking in on mine.

"From all the pain people are going through -- not just the ones who are dying, but the ones who are having to bury their sons, their friends, someone they love -- from all this pain is coming caring. There's something beautiful . . . "

His tears are spilling over from eyes that haven't stopped watching me.   "I can't help this," he says, wiping his face with his bathrobe. "It's what happens to me." I'm now having trouble swallowing, too.   As I receive a "last words" benediction from a man who is three years my junior.

"People are learning, really, to love again. To care. Not just the gay people, but straight people too.   My family, I'm talking my aunts and uncles, were always close-minded in the past.   But now they're supportive! One of my aunts . . . we haven't spoken in seven years because of a family thing . . . she was here and we were crying and hugging. It's incredible how much love is coming out between people, from the pain.

"I've never hidden my being gay. I was always been a bit flamboyant. Like dyeing my hair whatever color I wanted. But much of my family didn't know what my lifestyle was. Now they've cared enough to do 'research.' About me and about my life. And about AIDS. They've found out more because they care about me."

Neither one of us, now, is bothering to hide the fact that we are each gently crying. I am moved this man's appreciation of his family, of the aunt he now can hug.

"They're helping me die. I asked them, 'don't help me go through a research program in Washington. Help me go through my death. Let me go away knowing that everybody, all of you, were there behind me, with me, caring. The love and the compassion that is coming into the world now, because of this horror . . . that love is incredible.

"I'm dying, Mike. But at least I've made it to thirty-eight. At least I've accomplished things, I've travelled. When I hear about a twenty-four year old, a boy, just a boy, who is dying . . . well, out of all these tragedies, people are learning to love.

"I would like to tell the public, Mike, about this love I'm now experiencing. I wish people could open up more and show their caring. Not hold it in. Tell somebody else, while they're alive, that you love them. Don't wait to look at them in a casket and say, `I loved you.'

"I believe I was put on this earth to learn a lesson, put here for a purpose. I believe that purpose is connected to the friends I've told you about. Do you realize, Mike, that I'm the *only* gay person in that group of fifteen people? All the others, the men, the women -- they're all straight. I celebrate their pregnancies, the births, right along with them. We celebrate each other's lives, as people, just as people, regardless of different lifestyles.

"That's the lesson I was put here to learn -- loving other people. And that's what I'd like to share with someone reading this. The opportunity exists to share your love with all kinds of people. If you let the sparkle happen, you'll find the love can really be there."

Chapter 17:
A Bathhouse and Politics

One of the social ramifications of AIDS is the political reaction to it. Reaction of all kinds. Don Boys (see the "Indiana" chapter) believes he will be better able to pass a sodomy law in Indiana as a result of AIDS "backlash." Councilman Joel Wachs (see the "Los Angeles" chapter) was able to pass an anti-discrimination law on behalf of people with AIDS.

In mid-October in New York City, Diane McGrath, the Republican candidate for New York City Mayor, called for the closing of gay bathhouses, along with bars, theaters, and pornography shops catering to homosexuals. She also suggested that people in "intimate" contact with the public -- she cited doctors, dentists, nurses, teachers, food handlers, barbers, beauticians, and prostitutes -- be tested for AIDS antibodies.

A spokesman for her opponent, Mayor Koch, responded by saying, "The Mayor hopes no one will make political the calamity of AIDS."

By the following Friday, the Mayor had asked the city's health commissioner to reexamine the question.

Amidst worried alarms for public health, and equally fearful expressions that civil liberties would be lost for the sake of political gestures, I decided to obtain for CHRONICLE readers a closer look at a bathhouse -- a snapshot of this controversial piece of geography.

This chapter contains my report of a bathhouse tour and an interview with one of its owner-managers. Here also is my encounter with New York's Mayor Koch on the steps of City Hall (photographed in TIME Magazine, November 25, 1985.)

Visit to a Bathhouse

My appointment is at 4:30 in the afternoon. The East Side address is in the heart of prime Manhattan real estate -- convenient walking distance from prestigious Sutton Place and Park Avenue co-ops and condos. A stroll to the Madison Avenue headquarters of IBM and AT&T, elegant restaurants, and Bloomingdale's.

I take an elevator to the fourth floor business office. There I meet several shareholders in the business. Steve will give me a tour of the bathhouse before our interview. He is thirty-six years old, wears a red flannel shirt and dungarees, and is slightly overweight. I have noticed with surprise that three of the four men in the office are more heavy than trim. It's not a gymnasium, I remind myself, even though men walk around in towels upstairs.

The bathhouse itself covers three floors of the building. Steve explains, as we walk through narrow, carpeted hallways, that all the rooms and halls are now more brightly lit than they used to be. Voluntary bathhouse practice, in New York City, is to enable anyone "at arms length" to clearly inspect someone else's body for lesions or other signals of disease.

He shows me the locker room. Two men and I exchange stares, fellow goldfish in the same bowl.

We visit the "Ultra Deluxe" room. I immediately notice, that "ultra" is a relative term. You've been to too many Hyatt-Regencies, I tell myself. I'm inventorying -- no plants, art work, chairs. But men don't come here, after all, to read a business report and order ham and eggs from room service. The room is spartan and sterile, but it is spacious and absolutely clean. It features a window (very rare, Steve says), mirrors on two of its walls, and plenty of space around the double bed. There's a free-standing armoire and one cushioned window ledge to sit on. Depending on the time of day, the room rents for as much as $25 for three hours.

Regular "Deluxe" rooms renting for a few dollars less have no wall mirror and less space around the bed. Standard cubicles have simply an orange light bulb and one narrow bed. A locker is eight dollars for eight hours on weeknights.

Steve shows me the "group room", the centerpiece of which is a ten-foot black leather hassock. Matching black couches wait on the sides of the stark, gray room.

Next, the video room, where men of various ages sit tranquilly on benches nested into the wall. They're watching a ceiling-mounted monitor on which other men are being noticeably more active.

Sauna. Steam room. Snack bar ("coffee, soft drinks, and junk food.") An observation loft is perched many feet above a giant hassock. And there's a slide room, if you prefer a quieter medium than videotape.

On to the "glory hole" closets, where formerly — pre-AIDS — there were penis-sized holes at appropriate heights from the floor. Now the holes are boarded up, and the brightness of the light simply make it a place "where two people see each other."

I pass a man standing in front of a doorway, his penis erect, as he faces the cubicle's occupant. Altogether, I've seen perhaps ten or twelve men on the three floors. A few stroll slowly through the dim -- but visible enough -- corridors. Others have settled into choice locations, or wait within cubicles with doors invitingly opened. Most businessmen are not yet out from work.

My overall impression is of being on shipboard. Yes. Everything is "ship shape," I hear myself thinking. The beds are all neatly made. The gray carpet and the white sheets, the sense of command I feel in Steve as Operations Director, the long, perfect row of lockers and cubicle doors . . . this entire operation seems efficiently planned and run.

I notice an illustrated poster on a prominent bulletin board --

> Great Sex
> Don't Let AIDS Stop It.
> Don't let him come in your ass.
> Don't come in his.

The poster continues its explicit instructions, closing with "Jacking off is hot sex" and "Affection is our best protection." I find myself appreciating the lack of ambiguity in the writing. There is, after all, a life-and-death motive for the existence of this poster.

There are stacks of pamphlets, available free of charge. "Healthy Sex is Great Sex" says one, with expanded instructions and illustrations. "AIDS Information for Gay Men" says another, with Help Line phone numbers covering all of New York State. Steve shows me the package given to every client upon arrival: two pamphlets from the Gay Men's Health Crisis with guidelines for healthier sex, one lubricated condom, and a letter:

Dear Patron:
The contents of this packet can help prevent an epidemic!
Please use the enclosed CONDOM with our compliments.
Also, read the information contained in the LEAFLET
and try and get your partner's name and phone number
on the CARD supplied.
These few precautions can help curb the AIDS crisis.
Whatever enclosed items you do not use,
Please leave in your room or locker.
Thank you.

172

Included in the envelope is a card on which to jot a name and phone number. On the back of the card are safe sex guidelines in summary. Also, a caption: "Keep sex free of disease. Insist on infection-free encounters. Learn to trust yourself. YOU are responsible for your good health." A twenty-four hour GMHC hotline number is provided on the card, along with a note that all these materials have been provided free by GMHC as a public service.

The absolute, can't-miss-it level of communication about AIDS surprises and impresses me. My sense is, this is a place established quite clearly as a meeting place for sex, all kinds of sex, but there is strong, insistent encouragement you cannot escape: let the sex be safe.

Steve and I return to the "Ultra Deluxe" room where I set up the tape recorder for his interview. We sit at opposite ends of the bed, with the tape recorder between us. I'm reminded of my interview with Jenny, sitting in much the same way. By comparison, these surroundings are a clean but empty laboratory, despite the disco music piped in over the speaker next to the bed.

Steve tells me his first job was in IBM's "repro graphics" department, keeping track of reports people wanted duplicated. "I was very corporate -- three-piece suit, wing tip shoes. I make a reasonably good impression, and people in the mail room liked me. I became one of the only people in the world ever promoted *to* the mail room instead of out of it."

He also worked in an antique shop, as a bank teller, and in his uncle's New York plumbing business. He found his uncle difficult to work for, however, and became a manager at the bathhouse eight years ago.

"You know I'm here to learn about bathhouses and their link, one way or the other, to AIDS," I say. "Has your business changed dramatically since AIDS?"

"Yes. It's dropped off quite a bit. We keep a graph, and you can see that it's plummeted. It dropped last year, too, in late July and August. It started coming back in October, though, and through the winter. Right after the Rock Hudson story broke, it went down again."

"How many people visited here each week, normally versus now?"

"I guess we were doing about 200 people a day, and now it's about 100 to 150. It adds up to a great difference each month."

"What kind of people come here, to this location?" (The management owns a Wall Street bathhouse as well.)

"They're all professional men. The three-piece suit is often the costume of the day. A lot of attorneys. Decorators. All kinds of white collar professionals."

"When is peak time?"

"Weekdays we've always done a good business during the lunch hour. I call them the `Sex for Lunch Bunch.' They're here from 12:00 to 2:00. Then it empties out, despite a few stragglers, till after work, 5:00 or so. The `Honey, the train is late guys,' and they'd spend about an hour or two and head out to the suburbs, whereever."

"Steve -- do you have any true, personal sense that a lot of the people who come here are married and do live in the suburbs, versus the urban, unmarried gay?"

"Yes. The lunchtime crowd is predominantly married, that's certain. Then it gets mixed up at 5:00. After the commuters leave, it's mostly full-time gays. But, honestly, there's always a mix of heterosexually married gay men versus out-of-the-closet gays. It stays busy till midnight, and then slacks off. Sometimes at 3:00, 4:00 in the morning it gets busy again, when the bars close. People just come in to sleep it off, or they didn't get their chances at the bar, so they figure they'll come up here."

"How have sexual practices changed?"

"I don't peek into the rooms, you know!" he says with a laugh. "Once the doors are closed, that's that. But I do inspect the place almost every morning. The rooms are vaccumed, the trash baskets are emptied, the ash trays are cleaned, the linen is changed after each customer has been and gone. I notice there are a lot of used rubbers around now. They're genuinely being used, which is good. We try to recycle the plastic information packets, and they generally come back without the condoms.

"Prior to handing out the packets, we were also seeing strong sales of condoms from our vending machines. Even before Rock Hudson. And even before the Coalition for Sexual Reponsibility stepped in and told us that every customer should get one . . . people had begun to use condoms."

"What is the Coalition for Sexual Responsibility?"

"It's just a group of people who formed a coalition, however loosely, to get bathhouses to conform to health codes set up by doctors, and to see that we were sticking to it voluntarily. Like turning up the lights. They're the ones who came up with the requirement to see a mark on someone's body at arm's length."

"How typical is this bathhouse in that respect?"

"They are all supposed to be conforming to the requirements. There are ten bathhouses in New York City. They each have different clientele, but we're all trying to promote healthy sex. St. Marks' gets more of the Village clone-type guy. We get the business people. It varies from location to location. Our customers here have always complimented us on how clean the place is. We're inspected at least once a year by the health department. Also, the Mayor's Task Force inspects us -- that's someone from the building's department, the police department, the health department, and the fire department."

"How long have you had the AIDS posters up?"

"Must be about nine months to a year. As soon as they were printed and we were told by GMHC to put them up, we put them up. A GMHC volunteer comes here once a week to answer questions for anyone who attends his meeting."

"What is your sense of what Diane McGrath is recommending as a Mayoral candidate?"

"She wants to close bathhouses, and I think gay bars also. But it's impossible to police people. People will have sex whereever they want. Especially men. It's so much easier for men to have sex, man to man. You don't have to get undressed even. It goes in the bathrooms of Penn Station, Grand Central Station. She's just not informed about these things."

"The suburban, married types who come here during lunch hour. If this place were closed, what do you imagine they would do?"

"Hmmmm. I don't know. Some people come up here with a partner. Maybe they'd go to a hotel or motel instead."

"Governor Cuomo said in a television interview that the feeling used to be that bathhouses should stay open as a place to educate but that, maybe, we're beyond the need for that here now. What do you think?"

"Yeah. So everybody's been educated, so what? It's better to come to a place like this, than to go to a bathroom someplace. At least here we have soap, and a shower room. You can shower, and the lighting is increased and you can look at your partner and really see him. If a guy has his clothes on in a men's room, you don't know. He could be covered with Kaposi's marks all over his body, and you wouldn't see them."

"Do you worry that the bathhouses really will be shut down?"

"Sure we worry. But we intend to fight this legally. We employ twenty-five, thirty people on staff. We pay about $100,000 a year in city taxes. That ain't hay."

"You pay $100,000 a year just in CITY taxes?"

"Sales tax. There's also occupancy taxes, etc. New York has 8 and 1/4 sales tax."

"So that implies sales of something like $800,000 a year. Yes?"

"Yeah. Sure."

"That's a big business. Is that the Wall Street location too, or just here."

"Just here. Right from here."

"Steve, usually, when I interview someone, I give him the opportunity to say something directly to the public. What would you like to say to readers?"

"Well, we've been trying to educate the public at large. Follow the safe sex guidelines. That's all I can say. Use the methods we're all telling you about. That's the best thing to do. We're not telling you to be abstinent.

"To all readers: just be careful. Let's all be that way, homosexual and heterosexual."

Downstairs, as I leave the building, six men -- most in suits and carrying brief cases -- get on the elevator. None of them seem to be looking at each other. Not yet. I look at my watch. 5:45. The work day has ended.

Mayor Koch

"I'm sorry. The Mayor has a very busy schedule. It's just not possible, Martin."

"Mike."

"Sorry. It's just not possible, Mike."

Governor Cuomo has just now given permission to New York City to close any bathhouses harmful to health. What does that mean?

WILL they be closed? Which ones?

What about legal action from the bathhouse owners?

What about civil rights?

What about patrons, including men in heterosexual marriages, who may continue their sexual practices elsewhere -- without the free condoms, educational posters, and bright lighting provided at some of the baths?

Is this action by the Governor, and presumably soon by the Mayor, a response to the spotlight that Republican Diane McGrath has put on the gay bathhouse issue and AIDS? Does it effectively remove an issue from her campaign?

Those are the kinds of questions being discussed in the media and by reporters I've spoken with. I've been wanting to interview Mayor Koch himself, but am unable to approach him -- until *TIME* magazine calls his office.

Oh? *TIME*' is doing a story on how people use computers, including reports to readers about AIDS? Why of course Mr. Greenly can have his picture taken with the Mayor for your article! Have him come right down to the press conference on the steps of City Hall. We'll give him and your *TIME* photographer prime positions for the event. Thank you so much!

City Hall is an antique. Beautiful, broad stone steps rise to classic stone columns. Planters of tan and pink chrysanthemums lead up to them. In the end-of-October chill, the flowers themselves look like history.

Inside, I pass security guards.   The men's room is a stage set for old, shopworn politics: dim yellow light comes from unmatched fixtures hanging down in fatigue from the dull gray ceiling.   The light spreads like fog onto the gray and yellow tile of the floor and onto fading yellow walls.

The basement corridor by the men's room is vaulted, as in a picturesque monastery. Old wooden church pews line the hallway. The main floor public areas are gleaming white and chandeliered. They lead from a grimy, weather-beaten press room at one end, to more security guards at the other, and the glamour of the Mayor's personal office.

"No one knows anything for sure," says the exasperated *Daily News* reporter across the desk from me in the press room. "You'll just have to ask around yourself and hope for the best."   Eight or nine reporters are at various desks and equipment.   An old Royal typewriter. Shabby desks stacked with press releases and newspapers. A huge machine that looks like the first word processor on earth. The room is a holding pit where reporters wait between events, where they can type and phone stories to waiting editors.

A local TV newsman enters the room. I feel the confidence in his subdued strut.   He is not nationally known, but to local viewers, he's a celebrity.   Here, at City Hall, is where his best performances occur.

"Hi!" says a print reporter eagerly to the TV star.   The acknowledgement in return seems perfunctory.

The *TIME* photographer arrives. Together we go to the opposite end of the hall to announce ourselves to the Mayor's contact. Now that I'm under the halo of *TIME* , the official could hardly be more cordial.

Alan, the photographer, has camera equipment and credentials dangling across his chest. He's been doing this work for twenty years and he acknowledges that he's become jaded.

"It all seems like bullshit after a while.   You see too much of how things are set up to produce an image."

"Do you have to be aggressive in this job?" I ask him.

"Yes, I have to make myself more aggressive than I really am. When it comes to getting the picture or not, you just do it. If you have to knock aside the old lady, that's it. Some of these guys are animals, they don't have to work at it like I do.   You learn how to physically move through a crowd — handling the camera, anticipating the moment.

The Mayor's aide escorts us outside to the steps. A pack of TV technicians and print reporters are already assembling. Two competing TV reporters stand next to each other, each with his crew in readiness.

Joining the men I so often watch at home creates an unreal quality to what's happening. "Mike, why don't you go over to Spider Man and Batman?   The three of you will be interviewing the Mayor."

We're assembled on the sidewalk at the foot of the stairs. Now, like a bride emerging with flowers for the ladies in waiting, comes His Honor.

"Probably the last time I'm coming out without a jacket," he announces to the wind. He's in blue shirtsleeves and looks commanding and hard at work. My photographer is delighted with the overcast light.

There are two press events. First the Mayor endorses a black politician for City Council. The Mayor's speech is short and effortless.

"I'm supporting him," he concludes, "and I'm delighted he's supporting me." There is an awkward silence. The endorsee doesn't seem to realize that it's his turn to speak.

"Would you like to answer that?" prompts a reporter. The man answers with a rambling muble, like most of us would. He lacks the years of practice of Mayor Ed Koch. ("He's a living Press Conference Machine," a *TIME* editor had said to me.)

The endorsement is done. Politician and entourage disappear. In a few minutes, State Comptroller Regan will join the Mayor for Conference #2. My photographer is unhappy that I haven't gotten close enough to His Honor.

"Get up there!" he says with steam. "Hold your little computer high along with your microphone." I've brought an airline shoulder bag to carry the tape recorder and leave my hands free. "Excuse me," I say. The man who's standing next to the Mayor is surprised when I try to take his place.

"*TIME* Magazine's doing a computer story!" I hear the whisper from several steps above me. We are like a Chorus in Greek drama now, at our different positions on the stairs. With the mention of the magazine, a spot to place my feet has suddenly appeared next to the Mayor's. I hold my tiny microphone directly in front of the Mayor, next to the large ones with TV logos.

The two competing star reporters are taking turns asking him questions. They seem to calibrate the exact millisecond when the Mayor's answer is completed and a new question can begin. They also — I believe this is true — have a tacit agreement. They're like the two tallest players on a basketball court, trading the ball back and forth only between themselves. "Shorty" Greenly's having trouble getting the ball.

"Uh . . ." I hear myself say loudly. The Mayor glances my way for an instant until the network man asks him a question again. His head jerks back to face the camera.

I'm enjoying my realization that some of the network guys' questions are halting and awkward. Of course, their pauses and meanderings will be edited out for broadcast. But it's a comfort to see, despite their smooth visual impression in my living room, that these luminaries I watch every night are not as flawless as I'd thought. This observation comforts me in my involuntary silence. I try to think professional thoughts as I listen to the clicking of the photographer. He gestures -- hold the computer higher! It is practically at neck level now.

So it's the four of us -- the Mayor, the two TV stars, and me with my miniature microphone, as I edge my computer closer and closer to the Mayor's face.

"Mister Ma-- " I ask. It's as though I've simply coughed to myself. One of the stars now switches from a local shipyard topic to bathhouses. The Mayor reponds to criticism from State Health Commissioner Axelrod -- is the City moving too slowly in closing bathhouses? And is the Mayor angry at Axelrod for saying the City is slow?

The newsman seems to be fishing for a controversial response, something juicy for thirty seconds at 6:00. The Mayor isn't biting. The City and State commissioners had been in disagreement on whether the bathhouses should be closed, he says. But now he and Governor agree. The Mayor endorses the "conservative" approach: "seek to reduce, and eliminate where we can, the contagious aspects of AIDS, as much as we can, even though it's very difficult to have people stop doing things that are killing them. Nevertheless, we will try."

The State regulations are "broad," the Mayor says, but the City will in fact implement them. New York is proceeding "in a very careful way to document the violation of the [health] rules and regulations, so that when we go to court, the case won't be thrown out." We could close them inappropriately, he says, but that wouldn't hold legally.

"I agree that the bathhouses should be required to prevent certain sexual practices which the State Health Council has said leads to AIDS," the Mayor says. "Anal sexual intercourse and fellatio, which is oral sexual intercourse," he says. I notice he was careful to define "fellatio" and I'm wondering if these words will be included in the edited footage. What is the social impact of television set bringing "anal intercourse" into the living room, given the life and death topic that occasions its discussion?

The Mayor says the City is now dealing with the problem of how to collect evidence of violation. How and when can you prove that a bathhouse is promoting unhealthy sex?

Ah! One of the TV reporters clears his throat. That is my opening.

"What about the fact," I say, "that the bathhouses give education for people who otherwise will go ahead and have sex?"

He turns to me full on. The two larger TV microphones must now enter the air space between me and the Mayor. My computer, propped up by my right hand, is like a helium balloon stopping by for a visit. The Mayor's gaze is direct as he answers my question.

"That's what Dr. Sencer said. But Dr. Axelrod believed that if you balance all the interests, including that which you just referred to, the net-net would be that some lives would be saved. I am for saving those lives."

"So you think that this is actually going to have SOME practical benefit, other than political?" We both know it was really the Mayor's Republican opponent, Diane McGrath, who first raised the bathhouse issue.

"There's no political benefit here." His voice has turned somewhat sneering. "You know, it's outrageous for people to think that either the Governor or I benefit by keeping them open or closing them. I don't believe it has any political repercussions, one . . . way . . . or the other!"

I believe I am supposed to feel embarrassed for having suggested that AIDS could have political repercussions.

"Will closing bathhouses, then, have some practical benefit?"

"Yes! It may save lives. And that's a very important benefit."

My moment has come and gone. The nearest network reporter takes the ball back. I am privately tickled to hear him stammer as he regains momentum.

As the press conference concludes, a man from the watching crowd grabs the Mayor's hand. "Mayor? I saw the musical about you, Mr. Mayor," he says. The show, *MAYOR*, has been successfully playing off Broadway for some time.

"Thank you," says the Mayor. "Did you like it?" As the man responds, the Mayor says, "It's good isn't it?"

"Yes, very good," says the fan. He starts to add something about telling all his friends to go see it, but the Mayor overrides him.

"You should write to them and ask them to make it into a movie," he says. And he disappears up the steps.

Chapter 18:
Vivian Shapiro: Fund Raiser, Businesswoman, Lesbian

Vivian Shapiro is co-chairperson and an active force within the AIDS Campaign Trust, a Political Action Committee which seeks to support government officials who favor legislation or other action on behalf of research, health care, and education about AIDS. ACT is specifically AIDS-related, with no regard to sexual preference. *(Vivian is active in separate, gay-oriented organizations as well.)*

It became clear to me in writing this chronicle that politicians who are willing to champion the needs of AIDS can, in fact, use ACT's support. They can often become involved in the controversies of drug addiction, minority sexual preferences, etc. Portions of the author's royalties for this book are therefore being donated to ACT. Reader contributions may be sent to: AIDS Campaign Trust, P.O. Box 1396, Washington, D.C. 20013.

I'd been urged to meet her. She's one of the people in this country having considerable 'back stage' effect on the American political process as it relates to AIDS. Once I heard her speak at a fund raiser. She was strong, direct, and clear. To be honest, I'd felt slightly intimidated as I saw her up at the microphone -- a personal distance I thought I'd keep.

I think it's partly my growing up in the rural South, the way I first reacted to this native-Brooklyn dynamo. I had learned to acquire a kind of easy, relaxing surface. ("Ya'll want some lemonade before we talk?") Then working at corporate Avon, travelling across the country and even the world, I learned the value of holding back. To eeeease into the ideas I was selling. ("Well, we certainly do appreciate your feedback, Barbara. I'll be very sure it's considered back at the home office. But I wonder if I could ask YOU to think about this point . . . .")

For a while, I received formal training as a psychotherapist. There too, I learned to stand back, not to get in the way of my client. ("But how does the news make YOU feel, Joe?")

I don't think Vivian Shapiro is very interested in 'standing back.' There are too many things she wants to accomplish *now*.

"OK, Shoot." I'm in her West Side apartment after work.

"Well, okay. Um. . . " I'm momentarily discombobulated. I sit across from her on a comfortable gray couch. She must like that color. The carpet is gray. Her pants are gray. She wears maroon oxford shoes and a maroon sweater, but her shirt is gray, and she wears a gray necktie.

"Let's get some biographical stuff on you then." I'm looking for a way to gentle my way into the interview. To my ears, I sound falsely chipper.

"What do you want to know?" she says practically.

"All right. Where are you from? Where did you grow up?"

"I'm from Brooklyn, New York. I went to college in New York. I've been in New York most of my life. After college I spent a year working and teaching my way through Europe. Went all the way round to Russia and Japan. I came back. I was a social worker for a few months and paid off my debts. Then I to went to Mexico for six months. Eventually I got the job I have now, which I've had for thirteen years." She talks fast. A computer printout.

"What kind of job?"

"I'm vice president of a newspaper rep firm. It works with every major newspaper in America. We sell advertising space for them in one category -- direct response. Book clubs, record clubs, etc."

"How old are you?"

"Thirty-eight." She says almost to herself, "I'll be thirty-nine next month." We are sitting in such a way that the track light above the couch is focused on me, not on Vivian. I am in the brightness, she is in shadows. I wish I had gone for the other side of the couch first.

I see a menorah. It's not Chanukah yet, so I assume it's just part of the decor. An arrangement of fresh flowers and autumn leaves. A small gray polar bear.

"How many people in your family?" I'm feeling like a visiting census taker. But I see something I've said isn't clear.

"You mean --?" Ah. Switch gears again. Vivian is a highly politicized woman. She has a different kind of consciousness than some of the people I talk with.

"I meant *traditional* family." Her point of view, surely, is that close gay and lesbian associations are also properly considered 'family'.

"My traditional family. OK. I have an older sister and a mother. My father died about four years ago." She answers in a powerful monotone. Not weak, or dull, or absent of energy. Suddenly I realize she reminds me of Jack Webb, in the black and white 50's TV show. 'Just the facts, ma'am,' was the detective's query.

"I have two nephews and a brother-in-law."

"Vivian, when I asked you that question, 'how many people in your family,' what was the other kind of family you were thinking of?"

"Well for eight years I was living with Marie Manion and her daughter, Sheila. We lived together, here, for about five and a half years. When we moved to our house in East Hampton, Sheila and I remained together in the City. Sheila's now studying at Pratt. She just got her own apartment last Sunday."

"Um. So do you define yourself sexually as a 'lesbian'?"

She laughs at the question. "Absolutely. Yes." I was just getting it officially on the record, I think to myself. I wouldn't be good in the Jack Webb role.

"And how long have you thought of yourself that way?"

"The past twelve years. Since I came out. Since my first sexual experience with a woman. I think I knew I was gay for many years, but I always wanted the shoe to fit. During college I went through a whole -- I lived out the 'party experience.' I had very many boyfriends.

"Very traditional things up to the age of twenty-six, when I actually fell in love with a woman who had become my friend. She and the man she was seeing, and I and the man I was seeing -- we'd all play bridge together. We were real traditional. Preppies."

"How did it happen? Your first sexual experience with a woman?"

"Um . . . because, I think we wanted it to?" For the first time now, she's softer, less rat-a-tat.

"When I was about twenty-one and I came back from Europe, I went into therapy. I said to the therapist, 'I think I'm in love with this woman I travelled with in Europe. I think I am gay.'

"He had said, 'absolutely not.' I said, 'GOOD!'

"Then I just proceeded with life, you know. But when I think back to being ten or twelve years old, I believe even then I had strong attraction to women. I can feel those instincts within me. So at twenty-six, this one woman in particular had . . .I guess she had experienced many of the same things. One of her graduate school roommates was gay. She told me she'd gone to a gay bar with her roommate -- and I got jealous. All the early feelings were surging up again. I told her that I thought I was attracted to her. And we ended up in a relationship."

"Was it -- ?" I am picturing the foursome at the bridge table. The two men must have been surprised. "Was it hard telling the men that each of you were seeing . . . ?"

"I don't really know how we dealt with that, you know. I think I blocked it out completely." I can see why. It seems a socially awkward situation to handle gracefully over the bridge table. Murray? Arnold? Viv' and I will be switching to Gin Rummy.

"The man I was seeing was divorced. His wife divorced him because she'd left him for a woman. I don't remember how I dealt with it, Mike. I had trouble being 'out' for many years. I think my problem really came from my parents not knowing. Once I told them, nothing else seemed to matter. Then I could tell my boss, and now everybody knows."

"What was your family's occupation?" I am careful not to say 'father's,' not to presume that the male earned money while the female did not.

"My father was a podiatrist. But we were lower middle class in many ways. My parents were both socialists, politically active. I can't conceive of him as a 'serious' doctor. If people didn't have money, he'd treat them anyway. Lots of his patients were like that."

"Was it hard telling your parents about yourself?"

"Yes. I sent them a letter. I was thirty-two by then. The coming out process is no easy trip for anyone. You do it to really be part of your family, to establish honesty. You tell them when you're ready, but they might not be set then to hear it. They may need time to readjust their aspirations. They're giving up traditional dreams when they accept your other kind of life. That can hurt them at first.

"Last week was the second time my mother went with me to the 'Parents and Friends of Lesbians and Gays Dinner.' It's very rewarding, you know. I love that dinner!"

I am beginning to feel her warmth. She smiles a soft smile I haven't seen on her before.

"It's everybody's parent represented there. Parents who don't yet know about their children. Parents who have trouble accepting. Parents who can't be present. The hundred or more who attend are symbols of our fathers and mothers everywhere."

"How do you think society views lesbians, and how do you feel about it? Two questions."

"Society doesn't 'view' lesbians at all. When we talk of 'gays,' we're really talking about men. If you were to survey 100 people in New York City, at least fifty would say they personally know a gay man. Only ten would say they know a lesbian. Lesbians aren't visible."

"Maybe there are fewer of them than gay men?"

"Absolutely not!"

"So you think the difference is only of awareness."

"That's correct."

I'm now enjoying the crisp nature of her replies. I'm seeing them not as abrupt, but as simply efficient.

"I don't even think it's 'awareness'," she adds. "Women in many ways choose to make themselves less visible. How many famous lesbians can you pick out in the theater? We could go through theater and ballet, the two of us, and in five minutes we'd have a list of 100 gay men who were stars in those endeavors. But how many gay WOMEN could you name? And yet, Mike, they're there! They're just non-visible."

"Why?"

"Two things, I believe. First, women tend to nest. They're just not out and around as much. Their socializing is in smaller groups. At house parties. They know each other but are not so known to the rest of the world.

"Economics, too, made women less visible for many years. They had less money than men. The most visible lesbians were the Lesbian Feminist Separatists. They were right on the front lines of the 'street people.' They were doing much more than separating from men; they were also separating from society as a whole.

"During that period, most women I know were developing their own careers, their relationships, lives. Today, everybody knows I've been living with a woman for eight years. I have many non-gay women friends. They understand I don't view them as sexual objects.

"My best friend in the entire world, my closest, best friend for the longest time, is a heterosexual black man. He's president of the Housing Police Benevolent Association in New York. He's the first black man in the country ever to be president of a police union. They bought a $2,000 table for our dinner. We bought an ad in the program when Jack was honored by the Italian-American Society.

"If I had a brother, it would be Jack Jordan. There isn't anything we can't share honestly. When things get really tough, he and I can sit all afternoon in a cafe. We can hug. We can cry. We can encourage each other."

I am touched by the picture of it: the black, heterosexual cop and the Jewish, lesbian activist, celebrating his tribute from Italian-Americans. In the periphery of my mind, I hear a song we sang at sixth grade graduation,

"One World, Built on a Firm Foundation.
Built on a Firm Foundation of Love."

I believed all of that hope, even as I used to find the swastikas on my locker at lunchtime, or heard people calling me "Jew Boy" in South Carolina of the early 1950's. Today, as an adult, I love to walk up to foreigners on the hassled New York streets. I can recognize a Frenchmen by his *Guide Michelin*, the slim green volume he may be studying as he puzzles what next to do.

"*Je peux vous aider?*" I'll say to the Frenchman. "*Sind Sie Deutsch?*" if I can tell he's a German. Even when they need no help, they appreciate the offer.

Now I stare across the expanse of gray couch, at this intense, strong woman with the wiry hair and the steady stream of words . . . she is warmer than I'd realized. I notice a toy on the floor, a white, plastic dumbell. Someone must have given her a playful symbol of her own strength.

"Even with gay men," she says, "something's happened since AIDS." She's sitting cross-legged on the couch. She leans forward as she describes the change. "There's more hugging. People are more open. AIDS took a lot of suspicion away. It brought us together. Men were willing to accept the nurturing women wanted to give. Women wanted to cry with the men. There's a huge number of women who have volunteered for GMHC. In its terrible way, AIDS is bringing us all together to fight it."

"And -- you think there'll be political repercussions from the solidarity that sprang from AIDS?

"Absolutely. Of that I'm certain."

"What are you doing politically? You're co-chair of the Human Rights Campaign Fund and of the AIDS Campaign Trust. What are you after?" She has summarized these purposes in city after city.

"We have two real goals. Our first goal, and our initial reason for being established, is to have a gay civil rights bill passed by Congress. The basic feeling is, I should be as free to love in Alabama, as I am in San Francisco. Everybody accepts our money, gay money, and we all speak the same language . . . yet it is determined where we are free to love in the United States as gay people. So the change has to happen at the Federal level.

"This year we have a second goal: we formed the AIDS Campaign Trust, a completely separate fund. It will give money based on a candidate's call for AIDS funding on key committees. Not only Appropriations. AIDS is overwhelming, so you have to break it into smaller issues. Social. Health. Education. You're talking about masses of committees. Anyone who can help us increase that funding, we will absolutely support in their election. We're involved here on the health issue only, not for civil rights.

"If a Senator is in favor of AIDS research, for example, we'll contribute to his election campaign and do whatever we can to help him. We think we can help make a difference. In that way, it turns out, the urgency of AIDS, and the way it brings lesbians and gay men together, is helping us create a national political force.

"I spent a good portion of my weekends on the road this year. Speaking in city after city. At the first Human Rights Campaign Fund dinner four years ago, there were twelve women present, at $125 a plate. This year, there were 300 women at $200 a plate.

"San Francisco, Washington, Dallas -- we're reaching the female doctor, dentist, and professional who may not relate to politics in the street but who's learning to write a check for $200. Or $1,000."

I can appreciate the phrase, "hold your head up high." Vivian's posture is actually different as she considers the accomplishment. It must not be easy pulling someone out of the closet -- and, by the way, do bring us your checkbook and ten of your friends.

"But Vivian, your first goal. Aren't the chances of passing a gay civil rights bill actually decreasing? Isn't there a backlash from fear of AIDS?"

"The effort's not over yet. Everything's a matter of consciousness. If people can understand the truth of it, 'gay' will be recognized as a person you love in everybody's family. And 'AIDS' will be seen as a vicious disease, just like cancer. AIDS and gay are not the same.

"It is only coincidental that AIDS lodged itself first in the gay community. You can get the disease from one single relationship. You don't get it from having twelve. You can have 800 and never get sick. Or you can get the disease from your first sexual experience.

"Maybe our promiscuity and the singles life helped AIDS' rapid transfer. But it could have begun in any community in this country or world."

She is on a roll, but I decide to interrupt her. "That's all fine," I say. "But there are vastly more heterosexuals than homosexuals. You're wanting homosexual rights from a worried heterosexual population." I've gotten comfortable enough with Vivian to enjoy the fact that I've pushed a "hot button." Her voice rises, and she is emphatic as she answers me.

"There are twenty million gays in this country. If each one has two parents, that's forty million parents. Give them one sister and brother. No! Give them each just one sibling. That's eighty million adults already."

"But, Vivian, many family members don't even know that these people are gay. It took years for you with your own parents, for example."

"Yes," she says immediately. "That's the problem with our image and we can only enhance it. But there's something great happening if you consider.

"When someone comes to our dinners for the first time they're astounded. `We're actually at the Waldorf Astoria?' A man handed me a check for $1500 the other day. Another man who's a Republican brought all his Republican friends. He bought a table for $2000. His nine guests agreed they would each sell a table next year.

"The event POSITIVELY REINFORCED THEIR IMAGE OF THEMSELVES! In a prestige hotel being addressed by Phil Donahue, for example. One year it was Walter Mondale. When a national figure speaks to *you* in an elegant setting, it's reinforcing. That helps you be more courageous -- maybe even telling your family, if you haven't, so when they vote on gay rights, they'll realize they're voting for you."

She pauses for breath.

"That and AIDS funding are the kinds of votes I care about. I'm not in this to run for political office. I want a cure for AIDS so my friends won't die. I want others not to get sick. And I want gay people to have personal freedom.

"The hardest part about politically related work is the abuse that comes with it, no matter what side you're on. But I'm a cause person, I guess. I've always been involved with them."

"Why so?"

"If I earned literally one dime, my father would ask me: `How much are you going to contribute, Vivian?' As an adult, if I got a raise or a bonus, my father would telephone: `Vivian, congratulations! Now how much of your raise are you giving to charity?'"

"Any charity?"

"Charity in general. Because you HAVE to give. In Yiddush, there's a word *'mensch '*. It means a solid, worthy adult. You cannot be a *mensch* unless you give to others. When people have a hard time giving, I think to myself, they didn't live with my father."

She's been making us tea from ground leaves, periodically going into the kitchen to pour hot water over them. Now as she brings in our cups, she tells me her married sister is on the school board in Stamford, Connecticut. Vivian has given her advice on AIDS and the schools.

"What do you think they should do?"

"They should tell students about AIDS and how deathly it is. They should teach them about safe sex. Unfortunately many school systems don't teach anything at all about human sexuality. I know that's controversial. But what's the great issue? Why not teach adolescent young men that when they're having sexual relationships, it would not be so traumatic to use a condom. It's not a birth control issue, it's about health."

Neither Vivian nor I are parents, and I try to represent them. "What would you say," I ask her, "to a parent who replies, `I don't want my child taught how to have sex. I don't want my child having sex early, and I don't want my school to encourage it. Keep your sex classes to yourself, Yankee meddler!"

"I would say, `Your children are going to have sex anyway. By teaching them about safety, all you may do is save your child's life.' It's just like drinking and driving. Parents may not want their kids to drink or smoke dope in high school or college, but kids do it anyway. So you try to make drinking a separate issue from driving.   Now there are bars with `designated drivers' -- if you're that kid, you can have all the free soda you want.

"The question isn't, should you have sex or not? Should you get pregnant or not? It's, how are we going to sustain life! In five years there'll be a lot of kids becoming sexually active. Maybe you're instilling a sense of morality into your child, and maybe you believe you can control it. Okay, but there's still no value in not telling them clearly, even now, that at whatever later point they do have sex, they should have it carefully until AIDS worries are history.

"AIDS is a national crisis. We talk about other disasters: mud slides in Puerto Rico, earthquakes in Mexico. Well this is a disaster too. And there are plenty of deaths to make it worth discussing. Much of society didn't care about homosexuals and IV drug users. But the disease is going to be less and less based there.

"Those of us in the gay community are very aware of men who 'trick' before going home to Westport or Darien. They're not all going to stay clean. They will transfer it to their wives. When the disease is transferred, some of those men won't ackowledge the truth of how they got the virus."

We sip our tea in silence.

"How I have experienced you, Vivian, in this conversation is that you're intense, you have a lot of gusto, and a lot of strength and energy. Is that really the way you are in general?"

(She murmurs comically in mock, subdued meekness.)   "I think so."   It makes me laugh, hearing her play at talking like a dormouse. "Sometimes I'm exhausted and sleep for two days straight, but I do have a huge amount of energy. This is really me."

"What are your fears and vulnerabilties?"

"One is that I'll have AIDS. I'm not saying that's rational.   But you can't live with the horror of this disease as much as I do and not be afraid of it. I also have tremendous fears of isolation. I think I could become a removed and isolated person, and then regret it too late. Maybe that fear is a leftover vestige of being 'different' as a youngster, secretly lusting after a twelve year old girl and being afraid to share that feeling. Learning to hold back.

"My father was very afraid for me that, as a lesbian, I might not have sharing relationships.   Who would take care of me when I'm old? Well he died and left my mother, so now she's taking care of herself. She is learning to live by herself in her seventies.

"I got some of my father's fears, I think. Just like him, I'm a scared person in some ways. There was a time when I was fourteen and I didn't leave my house for three months. It was maybe a kind of nervous breakdown. I've later had fears of that kind of depression. I don't know why I'm getting into all this!"

I laugh with her at her puzzlement, even as I appreciate her honesty.

"Well," I say, "I have to believe that 99.9% of the people you meet every day wouldn't spend a moment thinking you ever have those feelings."

"It is very intense, what I'm trying to do. It's consuming. For the first time in many, many years, I was so drained from all this political work two months ago, I was in tears three times a day." It's hard for me to picture Vivian that strained, and I'm affected by the thought of it.

"I cried at the office, I cried at home. I couldn't take the pressure. I mean we're dealing with a lot of immediacy here. We don't have twenty years to work this out. AIDS is now."

"Vivian, I always invite someone to say whatever they want to readers. What would you like to tell them yourself?"

"I mostly want to ask the public to care" she says right away. "It's really easy to love and care for somebody. It takes so much less energy to love than to be angry. With AIDS, you could be talking about your children or your parents or anyone else you care about.

"If we could only make our government responsible to help us find a cure, we wouldn't have all this business of people going to Mexico to get drugs. Or going to France.

"The only way we can really change things is if we each care. About hospital treatment. Developing the drugs we need. Experimentation to find a cure and protect all of us. We can be a finer and healthier society. We just have to care.

"That's it," she says. It's like her saying, "Okay, shoot" when we first began. But by now, I easily recognize her smile.

190

Chapter 19:
Indiana

I made a promise to myself to include in this chronicle something of "heartland America," the part of the country I used to visit — and learn from — as an Avon Products Vice President. AND I was determined to include as part of this history at least one person who very clearly and strongly did n-o-t feel especially sympathetic to people with AIDS, given the strong, early association of the disease with homosexuals.

Dr. Krim's office at the AIDS Medical Foundation helped me locate Amy Sloan, a heterosexual woman with AIDS. Art Kleiner, a San Francisco journalist and telecommunications specialist, drew my attention to Dr. Don Boys and his anti-AIDS research editorial in USA TODAY. Along the way, I met a successful businessman, "Lewis," whose views I also recorded.

My sense of AIDS and its conflicting human impact in our society was enriched by contact with these three individuals, and I'm glad for the experience of meeting all of them.

"Lewis"

We are on the plane to Indiana. He'll get off in Chicago, where he lives in a "progressive" suburb. I'm impressed when he tells me his title and company: he's the perfect client for my marketing consulting business. But I decide to interview him about AIDS instead of talking about advertising and marketing. He agrees to be "100% honest" if he can be anonymous. He is "Lewis."

He has three children, ages two through six. He has never had a homosexual experience in his life. He considers himself "fairly well informed" about AIDS. His concern escalated when a Kokomo, Indiana boy contracted AIDS and was refused school admission. He then decided he'd be following the disease regularly.

He appears to be the classic, conservative executive — white shirt, subdued tie, dark suit. About homosexuality he says, "people should be left to their own preferences, but I have a strong desire that my children not be influenced. I have a personal aversion to their being involved in school or Boy Scout counseling with anyone who might exert undue influence. I'd like my children to be taught only by people whos preferences lean toward the norm."

"You mean, taught by heterosexuals," I say.

"Yes. Heterosexuals." I think he's relieved to have expressed it so plainly.

"I honestly don't believe I'd have a problem if one of my children chose not to be, but I don't want that choice to be influenced by someone else, especially at a time of their lives when they're most formative."

"Let me ask you a few hypothetical questions." He agrees. "Some people say the chief protection of young people from AIDS is education in the schools. But that means overtly addressing sexuality there. What do you think about that?"

"I grew up in a small — really small — farm community. Ideally, I'd like each parent to teach his own children. Realistically, with the stakes on AIDS as high as they are, I guess there really should be some school education. But it should tend toward the norm."

"Well, speaking of 'the norm,' it's often said that a large percentage of heterosexuals actually do have homosexual experiences in youth, even though you personally never did, experiences they then outgrow and move away from. What if one of your children were to have such an experience, or be sexually involved with someone else who had? Wouldn't you want him or her to know how to have it safely?

He considers my question in silence for a very long time.

"Yes, I guess I have to say 'yes.' So I suppose all kinds of sexuality should be covered in education. But not by advocating those experiences at all. Just being clear about how to avoid getting the virus if one were to experience them."

"So after thinking about it more, you would now support sexual education, let's say of young adolescents, in the school system, including a clear depiction of safety in a variety of sexual situations? For example — let me be very specific — saying that if one has anal intercourse, whether it's male-female or male-male, one should use a condom. Right?"

"Yes," he says. He seems as objective and clear about his point of view now as I imagine he seems after making a business decision. "I didn't start out that way, and I don't want them to actually have those sexual experiences. But when you make me consider the fact that a young person might try an experience anyway, then of course I want them to do *anything* they do safely so they won't get AIDS. AIDS is too dangerous not to feel that way."

"I have to tell you, Lewis, that I was uncomfortable talking with you — a stranger to me, and perhaps quite a conservative man — about anal intercourse as we have our American Airlines dinner. Here we are, two businessmen. We each travel a lot. We each feel fairly well-informed about things. Yet I was embarrassed. If I felt embarrassed talking with YOU about the topic, I can picture how difficult it might be in a class room setting. Do you see what I mean?"

"Absolutely, I do. But one thing I do know from my own reading: we're going to have a major disaster on our hands, if something isn't done differently, even if it's uncomfortable to do it. We've got to have a national priority to coming up with solutions. I don't think the Reagan administration has any sympathy at all for this issue. I don't think the President would intervene at all if he could help it, because of what he believes philosophically. But we really need intervention on this one.

"You know, my wife says I'm pretty naive, but I didn't even know Rock Hudson was gay. That part of it was a shock. But the whole thing, including the publicity about him, could turn out to be a blessing in disguise for the entire human race. Maybe this will be the single most important event in beginning to shift the pendulum of pre-marital, adolescent, out-of-wedlock sex back toward the middle. It could actually have a major impact on improving the morality of the United States.

"It says to the entire American human race that they just can't get away with all the stuff they've been getting away with. I'm not talking just about a homosexual issue — I mean heterosexuals, too."

"Do you personally, to your knowledge, know any homosexuals."

"Yes. Someone who works for me. He's an outstanding person, and he takes his work very seriously. He's very competent. I've been responsible for promoting him twice. As far as I'm concerned, whatever he does in his own personal life, it's okay with me."

"And do you personally, to your knowledge, know anyone who might be called 'bisexual'?"

"No. It's not easy for me to understand that. As a heterosexual, you look at a female and mentally things transpire that cause you to have physical reactions. It's hard to imagine that same kind of reaction when you see a man. But even though I don't experience it, I really don't mind someone else being that way. I've had occasion to visit New Orleans for my work. You walk down Bourbon street, and two males hold each other's hands. It seems strange, but frankly I don't think they're hurting anyone.

"And if they go further than that behind closed doors, I think that's okay. I just don't want my children unduly influenced before they're old enough to make whatever their own, personal decisions might be."

"Let me ask you, Lewis, about what you think your neighbors might believe. You seem fairly tolerant, and you've been flexible enough to change your mind as we've discussed things. But what about the people in your community? Or in the community you grew up in?"

"I know what they think: `put homosexuals behind closed doors, lock them up, ship them away, there's no place for them, I don't want my children to be like that, and I don't want to talk about it in school!'"

"Well, based on your own point of view, that's a problem, isn't it? In schools, for example. If you now agree that heterosexuals, all adolescents in fact, need clear education in school about what's safe and what isn't, but if you think most of your friends and most of the parents in your community won't favor that -- then kids may be having experiences without real education. And some of them could get a killer disease because they weren't taught safety. Isn't that right?"

"I'm afraid it is. That's why I wish — usually I agree with Reagan, I'm really conservative politically on most things — I wish we had more aggressive leadership on this issue, because I think it's really a major problem. And it's everybody's problem."

"Is there anything you would like to say direct to the public as long as I'm typing your words right now?"

"I can sum it up. We started the interview based on the AIDS situation and its ramifications. America needs to take an active role in funding medical research and bringing about a cure for this disease.

"In addition to that, those people responsible for the education of our elementary and junior high school students have to understand that we're approaching a crisis. It's no longer a homosexual problem. It's a heterosexual problem as well. Therefore we have to take action to educate the youth of America and make sure they understand how to avoid this disease."

The plane lands. Lewis departs. And I head on to Indianapolis.

To Lafayette, Indiana

I have forgotten how flat the world is outside New York. I used to know. I used to come out into America all the time. Now it is novel for me to walk down Airport Lane to a hotel at the edge of the parking lot. Strange to look past all the rental cars and actually see sky meet an open sweep of land for almost all the horizon.

During my visit to Indiana, I have exactly two interactions with black people, notable here for their rarity. Both are members of the airport hotel staff who say, "Hello, sir," just to have said it. Everyone else on the path I follow this trip is Caucasian, including hundreds of men taking an Engineers and Land Surveyors Exam in the hotel ballroom. (Beauty Control Cosmetics is in Parlors A and B today.)

At 7:15 Saturday morning, a wonderful old man with badly fitting teeth helps me find my rental car and understand how to get to Lafayette.

"Sixty-three miles from here. Heading to the football game?"

Purdue is in Lafayette, and there's a game today. I am surprised on the highway to see we're all going seventy miles an hour. It's quite easy to get used to, despite the signs urging fifty-five.

Flat. Brown October furrows stretching off in uniformity onto flatness. A lonely barn. Some dull evergreens. A stand of barren trees, empty branches on a pale morning sky. And, unaccountably, one survivor in the group with flaming orange leaves still clinging and waving in the wind as I pass.

That tree makes me think of Amy. She's been described to me as "a Born Again country girl living way, way out there in the sticks." I picture a farm wife with gingham apron, bare feet, long brown hair, Bible in hand. That's who I'm whizzing along to see. Surviving, like the bright orange tree I've passed, despite the AIDS that courses through her bloodstream.

"Halloween candy will be X-rayed free of charge," offers a medical care center on the radio. I think of Trick-or-Treat apples with hidden razors inside and feel depressed. A car passes by, a blue Pontiac with a PURDUE sticker and a CB radio antenna. "B-Dry" says the license plate.

Highway patrolmen are already out directing traffic as I enter Lafayette. "Way out in the country," my New York contact had said. But the trees and open fields are gone, far behind me. I'm passing shopping centers, billboards, and fast food restaurants.

She lives in a housing development. I am early, so I drive by and spot her building. I head back to the Ponderosa restaurant on the corner for the "All you can eat" breakfast. Biscuits, gravy, spiced apples, cottage fries, grits, citrus salad, stewed prunes, eggs with sausage.

"What do people use the melted cheese for?" I ask someone in the buffet line as I consider the hot yellow mixture. "I'm from out of town."

"Me too!" he says, though his twangy Southern accent seems from a lot less far away than I am. "I think they put it on their eggs." I waive the cheese sauce, but try creamed gravy on a biscuit. I am feeling like a foreigner.

A Halloween skeleton is tacked up on the wall, hidden behind a plant. His bony hand points the way out to my car. Before long it's time to follow his direction.

Amy Sloan

She's not a bit like the plain Pilgrim I expected. Indeed, Amy Sloan is very pretty. She is twenty-four, has sandy brown hair, and is trim and stylish. She's wearing large, gold earrings shaped like tiny leaves. Her autumn red sun dress covers a ruffled beige blouse. I quickly sense her alertness and humor. She's one of those people I immediately like, purely on instinct.

She offers me tea. "I got it in England," she says, giggling with amusement because she so hastily announces that she was a guest on English TV: The Heterosexual AIDS Lady from Middle America.

She was born nearby, and grew up in Remington, a town of less than 2,000 people thirty-five miles to the north. After high school, she came to Lafayette to learn a skill and get a job. She went to "Ivy Tech" (Indiana Vocational Technical College) and became a dental assistant in Lafayette. "I come from such a small town, there were no prospects there. No people!" There were five children in her family; one brother was killed in an automobile accident. Her father is the Postmaster of Remington.

I am sitting on the couch, and she's in a lounge chair across from me. Her nine-month old son is asleep in the crib, where a dining room table might otherwise be. I recognize an Avon shipping carton underneath the crib. Even before I see it, I'm feeling that I'm in the classic Avon 'selling scene.' Instead of the latest brochure on her coffee table, with pictures and descriptions of my newest Christmas enticements, I've set my tape recorder.

"I grew up Catholic," she tells me. "We went every Sunday, you would never miss. That was a big part of my upbringing, but since then I've converted. Now I'm Protestant."

"When did the conversion happen?" (Is that how one refers to it?)

"March of '82. To Church of Christ."

"And when did you learn you had AIDS?"

"In May of '84. So my religious change was definitely before." She was a young girl, living on her own for the first time. Her dentist said the Pentecostals had excellent social events for young people. "It's a pretty radical church," she says. "Some people call them 'Holy Rollers.' They raise their hands, and you have to say 'Praise God' a lot. But they had a really big youth group. I met Steve right away. After six months, we got engaged. Then we went back to this little Christian church, just a middle of the road, mild-mannered Christian church."

"How come you had, uh ... did you stop feeling Catholic, or —?"

"No, I'll tell you what the deal was," she says. She is breezy and natural. One of the things I like about her, I now understand, is that I trust her honesty. "It just wasn't doing anything for me spiritually. For a long time, I didn't care about that. It wasn't important to me. But there came a point in my life when I felt I needed something. I needed more spiritual fulfillment, more Bible teaching. I needed Jesus Christ.

"Of course, the Catholic church believes in Jesus Christ, and that's what their basis is. But it was just too stale for me. I needed something more, you know, peppy ... and singing ... and acting crazy. That's what I got!" She has an easy, light laugh.

She and Steve married in September, 1982. The ceremony was held at the Catholic church for Amy's family. Steve works, stocking shelves, at a local supermarket. Until Amy got sick, they were both employed.

"Is your accent typical of this area?" I ask her. She pronounces her son's name "Bray-ant" as though "Brant" had two syllables.

"Ah don' know," she says in the same, natural way. The intensity with which she gives serious thought to my question makes me chuckle. "Does it sound like I have an accent?"

"Well, to me it does," I say.

"Maybe 'cause I've been to England for a few days!" she says with a smile. "Do you think?" To me she's just as charming and delightful as can be.

"I'm just kidding," she says needlessly. "Really, I know it's not such a big thing to go to England, but to us it really was a BIG DEAL, you know. We never in our lives thought we would do anything like that." She and Steve were flown to London for four days. "It was great! I'd love to go back sometime." I wonder if she'll ever be able to. I imagine she wonders the same thing herself. What happens when you know you have a "terminal" disease scientists are "working on"?

"You say it was May of 1984 when you learned you had AIDS. How did you get it?"

"Through a blood transfusion." She'd had ulcerative colitis, an inflammatory disease of the colon. She was losing blood and had become anemic. "They gave me three units of blood. I got better and everything was fine.

"Then in March of '84, I started having tightness in my chest. I would be at work and I'd say, `Boy, I'm having trouble breathing!' I'd get worn out and have to sit and rest a while. I'd feel fevered. We couldn't figure out what was wrong, y'know. I think everybody thought I was just complaining. This went on for a couple of months.

"Finally — it just kept getting worse and worse — so I started going to the clinic here in town. And no one could find anything that was wrong with me. Nothing! I'd missed a whole week of work, and I never miss work. I was flat on my back on the couch. I had terrible night sweats, waking up soaked. The pillow was soaked. And I couldn't breathe.

"I told this guy how sick I was, and he said, 'You're as healthy as the day you were born. Go home and forget about it.' Those were his exact words and I will never forget it. He said I had a mild case of pleurisy.

"I didn't give up. I couldn't, I was in too much pain. Finally I went to another doctor and ended up just breaking down. I just cried my heart out to him. `There is something wrong with me! I feel you guys think I'm just trying to get attention. But I'm not. Help me!'

"He sent me to a cardio-pulmonary specialist, a lung person, brand new n town, Dr. Emory. He immediately knew something was seriously wrong. I couldn't breathe! It was his second day in practice in Lafayette. He'd just moved here from Pennsylvania. The very first day I saw him, he wrote on his chart that he suspected pneumocystis pneumonia. He didn't say anything to me about it. But the fact that he was here, that he knew about it — that was such a miracle! He had treated two people in Pennsylvania with AIDS, but no one in this area had any inkling at all about such a new disease.

"That night, I thought I would die. I woke up on the couch so sick I couldn't talk. My lungs felt that big around!" She closes her index fingers into her thumbs as though holding a marble in each hand. "It was like my lungs were being squeezed. I couldn't get air. I would have to—" She pants to show me how hard it was to breathe.

"That's the only way I could get air." She tells me of Steve's fright when he came home during a break from his night job at the supermarket. His mother waited with Amy till he could get off work to take her to the hospital.

The mother-in-law had to dress her. "I couldn't put a bra on because of the constriction in my chest. I hadn't washed my hair in a week. I wasn't even able to make it into the bathroom, so she brought a little pan of water over so I could brush my teeth. I didn't want to go to the hospital without brushing my teeth. She put my pants on, put my socks on.

"Finally we made it to the hospital," she says. "They did a 'bronch,' with a tube into my lungs to snip a piece out for testing. That resulted in a collapsed lung, would you believe it?" I am following every word and am stunned when she adds, "We had found out the day before that I was pregnant." Photos of Brant sit on the television across the room.

"They were going to do a lung scan," she says. "They warned me: if there's any chance you're pregnant, tell us. Because it's so much radiation. I said, `I'm not pregnant, I'm just a bit late.' They did the blood test , and I was. Crazy!

"Then, when my lung collapsed from the biopsy, they inserted a chest tube in to blow it back up." She makes a pushing movement against her chest where the tube had penetrated. "I was in so much pain, I can't even explain it. The chest tube — they have to break through bone and cartilage, and cut you." She is acting it out.

"You were conscious during all this?" I ask her.

"Yes I was! I thought it was gonna ram right through me and into the bed." It sounds so real as she describes her fear, I almost feel the

198

thrust of the tube through her chest as she emphasizes her words.

"Amy. As you're telling me this story — I'm right with you. I can feel it, but tell me . . . ." She is leaning forward, graceful and delicate in her arm chair. "How are you feeling as you tell me this story? How are you feeling today?"

She looks at me gravely. Then she smiles. "I feel tough!" We laugh together at her own surprise. "I mean it. It makes me feel like, how did I ever get through that? I must be tough!"

Brant wails from the crib. "He doesn't want to nap," she says. She sets him into a chair in the center of a wide metal ring with wheels, as though into the middle of a space ship rolling on the carpet. "That's when I learned I had pneumocystis pneumonia, the disease `only people with AIDS get.' "

"`But how can I have it,' I asked 'em, `since I don't have AIDS?' They kept beatin' around the bush, they were pussy-footin," she says. I realize that in New York, I seldom hear anyone say "pussy-footin'."

Amy imitates the staff whispers: "`Oh my God, we got this girl here and she's got AIDS!!' A year and a half ago, Mike, that was a BIG DEAL in Lafayette, Indiana. They didn't know how it was transmitted. They probably thought Steve was homosexual, or I was an IV drug user. It was a hush-hush deal. They were tellilng us, `don't say anything.' It was an embarrassing disease to have.

"I kept asking them, `but how could it be that pneumonia?' They gave me no straight answers. Finally I was catching on. `Do I have AIDS? Just tell me!' There wasn't a positive test. They knew I had it, but they weren't conclusively admitting it."

"Why not?"

"I think they were nervous because I got it from a blood transfusion, right at Home Hospital. They were questioning my lifestyle, and trying not to admit the blood issue. Finally they said, `okay, you've got AIDS. But don't tell anyone. If the public finds out you got this through the blood system, there'll be an uproar and people will panic.'

"I said, `don't you think they have a right to know?' I asked my doctor, too. I think he agreed, but maybe the clinic was saying, `keep her quiet.'"

The hospital suggested an abortion, but Amy said no. "At that time, May of '84, I had an overwhelming faith. It was all in God's hands. I prayed every day. If God meant for me to have a miscarriage, okay."

As a dental assistant with AIDS, she could no longer work. The family income was cut in half, and they moved into a tiny apartment above a beauty shop. She was worried about the baby, and unhappy to have lost her livelihood. When family and friends said, "you should have a lawsuit," she and Steve agreed.

The blood bank and hospital refused an out of court settlement, so Amy and her lawyer held a press conference. Her lawyer told the press, "We've got a big story for you."

"It was the lead story that night," she says. "'PREGNANT LAFAYETTE WOMAN GETS AIDS FROM TRANSFUSION!' The blood bank, they just hate us, I now they do." She affects a strained and high-pitched attempt to soothe: "'Don't be worried! You can't get it from transfusions. Don't be worried.'

"But we were able to trace the blood," she says. "There were three units of blood. All three people came in. One was from a gay man. He tested positive for the virus. That blew away the blood bank's theory. The suit is still going on.

"Back then, they weren't screening blood donors, even though AIDS was already a known problem. I heard the man gave blood four times, and another woman has gotten sick too. He must feel awful. I'm not angry at him. I don't blame him. He didn't know he was infecting other people, or he wouldn't have given. He must be going through his own private hell right now."

Brant was born in January. He's been tested twice for the virus, and appears not to have it. Amy, however, is often feverish. "Mostly, it's like a mild case of the flue, all the time." Sometimes the pneumonia returns, with its breathing problems. She takes regular medication to control it.

"I still have religious faith," she says. "But I think I was hoping for a bolt of lightning out of the heavens to come and heal me. It didn't happen. I still believe in Jesus Christ. I still believe God could heal. But I don't understand His reasoning.

"Sometimes I wonder about fate, and is there a God at all. Is life just life? I have deeper thoughts now than before. I think about bigger questions, like why do some people suffer? Why must some die with AIDS while others live fine?"

Brant is wailing. She gets him a cracker from the kitchen. It's like a dog biscuit for babies. She must wonder all too often if she'll be the one to keep feeding him biscuits.

"If I could only have an answer," she says. "If they could only say, `Amy, it's because you pinched your sister when you were five years old.' Then you could say, `Oh, yeah! I knew I shouldn't have done that.' That's why my faith is different now. When I originally got sick, I had Big Faith, as though I walked around in a bubble. My faith let me live when I could have died of pneymocystis. Whether God got me through, or whether having faith did, it doesn't matter in a way."

The biscuit isn't working and Brant is screaming. She lifts him from the space ship and lets him crawl toward the coffee table.

"Maybe God can perform a miracle and maybe the miracle will be me. If my Christianity helps me through this, great. But I know some people died of AIDS and were Christians." Brant reaches for the microphone. I lift it away from him and point it to Amy. "People are acting more scared of me than ever, with the AIDS publicity. Everybody's thinking they have AIDS as soon as they get one symptom. People point at me now. In a restaurant, I'll see them nudge their friends. I hear them say, `that's the girl who has AIDS.' In the grocery store, too.

"When we did the TV show in England, the technicians wouldn't film it in the studio. They wouldn't let us in. The people who sell soft drinks wouldn't come to work that day. We went to a Working Man's club with a freelance crew. These were people who knew the score. They weren't afraid; they even hugged me. A doctor kissed me on the cheek, and newspapers ran the photo."

She lifts Brant, who is upset not to have the microphone. She kisses his cheek, as a kind of punctuation. "They're trying to teach people, don't be scared about casual contact." He is wide-eyed and comforted in her arms.

"Amy, let me ask you a question I guess you've been asked a lot: what is your attitude about homosexuality?"

"That's changed," she says. "I used to be die-hard against it, mostly from a Christian viewpoint. I still believe it's a sin. But..." She laughs at her own change of heart. "I've come to believe that the people who are sick, including all those homosexuals, are sick just like I am. They go through the same crap I go through, emotionally and mentally.

"I've met a few gay people I just love. To tell you the truth, right now I could care less if they're homosexuals. I don't care! That's my attitude now. I don't care, and I love 'em anyway.

"I have a friend I met on a TV show. His lover just died. They were together seven years. Steve and I have been together only three years. I keep thinking, those guys were together twice as long as we've been. That just has got to hurt, really bad. To see your friend be so sick. He died in his arms.

"Hearing that story, I couldn't have felt any more pain or love or compassion for any straight person than I did for that guy. I just really don't care. We're all just people and we all love. And if a man loves a man, like I love Steve, then I don't care!

"Some people are telling me, `Take a stand against homosexuality. Stand up for your Christian Faith.' But on the other hand, I'm thinking I've got these friends, and if I'm quoted in the paper that, `Amy Sloan thinks all homosexuals should be incarcerated'....come *on* !

"If you push me, I think homosexuality is wrong. But I accept it. We're all just humans." Brant is shrieking. I won't stay much longer.

"What would you like the government to do about AIDS?"

"I'm glad to see more research money being spent now. I think that's because of Rock Hudson. Until then, there were a lot of people sitting back saying, `who cares about a bunch of gay people? Just get a bunch of 'em off the face of the earth. We don't need 'em anyway.' But now that there are people like me coming public with it, and Rock Hudson, government people are finally aying, `oh, great, now we've got constituents coming down with it!'

"I wish the government would help free up these drug protocols. The FDA isn't putting drugs through fast enough, and there are people dropping like flies. I'm worried that a year from now, I'mnot going to be here. I want one of those drugs. Every day that goes by, I think — one more day. I've been around for a year and a half since they told me. I've got this little kid sitting here. I want one of the drugs my doctor thinks is promising, but I can't get 'em. If we're gonna die anyway, and they've given us the death sentence, then at least let us try the medicine. It's not like this is the flu and we're gonna get over it."

Brant is louder and more urgent.

"Last question, Amy. I always invite someone to address the public about whatever she wants to say. So, I invite you." She tucks Brant to the side and he's magically quiet.

"The thing I'd really like to share doesn't have anything to do with my personal suffering. But I've just seen so much prejudice against gay people in the last year and a half. I just hate that. I wish we all could treat each other loving — kind — whether we're sick, whether we're gay. I wish we'd treat each other like the brothers and sisters we really are. This world would be a better place to live."

"Amy, you say that, even though when I pin you against the wall, you say homosexuality is wrong? Despite that, your message is what you've just articulated?"

"Yes! It all comes back to — the whole message of Jesus Christ is to forgive, love, and accept. Jesus Christ loves us, accepts us, forgives us. That's what we're supposed to do with other people. So even though I say, yes, homosexuality is wrong, I still love and accept people that are homosexuals. It's not for me to judge those people. I still love them."

The magic is over. Brant is in torment.

From Lafayette to Greenwood

I'm headed south again on Highway 65. The drive helps me gain perspective. I'll be meeting a man with a very different outlook than Amy's. Don Boys is a frequent contributor to *USA TODAY*. He is described as a "writer, publisher, evangelist, and former member of the Indiana House."

From a recent commentary:

"Sodomites demand that I fund the research
that would produce a cure enabling them to
continue their degrading practices....
God's plan is for each man to have one woman —
his wife — and be faithful to her....
I am appalled, angry, and agitated that tax
dollars are being used to find a cure.
We are constantly told how successful homosexuals
are; let them fund their own research."

I drive past grizzled farmfields whose season has ended, past roads turning off to exotic and Biblical names. This way to Peru, to Lebanon, to Zionsville. Southwest on the map are Mecca, Palestine, Brazil.

Stay on the highway. Past a horse farm with impeccable fencing. Its horses are grazing near a satellite dish on the hillside. The radio is tuned to music I rarely here in New York City. Plaintive, sassy Country. "Hey, Bartender —" "I'll never stop loving you." "Do you think I'm such a fool?" The newscaster announces a new song written by Burt Bacharach; royalties will go to AIDS research.

I'm in Greenwood, in a virtual village of fast food restaurants. I stop at Hardee's because of the free "Finderscope" they are offering with a hamburger. This gift of lens and cardboard will enable me to "see Halley's Comet closer than most of the people on Earth have ever seen it in the past 2,000 years!" I think back randomly to thankful Pilgrims, to slaves dripping sweat as they haul the huge blocks of stone for Egyptian pyramids, to a fisherman in Jerusalem in the days of the Bible — none of them had the benefit of a Hardee's Finderscope.

My mind is sufficiently distracted from the previous interview. It is time to meet Don Boys.

Don Boys

Several of his neighbors are out working on their lawns on this late October Saturday. Don Boys lives in a classic picture of a well-kept, Middle American home. Unpretentious. Clean. A small ranch house on a small piece of property next to others that are similarly cared for. A placque below the license plate on his car says, "Remember Flight 007 - Larry McDonald was Right."

We shake hands and pass through a formal living room, a family dining room, and into a den. It's decorated in an early American motif — antique ornaments, wood paneling, decoy ducks, dried flowers, and a wooden sign over the fireplace: "Boys House Established July 16, 1954."

"Pardon the toys," he says. They are strewn on the orange carpet, near the sewing machine. Above all else, this room communicatews FAMILY.

"Before we start," I say, "and pardon me for not knowing, who was Larry McDonald?"

"Larry McDonald was a congressman from Georgia who was killed in the plane crash the Russians shut down. He was the most conservative man the House, and he was a Democrat, which was amazing. Yet if he'd run for President, I'd have been glad to vote for him."

"What was he saying that was 'right'?"

"He'd been the most vocal anti-Communist for at least ten years or so. He was involved in the John Birch society, about trading with the Communists. If in fact they're our enemies, it's insane to trade with them. I wouldn't send them a paper clip, let alone computer information. That's what McDonald was saying for years."

We are sitting on separate couches, the microphone on the table between us. He lies back and props his feet up; I notice what good condition his soles are in, and remember I must find time to repair an emerging hole in my own. I see that his socks are a deep, rich purple, chosen to complement his maroon sweater. He has thick brown eyebrows, and a healthy head of hair with gray edge-touches. He is trim, and he looks vigorously healthy. He grew up in a log cabin in West Virginia.

"Literally a log cabin?"

"Yes, for a number of years. Since I got involved with politics, I've gotten a lot of mileage out of that!" We both laugh at the Abe Lincoln aura the fact conveys on him. "I became a Christian when I was almost seventeen and it completely changed my life." After college and seminary training, including getting his Ph.D., he became an evangelist for Youth for Christ.

"I was pastor of a couple of churches and came to Indianapolis about twenty-five years ago. Taught in a college here. Travelled around the country as an evangelist. I've spoken in the largest churches in America."

He is cordial and polite, exuding the comfort and control of a man at home in his castle. I can easily imagine him speaking to large audiences. He projects assurance, certainty, and pleasure in himself and his beliefs. I think he must love to let loose at a podium.

"I got involved in Christian education, apart from the college level, in 1969 and 1970. I organized a Christian school that became the largest of its kind in the nation, over 600 students. Baptist Academy, here in Indianapolis."

Eventually, he had his own weekly television and radio programs.

"I was always yelling about those liberals and radicals. Almost in self-defense, I got involved with politics." He successfully became a state Republican congressman in his first election. "I was involved, of course, in the Equal Rights battle, parimutuel gambling, abortion, laetrile, Right to Work, and collective bargaining." The warmth of his memory, as he recounts the causes he's fought for, reminds me of a child almost tasting a Christmas wish list as he recites it.

Only a few days prior to Election Day, the brother of Dr. Boys' opponent was killed in a plane crash. "For the next six or seven days, every day, the newspapers had front page coverage — Mullendour, Mullendour — that's my opponent. I lost to him by two or three hundred votes. Even the people that hate my guts, the liberals and some of the Democrats, all said to friends of mine, `well, that was worth at least four or five hundred votes.'"

I ask him to spell his opponent's name for me, for the sake of accuracy. I am from out of town, of course, and do not even know whether the melted cheese at breakfast goes on muffins or onto the eggs. He gives a little gasp of uncertainty or exasperation and spells it for me.

"M-u-l-l-e-n-d-o-u-r...I think." Does he really not know the incumbent's name for sure? Or is this a politician's artifice — create an impression that your opponent is hardly worth keeping track of. I remember President Reagan rarely pronouncing Mondale's name.

Boys will be running again this year. The primary elections are held in the spring, and he is confident of winning. "Frankly, I have a better opportunity this time than when I won the first time."

"Do you think he realizes he's likely to lose?" I inquire about Mr. Mullendour.

"Yes, I think so." The office is mainly a January-April responsibility, which would allow Boys to continue writing, publishing, and speaking. The State House is only fifteen minutes away from his home.

"If the political side of your life is involved in running for that office," I ask him, "how do I capsulize the evangelist side of your life? Are you affiliated with a particular church right now, or are you nationally doing various things?"

"Well, I'm generally recognized as an independent Baptist. I'm like Jerry Falwell. You don't know me, but if you say, 'Jerry Falwell,' then you do know. I disagree a little with him, but it's so minor. We're part of the same group, a loose and independent Baptist group."

I remember, while covering the Republican convention in Dallas, attending a barbecue at the extraordinary Hunt mansion outside of town. There was Jerry Falwell — was it a bull he exuberantly mounted? — as the news cameras clicked like castanets. I stared then at the famous man, and sensed his gusto and delight at the photo opportunity. August, 1984. Some of the people I've met since then were already in lonely anguish over AIDS.

"So you talk with Falwell, or work with him...?" I ask.

"Yes. We're not bosom buddies. I had a bill called the Right to Decency bill which dealt with sodomy. And we had 8,000 people out. He was there, and Anita Bryant was there, and all that. He introduced me. He had a series of rallies on the State House steps in all fifty states, and he was here and introduced me. We're not bosom buddies."

"But," I ask to be certain, "I'm talking to somebody now who would be, in many ways, as though I were talking to Jerry Falwell? By position and stance on most issues?"

"Well, generally. But you know, Independent Baptists, we're as independent as a hog on ice. That's one thing you learn: you never speak for any other Fundamentalist."

I can't help laughing, even though I wonder about the image. How does a hog get out there on the ice? Where does his independence come from? Wouldn't he want to scamper off of that slippery frozenness? Or — surely the image is not indended to be as grizzly as my fantasy now becomes — a hog in a huge, styrofoam picnic chest, packed in with ice cubes. No, the idea must be more of a frozen pond, with a hog all by himself out in the center of it. Dr. Boys, who can surely see I've found the image striking, must have available many such vivid expressions, to call upon as he needs them.

"What about the publishing side to your life? You've personally written books?"

"Oh yes." He's written a half-dozen. His first book, *Liberalism, a Rope of Sand* , deals with issues he faced in the general assembly. It was "very controversial" he tells me — about the death penalty, welfare, sodomy, public schools, abortion, "all the hot issues." It's now used as a source book by laymen and pastors.

"I've got a lot of quips in there that's good for TV, ten second quips and all that." His most recent book, *Is God a Right Winger?* , is the most controversial to date, he says.

"How do you know that?" He chuckles at my question.

"Well I've been on a coast-to-coast radio and TV tour. When I talk with liberals and see them literally lose control, they start screaming at me on TV, I can see I've caused 'em a stir!" He laughs with delight.

I will not lose control, I remind myself, wondering if he could say anything to make me scream like they do on TV. No. We are having a pleasant conversation by the fireplace. I'm here for his viewpoint, a man who influences others' opinions. I'm not the type to lose control anyway. Unless the couch is wired for electrical shock, I'll be fine.

We're also quite physically separated from each other, he and I. That creates an emotional distance. We are each on his own couch, like independent hogs on ice.

"Of all the stands you take," I ask, "which one elicits the most screams from liberals? Which makes them the most uncomfortable?"

He considers the choices. "Well I guess my stand on sodomy and adultery. You see, I'm old-fashioned. I believe that God expects a man to marry a wife and stay with her the rest of his life, and be faithful to her only. I maintain that would solve the problem of AIDS eventually. And herpes and so forth."

He tells me about university debates he's been part of where the audience has booed him, has interrupted his debating. On the issue of audience respect for each debater's chance to speak, I have no disagreement at all. He tells me of a time when he addressed some college students who were hissing his talk disruptively. He lectured them about academic freedom, about forums where opposing ideas can be heard.

He told them, "I want to remind you that what I believe has been believed for hundreds of years. I'm not the one that's outrageous in what he believes. Some of you have never seen a real, fire-breathing Fundamentalist in your life. Well, here I am!"

Then, when he reached the topic of sodomy, "I talked about the brutish activities of men. I talked about the 'strutting sissies.' I got hissing again. I said, `I know three things that hiss: a goose, a snake, and a fool. Stand up and be identified!'"

He laughs at this. I think he expects more of a reaction from me than I feel or display. The comment, however, won audience approval, which lasted until he stated his point of view that Martin Luther King was a Communist. "I'm used to it," he says, grinning at how upset people become in response to him.

"I personally don't get much chance to talk to a 'real, fire-breathing Fundamentalist,'" I tell him. "And that's why I want to know more of how you feel about AIDS."

"First, I need to say I'm sympathetic for anybody who's going to die. An AIDS death is obviously a terrifying thing. And I'm especially concerned for innocent people who are dying of AIDS.

"Now — I take a hard-nosed position on sodomy. I think it should be illegal again, and if I get elected next year, I'll introduce another bill that will make it illegal as it has been for seventy-five years in this state. As it is, I think, in thirty-three states.

His voice is sharper now. Forceful and stern.

"My bill that I introduced, I had 32,000 signatures, 8,000 people out, and my own party refused to even hear the bill. That was liberal Republicans who did that.

"I take the position that AIDS is a plague, and that it's here because of the brutish practices of men. And whereas I'm sorry that many of them have this terrible plague, I maintain that just like thirty-four years ago with the TB epidemic and polio...let 'em form their own March of Dimes and fund their own research.

"I know that seems heartless. And I'm willing to say that, as more and more innocent people are involved, I would be less vociferous in my criticism of taking tax dollars for that. I'm very disappointed that they've recently doubled the research dollars again."

"You're disappointed because those are tax dollars?"

"Yes."

"Let me..." My voice exhibits the slightest cracking as I experience nervousness. I clear my throat, and he courteously offers me something to drink. A Pepsi Cola? I squelch the impulse to say I only drink Classic Coke. We are different segments of the market, he and I.

"I just came from Lafayette," I say, "where I interviewed a woman who has AIDS. She's heterosexual, and she got it from a blood transfusion. Do you have a personal or religious point of view on why she, as a heterosexual, has AIDS?"

"The same as anybody with any problem," he replies immediately. "My wife just had a cancer operation eight or nine weeks ago. I see no difference at all. It does incense me that someone like this woman you mention would get AIDS. But the disease is a natural consequence of sodomy. That was the catalyst, even though the problem has now 'jumped the tracks' and is in the heterosexual community."

"Now — " Maybe I should have accepted the Pepsi. "I need to be very clear here on this question, and very specific. When you say 'sodomy,' I don't know whether you mean sex between men and men, or whether you mean any kind of sex, male-male or male-female, which involves anal intercourse. Which way do you mean that please?"

"Basically I mean anal intercourse." My impression is that he slurs the word "anal" as he answers me; perhaps he is feeling some of the same discomfort I am.

"Even between man and woman?" I am sounding clearer and more focused now.

"Well, yeah, it could be, but I, I don't know...."

"Because, from what I've been researching, AIDS could certainly be passed that way too."

"Oh, yes, there's no doubt about that. And the bisexual who has sex with a man and then infects his wife — that man is a scum-bag. I have no respect at all for such a man."

"But do you have a religious point of view on a man having anal intercourse with a WOMAN?"

"Oh, I think it's abnormal. Yes. I would say it's an abnormality, of course. I guess I don't feel quite as — it's probably a matter of degree. I don't think it's quite the perversion as it would be with man and man. And, as somebody said years ago, God created Adam and Eve, not Adam and Steve!"

Once again, I have the feeling my reaction to the quip is deficient.

"I haven't seen any figures on man to woman..." he says. "But there's no doubt that, because of the lining of the rectum, it becomes super-dangerous."

"Do you personally know any homosexuals?"

"Oh, yes. I've talked with a number of them. I've counseled with 'em. And then I've talked to others who weren't interested in any kind of counseling. Truck drivers...." What a vast difference, I imagine, between the homosexuals who welcome his counseling and those who disdain it.

"What is `talking to them?'" I say. I change my mind about my approach and ask, "have you ever had anyone as a close friend who was gay?"

"Yes," he says.

"Do you still?"

"He's dead. He was a younger man. He was younger than I." He sighs. "I won't tell you what community he's from. Frankly, I don't even want to tell you what state he's from. He left his home and went to San Francisco and started making a bunch of money. His parents and their friends knew he was homosexual. But before long, he was found dead." I see and appreciate his honest distress as he tells me this story.

"You know, after a while, regular homosexuality is not enough. They have to go a little further, a little further, a little further. More kicks." He seems secure in his knowledge of the process, the rising Graph of Kicks for homosexuals. He is an intelligent and highly intelligent man, I remind myself. But our couches could be at totally opposite poles of an icy universe.

"I'm the only person who's ever mentioned this on radio or TV," he says. "Everybody talks about exchanging body fluids, but nobody says what it means. I did, on a Pennsylvania station. I mentioned that someof them have a fetish for urine and feces. That they ingest each other's waste. And others go on to strangling.

"The boy's lover — you put a chain around someone's neck and twist it. You release it just before the person suffocates. In this case, the lover didn't release it quick enough."

"That's how the young man died?" I do not doubt the truth of the story. I feel heavy, pulled by gravity on the Couch of Planet Jupiter. So *this* is the homosexual Dr. Boys has personally known? This is his reference for what "they" are like and what they do?

"Yes. His family are fine people, too."

"What do you say, when you're counseling someone and the person says, `Look! I've always been attracted to my own gender. That's how I really feel.' What do you say to that?"

"I hear it all the time, of course. The fact is, all the time they tell me, `I was born this way,' just like blacks are born black and so forth. Of course, I maintain that's a fairy story. That's not true at all." I note the "fairy story" pun and have no reaction in exchange.

"I believe it's possible for a person to have effeminate tendencies without being homosexual. But there's no doubt in my mind that homosexuality is a choice. It's a set of learning factors. What can be learned can be unlearned.

"I will not for a moment permit someone to make that statement, that they were simply born that way, without a rebuttal. If someone says, `I can't help it,' I say, `It's a choice.' Maybe the choice is made at fifteen years of age. Or at twenty. If anyone can prove the fact that they were born that way, then the position I'm taking could be altogether wrong. And we've been wrong for 2,000 years in having laws against it, see?"

His wife and daughter-in-law enter the house with groceries, and we are briefly introduced. He presents me politely as "Mr. Greenly." I ask them to please call me "Mike." We resume our respective couches.

"What would you say if someone said to you, `Well, look. Fine if it's a choice, but it's *my* choice, not yours. This is America. And the whole point about America is individual pursuit of happiness. Suppose I'm a person who is attracted to my own gender and is not hurting anyone else. What is that to you?'"

"Obviously," he replies, "that's perfectly legal in many states. It's legal in this state at the moment. The basis I come from, of course, is the Scripture. I believe the Bible is applicable in every state. Every state and every nation. The Scripture is quite clear — it is perversion, it is wrong, it is always wrong, it is abomination."

I understand I'm not asking anything he hasn't answered many times before. There is a kind of ceremony taking place for both of us now, I think. I'm pitching, he is at bat. An American pastime.

"But what about the reply, `it's fine that you believe int he Bible and can quote it. But because this is America, Church and State are supposed to be separate. Your Bible and your beliefs are private, not governmental.'"

"Yes, that's exactly right. Church and State are separate. The fact is — you see — here's — it seems that the liberals have all the rights, they've been doing this for years, to try to bring pressure upon legislators, to get laws changed, to be what they want them to be. But when we conservatives, and Fundamentalists, and Christians get involved.... Most

210

of our law is already based on Biblical precepts! Thous shalt not kill, thous shalt not steal, and so forth. You know, it's hard to sit down and defend something that, if it's continued and pursued, will call for the depletion of the human race. By not having procreation."

"But — what about this reply: `You really don't have to worry about the human race being depleted, Dr. Boys. People have been attracted to their own gender for thousands of years. We're all still here. In fact, earth has a larger population than ever.' What would your answer be?"

For a moment, I think of market segments as an illustration of the point, of varied human preferences. I think back, as I have before, to Jenny, the prostitute who startled me when she told me of the existence of 'Mother's Milk Sessions' with her clients. On reflection, I decide to leave Coke and Pepsi out of it. And "market segments" like price brands, and juice-flavored sodas, and diet brands...let alone coffee, milk, papaya juice. I doubt that my points on consumer preferences would be considered relevant to a Biblical interpretation.

"So, then — `don't worry about population!' " I summarize again. "`The issue has always been a choice for only a small segment of the population anyway.'" I lean back and await his response.

"Yes, well. First of all, it's never been as legal and as accepted as it is today. Fifteen years ago, a man would not have even considered sitting on a television state and boasting about his homosexuality. Not even if he was having an illicit affair with a woman. Today, it's done all the time. It's done without shame. You never hear any remorse, there's never any blushing. I think that's an indictment of our civilization."

"But what is your stance to the heterosexual couple who says, `Dr. Boys, we'll do what we want in our own home. We don't need you to pass a law saying that what a man and wife do in the privacy is illegal."

"I would say, `I'm not interested in putting a camera into your bed room at all.' I think it's an abnormality, husband and wife. But to me, it's not the same, man with man."

"But a sodomy law would include heterosexuals...."

"Yes. Yes. It would. But the very fact is that, if it's against the law, it will eliminate some participation in sodomy. At least, even if people disobey, it won't have the acceptance. It won't have the respectability. That seems to be what many homosexuals want. They already have acceptance in many areas, but they want respectability."

I have never studied a sodomy law. "I need to be precise again now, for the sake of clarity. Would a sodomy law include in it, or are they separate things, cunnilingus and fellatio?"

"Well, my bill covered — I don't remember the terminology now — it covered a number of sexual crimes. That have always been recognized as felonies. I'm not sure how I'm going to write it if I get elected next time, but there are hundreds and hundreds of sexual aberrations. If they're asking us to accept sodomy as legal, my question is, what comes next?"

Sexual crimes. The phrase is still in my head as he continues.

"Are we going to say, `Anything goes?' I don't think there's any doubt that's where they're headed. Sex with animals. Sex with dead people."

I have read too many Steven King novels, I know I have. I quickly squash my fantasy of the kind of lobbyists Dr. Boys worries would ultimately press for legalized sex with dead people.

"What about: `Dr. Boys — why don't you just deal with those issues if and as they happen?"' The ghouls are not yet at the doorway.

"I maintain that, no — we've backed up enough. By 'we' I'm talking about Christians and conservatives. Thirty years ago, it was illegal to go to a motel with a woman who wasn't your wife. Fornication, adultery was illegal. Today, you talk about that and you get laughed out of the legislature. I'm saying we Christians have backed up far enough. We're not going to accept homosexuality, we're not going to make it respectable. We'll do our best to make it illegal again." I am listening closely. I believe his opinions are of genuine social significance.

"I'm not interested in hanging homosexuals from the maples of the State House lawn."

Perhaps in case I've misunderstood him, he repeats: "I'm NOT interested in doing that. But I am interested in making it a felony again. In Indiana law, you once got seven to twenty-one years for sodomy. I'd like to see the same thing again."

"What would you say are your chances of getting the law passed?" I ask him.

"Far, far, far better now than before."

"Do you think some of the reason for those improved chances has to do with AIDS?"

"A reaction? Yes. I have no doubt of that at all." He leaves the room and returns with a folder of papers.

"You see...Dr. James Curran, Harvard health official, said, `This is a plague. I see nothing wrong with quarantine.' I'm seeing that kind of statement or something similar quite often now. But frankly, I don't think it should take a potential plague to form our principles. I don't think AIDS should be the reason we get the sodomy law passed. I do think it will be helpful, though."

I ask him, in case readers want to order his books, where they should write for information. The address is Goodhope Press, P.O. Box 27115, Indianapolis, Indiana 46227.

I also ask what message he would like conveyed here. He looks through his folder and selects a quote. "I guess my statement to the public would be, `There's nothing gay in the homosexual way.'

"And, as I quote in my book, *Is God a Right Winger?* — psychiatrist Dr. Daniel Cappon wrote in his book, *Toward an Understanding of Homosexuality* :

"`Homosexuality, by definition, is not healthy or wholesome....the homosexual person, at best, will be unhappier and more unfulfilled than the sexually normal person. There are emotional and physical consequences to this protracted state of mental dissatisfaction. At worst, the homosexual person will die younger, and suffer emotional, mental, and physical illness more often than the normal person. The natural history of the homosexual person seems to be one of frigidity, impotence, broken personal relationships, psychosomatic disorders, alcoholism, paranoid psychoses, and suicide....'

"There's nothing gay in the homosexual way."

I reach for my jacket. "Now it's accurate?" I say to him. "I've just had an interview with a real, true Fundamentalist, right? The real thing." He laughs with me.

"Well, I hope, with a capital 'F' — but notice, I don't handle snakes! That's what a lot of uninformed people think, that Fundamentalists are snake handlers in our services, which is ridiculous. Thirty years ago, I was uncontroversial in every respect of my life. So I say, at the least, I'm not the one who has changed. I'm a traditionalist. I'm not a nut. I'm a Christian, I'm a conservative, I'm an American. I can defend my position and I have, at Universities and on radio."

I explain to him that I will try to be absolutely faithful in representing his point of view in my writing. I warn him, however, that his opinions will be accompanied by those of people feeling quite opposed to them. He understands.

"Real good," he says. He gives me an autographed copy of *Is God a Right Winger?* I promise him a copy of *CHRONICLE* whenever it's published. We shake hands.

I cross his well-tended lawn to my car. I'm going home.

Chapter 20:
Bishop Paul Moore

I sometimes feel defensive admitting not only my personal lack of religious belief, but also how uneducated I am about organized religion, or even disorganized religion. Documenting various glimpses of the human side of AIDS, however, inevitably led me to include at least some word from religious leadership. I also began to reflect more about religion myself, as various people I met talked about what their own faith meant to them (Doris Williams and Manuel Ortiz, for example, in previous chapters.)

My talk with Dr. Don Boys ("Indiana") gave me one end of the religious spectrum. By his reputation, I knew that Bishop Moore, leader of the Episcopal Diocese of New York, represented another.

Here is my experience in several encounters with the Bishop.

Bishop Moore's Speech

(October 21, 1985) He is Chairman of the Governor's Advisory Council on AIDS. I have an interview scheduled with him in a few weeks. Tonight, in a high school auditorium in Greenwich Village, he sits behind a chipboard table on a stage backed by stained, canvas curtains. He is joined by other AIDS experts including Dr. Mathilde Krim.

Each speaker has volunteered time for this event, which is sponsored by Citizens United for Research and Education (CURE) for AIDS. CURE describes itself as "a broad-based citizens' group concerned about the lack of treatment, research, and reliable, coherent information regarding the health crisis. . . . concerned that the health crisis is still misrepresented as a tragedy affecting only specific target groups."

I am glad to have tonight's 'preview' of the Bishop. I learned from his office that he leads 70,000 Episcopals in the New York area. I know nothing else about him. Before I tell you about Bishop Moore, I should probably provide my own religious perspective, so you can make any necessary allowances for the impact he had on me.

214

As a Jew and as a good boy, growing up in South Carolina, I received thorough religious training. I went to Synagogue two days a week for Rabbi Fischer's after school classes. I learned to read Hebrew and then to sing it for holy occasions. I loved the stories that were like mythology.

Ultimately, when I turned thirteen, I wrote my own Bar Mitzvah speech. (Most boys had their speeches written for them by the Rabbi.) My close friends were all Christian. As an adolescent, I hated the fact that Jewish services were on Friday nights, PRIME TIME for socializing. Why can't we go on Sunday like everyone else?

Occasionally I would visit friends' churches. Those excursions made my parents fidgety and short-tempered, but they held themselves back from begging me not to go. They went with the tide and allowed my occasional Sunday reconnaissance, provided I'd to our Friday night services that same week.

I visited the Baptist Church one Sunday morning with Bill. I squirmed in my seat when the hymn rose around me, "Put Your Hand in the Nail-Scarred Hand." I focused on social aplomb and politeness and quietly kept my shivers to myself.

I visited Mollie's Catholic Training on a Tuesday night. That's where I heard a nun describe what I was afraid of: Jews are "Christ Killers". I don't follow religious news, but I understand this judgment has since been modified. If so, I'm appreciative.

Later that year, Mollie's mother phoned mine and asked that Michael no longer see her daughter. He was causing Mollie to 'lose her faith.' I don't know if you'll be willing to take my word for it or not, but I believe Mollie's faith was in serious jeopardy without any help from me. I was a laissez-faire person even then; I wouldn't have tried to change what someone else believed about God.

That incident formed my adolescent opinion of Catholicism. My naive religious stereotypes were, in summary:

Baptists are the most conservative.

Methodists are like Baptists, but not as strict. (Rumors of a secretly homosexual Methodist minister, with a wife and children, seemed to confirm that Methodists lacked Baptist discipline.)

Catholics are Mollie's Mother.

Episcopals are wealthy, and they like a lot of ceremony just as Catholics do. But they're not as uptight about Jews.

There were numerous other churches in my small town. I would often hear the clapping and whooping and singing of black gospel, like the smell of forbidden cake tempting you from the oven.

215

As a Duke University student, I took a "Religions of the World" course. That requirement accomplished, I left religion behind. Survival in the secular world commanded every ounce of my soul. Eventually I learned to balance fear and pain with pleasure. "Survival" became more optimistic — "personal growth."

The auditorium is totally filled. The event will be broadcast on WBAI, New York's "listener-sponsored, free speech radio." An NBC television crew is setting up. The woman from WYNY approaches most of the speakers with microphone and portable recorder.

The Bishop is tall and distinguished. He will soon be sixty-six. He wears a charcoal gray suit and a plum shirt and collar. I don't know the formal name for that article of clothing. It is set off by a gold chain across his chest, under the jacket. To me, he is startlingly elegant.

He has thin-rimmed glasses, and rich, perfect silver-snow hair. He looks serious, warm, formal, and loving simultaneously. A religious "Father Knows Best." All of the speakers are effective. But no one makes a stronger and more unexpected impression on me than Bishop Moore. Here are excerpts from his speech:

"Good evening. It's nice to see all of you.
"It's hard to know what to say leading off a forum of this kind. I was sorry to hear I have white hair. I thought it was blond." (laughter) "We all have our little hangups." (More laughter. He's easy, and more wry than I'd expected.)
"I am a clergyman. In a sense, I hesitate to come here to speak to you because, as a group, the Church and religious people in general do not have a very proud record about their relationship to the gay community. Therefore for any of us presuming to speak to a community like this, to an audience like you, I think is perhaps presumptuous.
"I also hesitate to speak because I know that many of you have lost even more friends than I have to AIDS. I know the fear that you have, many of you, and that we all share. And so I do speak to you, I hope, with a sense of real humility.
"I went through two wars -- I include Vietnam -- the convulsions of the 60's, the threat of atomic war. But somehow the epidemic of AIDS is to me one of the most deeply threatening events that I have ever experienced in my whole life. It is different than any other epidemic or any other corporate experience our community, our City of New York, our nation has ever undergone.
"I think that's one thing I want you to remember tonight -- that this is different. Therefore the guidelines, the presuppositions, the hypotheses by which people figure out how to act, one with another, in

216

other areas of disease or in civic crises, do not hold necessarily. In a way, we start from scratch with this epidemic.

"Never in modern times have we seemed so helpless. I remember as a child, I was that generation when some of my friends fell to polio, when all of us were forbidden to swim during August. That terrible dark killer came to strike down children in their beautiful prime — in that beautiful, splashing, watery summertime. Yet, at least with polio, there was some hope of recovery. With AIDS, we are not sure that there is."

(His image is still reverberating in my mind: "that beautiful, splashing, watery summertime." As he talks, cool and deliberate, I find I'm not interested in making notes on my lap computer. I look and, yes, the tape recorder is capturing his words. I want only to surrender myself to his message . . . and to the fact that this is a religious authority, speaking in a way that I long ago decided they do not speak.)

"Furthermore, because it attacks two of the tragically least respected groups in present day society, AIDS is an even more evil and demonic disease. It attacks those who are narcotic addicts and use IV, intravenous needles. And the gay community which, because of its courage, began to gain respect starting with Stonewall, and was getting to the point of high respect in the community — then, AIDS comes."

(Another surprise. To hear a Bishop talk supportively of the "Stonewall" riots on June 28, 1969 in Greenwich Village that started 'Gay Pride.' To hear him talk without the sneer I usually hear -- and have sometimes felt myself -- toward drug addicts.)

"Not -- believe me -- as an act of God. But rather, perhaps, as something which has happened to a beleaguered community which may, despite its terrible tragedy, have a deeping effect on the Witness and the love and trust within that gay community.

"Yet unfortunately, despite the fact of the gay community's courage and endurance and decency and trust, one with another, and forgivingness, even to the Church -- despite this -- the gay community and the IV community, if I can call them that, are still less respected than most other groups in society. Therefore, AIDS, because it attacks these two communities primarily -- instead of eliciting compassion and support as polio did, as the Legionnaire's Disease did -- it elicits horror and disgust. That's what I mean when I say it is different....

"Politicians reach out in a dull mayoral campaign to some issue that will be exciting and controversial. What do they go close in on? AIDS. Close the bathhouses. Test everyone. Quarantine gays. Quarantine single persons. Quarantine friends of single persons. Quarantine parents of friends of single persons." (Huge applause.)

"I'm glad to say that our Council on AIDS has come out as, thank God, the *Daily News* and *New York Times* both have come out, not to close the bathhouses at this time, because that is a place where much can be done in terms of education, and also a place of gathering dearly won in the civil rights struggle of the gay community.

"The Army, testing recruits with complete disregard for the ambiguities of the present test. Do they not realize that a man's life could be ruined forever, because he's tested positive, even though he's by no means proven to be a person who can get AIDS?

"Perhaps even more dangerous than the physical danger of the epidemic of AIDS itself, is the epidemic of fear which I've been touching on already. The epidemic of 'fear of AIDS' may last longer in its harm to the nation than the epidemic of AIDS itself. There may be a vaccine for AIDS. I hope, pray God, before long. But when the very heart and soul of an ultimately decent nation is destroyed, there's no vaccine to heal it.

"If we ostracize the AIDS community, we will be next ostracizing other 'useless and dangerous' communities. The homeless. The hungry. I believe all of us need to fight with everything in us against this leper-phobia, this hate, lest it become part of the culture of America that when a group of people's in trouble, we ostracize them, we get rid of them, we lock 'em up as we have with mental patients over the years.

"This is a very dangerous threat to the soul of our nation and our City, and must be fought with everything within us....

"I think the attitudes of our churches and synagogues with what they assume, in this regard, will test our sincerity. Even through people who are not institutionally religious: their attitudes will test whether or not they believe in what we stand for as a people.

"Please don't become cynical, my friends. Stand up for what America stands for. And all of our old-fashioned patriotism, for decency, and democracy, and freedom. And equality of opportunity. For you. And for me. And for persons with AIDS.

"Don't let them take the American flag away from us. Because the rights we claim in this crisis are the rights that belong to every American. We must mount a campaign to elicit an even more urgent program of research. And lobby insistently for adequate hospital care and housing for persons with AIDS. To dissipate as best we can with education, the panic of ignorance and fear.

"There is much to do. God bless you."

(The applause is overwhelming. Loud and enduring, it is a communication up to him on the stage. I realize, personally, that my own simple, monolithic picture of what "religious leaders" are like has been closed and narrow-minded for decades.)

Excerpts from the Biography of
the Right Reverend Paul Moore, Jr.

- He was born in Morristown, New Jersey, on November 15, 1919. He has a B.A. from Yale University, and an S.T.B. degree from General Theological Seminary.

- From 1941 to 1945, he served in the U.S. Marine Corps. He was seriously wounded as a platoon leader in the Tulagi-Guadalcanal operation of the First Marine Corps Division. He has earned the Navy

- In Indianapolis, Bishop Moore served as president of the Standing Committee of the Diocese. (He was Dean of Christ Church Cathedral in Indianapolis from 1957-1963.)

- He became Bishop of New York on September 23, 1972, "in the ninth year of his episcopate."
Cross, the Silver Star, and the Purple Heart.

- He serves on the National Board of the NAACP Legal Defense Fund and is chairman of its "Committee of 100."

- One of his special interests is the relationship of the ministry to psychiatry. "His deep and unflagging interest in the plight of the cities and his concern for their survival is well known and on that issue he has spoken out many times. He has received the Social Sciences Award and the New York Urban League Award."

- He is the father of nine children.

Interview with the Bishop

It is 4:00 on a raw and darkening afternoon. I've taken the wrong subway and self-consciously walk back from Lenox Avenue and 111th. I'm the only white on the street, and I wear the only suit and necktie.

The gigantic figure of the Cathedral of St. John the Divine looms over treetops and dingy tenaments. I remember that Bishop Moore is famous for his concern for the poor and the underprivileged. It seems appropriate that my path to his towering Episcopal castle should detour through a kingdom of Urban Poor.

I pass a bent, human form, wrapped totally into a blanket, an unknowable person who sits or leans on a stoop. No head, no arm, no inch of skin is visible -- an impoverished turtle in hiding.

The door to the Bishop's administration building is massive. A sign warns, "This door is heavy. Push hard." His assistant greets me cordially in the anteroom.

I wait for the Bishop to finish his phone call, and I realize in dismay that I left my microphone at home. Ditto, my computer.

"I can handle things okay with just pen and paper," I say to Peter. "But is there a chance that the Bishop has a tape recorder I can use? I've got a cassette." Why, for the Bishop of all people, did I have to be so sloppy and hurried as I left home? "This hardly ever happens to me," I add, which makes me seem still more scatterbrained.

"Well he does have a machine," Peter says. "But it may not be here tonight."

"Okay," I say. "I'll just ask him."

Peter frowns. That isn't how it's done with a Bishop. Peter will ask him for me, and in advance. I have not been granted an interview, after all, to watch a Bishop rummage through drawers in search of a tape recorder. Peter exits and I hear one word behind yet another thick door, this one leading to the Bishop's study: "Alrighty!"

He returns with a tape recorder for me to test, and he invites me to have some coffee from an urn near the desk. I am filling a styrofoam cup when he offers a china cup and saucer. An Episcopal emblem is stenciled elegantly on the porcelain. Such is my picture of religious royalty that I imagine it might have been rude to enter the Bishop's office with styrofoam. You are already mooching off the man's tape recorder, I warn myself. Mind that you don't slap him on the back, or set your feet up on his table.

The Bishop enters the room. He is as tall, and as sunny, and as warm as I remember. He pours coffee for himself into a styrofoam cup and leads the way into his office. He helps me set up the tape recorder. He tests it for me. And he sits across the conference table with a direct and unwavering stare.

"Before I forget to ask you," I say, "what do you call this garment?" I gesture to the -- is it a 'tunic'? a 'smock'? some difficult Latin title?

"This shirt?" he asks.

"Yes."

"It's a shirt."

Oh. We laugh together at the mystique I obviously expected.

"It's a purple shirt," he adds. "Bishops wear purple, it's a Bishop's color. But all it is, is a . . . shirt."

I tell him I recently interviewed a Fundamentalist evangelist and politician near Indianapolis who has very different views than the Bishop does on AIDS, and on the lifestyles of gay people.

"I was in Indianapolis for six years," he says with a twinkle. "Apparently I didn't reach him!"

I ask Bishop Moore to tell me about his own point of view on gay people, and on the stance about AIDS he recommends for heterosexuals. And how did the Bishop develop his own ideas? Numerous religious leaders say the Bible is very clear: homosexuality is a sin.

"I imagine I'm not the first person to ask you about this," I say.

"No. You're not."

He mentions a book he wrote three years ago, *TAKE A BISHOP LIKE ME* , which discusses in depth how he formed his opinions. It's the story of how he actively got involved with the ordination of women as priests, and of a lesbian priest in particular.

"Ever since I've been involved in the ministry," he says, "I've for some reason felt particularly strongly about people who are poor and rejected and don't seem to have much of a chance. One thing the Episcopal church does have is a certain amount of respectability. The Episcopal clergy have respectability and therefore a certain amount of power, in the general sense of the word. One of our jobs, really, is to be stewards of that power.

"If we find someone who needs an advocate, we should try to help, whether it's a homeless child, or a black person who isn't allowed in the front of the bus. Whatever.

"The most recent group of people who have come to the public's attention and don't seem to have enough advocates are people with AIDS. Gay people have been persecuted over the years, and they were just beginning to get their heads above water . . . now AIDS has, in a sense, knocked 'em down again. I would feel that, because of the very fact that persons with AIDS are in such terrible trouble, there's a special obligation for the Church to stand with them. With anybody in trouble."

As he talks to me now, wanting to state clearly his perspective on AIDS and homosexuals, he no longer looks at me directly. His eyes are closed, as though to concentrate only on his message.

"The second thing is, as far as my relationship to the gay business, it goes way, way back. A priest who first got me interested in the ministry was a school teacher. I guess I was about seventeen, and a whole bunch of us used to go to his room and talk, and he got me into the ministry and I eventually became ordained. It was many years later, but he's the one who planted the seed.

"But he, poor guy, went in the Army and was out in New Guinea for a couple of years, and started drinking too much and made a pass on the beach at a soldier. He got busted from the Army, dishonorably discharged, deposed from the ministry. The Bishop in charge of the armed services was a tough New Englander. 'A homosexual? OUT!'

"I got home from the war and found my friend in deep alcoholism, living with his mother on Staten Island. Another friend and I got out to see him, tried to get him dried out, tried to get him a job. This went on for about twenty years. In and out of hospitals. In and out of alcoholic episodes. Get him a job and he'd get drunk. He'd lose the job and wind up in the mental hospital at Bellevue."

His voice is weary. His eyes have remained closed all along and now he opens them to see me again.

"If he'd had decent treatment early on, and if he'd been able to respect himself in his homosexuality, none of this would have happened. He was a valuable, wonderful person who meant everything in my life. Thank God he was eventually restored to the priesthood. I helped do that. He presented me when I was presented as Bishop; he died a few years later.

"It was through getting to know him that I first truly understood the kind of terror the Church has visited on gay people. Over the years I've gotten to know a lot of other gay people as well. A number of my own clergy are gay. I talk to them openly. So it's not a foreign group of people at all, but amongst friends. My uncle was gay."

I suppose it's the enormous naturalness of this man that is impressing me so. And the sense of his readiness to accept people, and to care about them.

I see behind him a handsome wall unit, with leaded glass. The leading forms the Episcopal crest I see on my coffee cup. Also on display are perhaps a dozen different chess sets. But the most prominent area of decor is the wall of photographs just above his desk -- friends, family, children. The wall is crowded with people he loves.

"You know," I say, "I'm not at all sophisticated about religion. I've had very little real exposure since my survey course in college. So I'm still startled -- now -- when I hear you mention easily that some of your priests are gay."

He has been grunting and nodding gently, following me closely.

"If some of your priests are gay, that means that they are having -- I'm assuming -- they're having gay sex with other men. Is that true?"

"Yeah," he says. "Presumably."

"And -- that's okay with you."

"Yes, it's -- well, let me go back a little bit."

"I'm sorry not to be more informed," I say.

"No, that's all right! This is new stuff. Even if you were very sophisticated religiously, you won't run into many Bishops that talk the way I do."

"That's what I was hunching," I say.

We both laugh at my understatement. I don't know much at all about religion, but I realize I really do LIKE this human being across the table. In his purple shirt.

"Being in a job like mine," he says, "you're always thinking on two levels. I don't think anyone should close his mind. The mind should always move on ahead -- and behind, and sideways. Exploring new things and trying to understand reality, whether it's God or fellow human beings.

"Meantime, if you're in an official position, sometimes your formal statements have to be where you used to be, while your own head is going out here -- " He gestures to the end of the table.

"Okay? I still really have to talk on two levels. Our Church teaches .... I guess the latest pronouncement they made was that they urge Bishops not to ordain homosexuals. Well, in the first place, what is a homosexual? Does it mean somebody who is bisexual? Somebody who's had one episode? Someone out of the closet? In the closet? Oriented --? It's a ridiculous statement. So -- I pay no attention to the resolution. It wasn't mandated, it was urged."

"Who does that come from?" I ask.

"The General Convention, which is our triennial convention that makes the laws and canons and statements for our church."

"If a Bishop reports to somebody, is it to --?

"I don't report to anybody," he says firmly. "I'm like a Governor who doesn't report to the President. We have a presiding Bishop, who's like a President, but he's not over me any more than Reagan is over Cuomo. He's not like the Pope. He's a presiding officer in the House of Bishops. He runs the Executive Council in between conventions. But he doesn't have power over the convention any more than the President has power over Congress.

"So," I say with some wonderment. "as an Episcopal Bishop, you really have autonomy to lead people as seems right to you."

"Within the teaching of the Church, yes. Our Anglican heritage makes that a little fuzzy. If you get out too far, people jump you. They jumped me on this. I almost got censured by the House of Bishops because active, sexual behavior outside of marriage is still not accepted, whether it's gay or straight.

"However, we're in sort of a transition period. A lot of Bishops, including myself, have counseled people over the years whom we knew were living with somebody before they got married. We haven't raised any trouble about it, but we can't get up and *preach* that, flat out.

"I'm being very candid now, but that's how it is. The same would be true of the gay situation. I think many of us are gradually beginning to understand that when the Bible was written, the knowledge of in-depth psychology had not gotten to the place it is now.

"So, homosexuality, insofar as it was said to be sinful -- there are very few references in the Bible about it, by the way -- it would be as if someone were doing something perverted just for the sake of its being perverted.   Rather than someone being made in such a way . . . either born that way or, or from an early influence, discovering that they relate to the same sex when they begin to experience sexual desires. This isn't exactly a sin. You cannot help that."

I am continuing to note the directness of his eyes, his lack of hesitation in saying what he believes.

"Let me ask you about something," I say. "The Fundamentalist preacher I interviewed disagrees. Whenever he counsels someone who says, 'But, sir, this is the way I really feel,' he answers, 'Nonsense! You learned to feel this way. What is learned can be unlearned.'"

"Yeah," he says. "I don't think that's true. I think it's possible, perhaps, that someone's bisexual, somewhere in the middle. They might be able to push themselves in one direction or another.

"But as far as someone who's strongly homosexual, no. I've known people in psychoanalysis for years. They've gone through some of these brainwashing things. They've gone through evangelical experiences. It simply doesn't work. I don't know of one person who's really been shown to have a psychosexual personality change."

"Therefore," I ask, "in your view, there's not a question of whether or not God can forgive such a person, because that person is merely being who he is?"

"That's right. And that gets you to the next point."

"Okay."

"Which is -- what do you do with your sexuality, whether you're straight or gay?

"The traditional rule about it is, you get married and have children. You marry one woman, and you never have sex before you get married. You never have sex outside of marriage. Well, even in the most rigid church, that simply doesn't happen. So, traditionally, it's a sin. If we have sex outside of marriage, we confess our sin, and we go about our business.

"That's okay, but -- suppose you can't get married? Does that mean you're supposed to be a monk your whole life? Celibate? No way. Being a celibate is a very special vocation. Some few people have it, if anyone. I often work with monks and nuns, and I understand a lot about that psychology.

"Therefore if you were made a homosexual, or became it so early it's as if you were made one, what do you do with your sexuality? The Church says you can't have any sex. That means the Church won't allow you to have a dignified, faithful relationship with one person. Which tends to kick you over into hidden sex, promiscuity, and all kinds of screwed up sexuality.

"I think that where we should be getting to -- and the position I'm in now, just about -- is to encourage homosexual persons to have good sexual relations, if possible, with one person. It will take quite a while before most homosexual persons can establish the kind of stability between two gay people that a lot of married people have. But I've known some gay people who have been together thirty and forty years. It's been the equivalent of a marriage, and I think that should be the goal.

"Should it be permanent? I don't know. This is something for the gay community to work out. Maybe you make a commitment to someone for several years. Or as long as you can live together in joy and fulfillment. And you don't necessarily commit yourself to a lifelong commitment."

"Why wouldn't that be true for a man and a woman as well?"

"I think it might well be," he says. "But we're talking about the gay scene now. If the gay community is beginning to build its own sexual ethic, let's have its members start from scratch with whatever is the best way for them to be living together in responsible sexuality for as long as that may be, lifelong or temporary.

"The main bottom line is that they don't hurt someone else in the process. I think that sex is neutral, like money or liquor or anything else, and it only becomes sinful if it is abused. If your homosexual sexual practice hurts you physically or psychologically, or if you are a predatory person who is seducing kids or people who don't want to be seduced, or being so promiscuous that you're spreading AIDS all over the place -- or before AIDS, gonorrhea, herpes -- then you're hurting the community, you're being irresponsible.

"But as far as sex between two persons of the same sex, carried on with affection and fidelity, I do not think that that is a sin. Now this has been a long way around to answer your question, but you have to set a context.

"The other thing to say about the Bible, is that many of those passages are now thought to be, by Biblical critics, not passages against homosexuality. The Sodom and Gomorrah story may well have been God punishing them for a sin against hospitality.

"Many places in the Old Testament which are anti-homosexual are really, apparently, more against the whole business of temple prostitution, whether female or male. There are several books on that.

"Our Anglican way of dealing with the Scripture is not Fundamentalist. But we take the Bible in a deeply serious way as inspired by the work of the Holy Spirit through people who wrote it. One realizes it was a developing document, starting actually as a very primitive document, working up to the sayings of Jesus and the New Testament.

"Therefore you cannot take something which is about throwing babies against the rock and say that's just as much the Word of God as the Sermon on the Mount. There's a passage in the Bible about throwing babies against the rock, and another about `an eye for an eye, and a tooth for a tooth.' And Jesus says `Turn the other cheek.' You cannot be a Fundamentalist. There's no way. Because the Bible disagrees with itself.

"You have to have a criterion by which to judge the various texts. The criterion relates to the whole message of the Bible. The whole message of the Bible is the development of our understanding of God as the God of love and justice. And of human beings made in the image of God, which is a way of saying each one is of infinite dignity and possiblity of fulfillment. So you judge the passages against the overall message. You test the validity of individual passages since they can disagree with each other. That's why I think it's perfectly legitimate to pick and choose with some of these very primitive passages."

I don't remember clearly enough the details of Sodom and Gomorrah, or fully understand his hospitality allusion. But I know our time is limited, and I do not want to use it by asking the Bishop to tell me a Bible story. I will read the story again for myself.

"Does it not happen very much that someone like you is in a dialogue with someone like the Fundamentalist evangelist I interviewed? It sounds like you're on two different planets!"

"We are, I think. Probably I would disagree more with him than I would with some secularists that say they're agnostics, or atheists."

"And, as you project ahead to maybe the next twenty years, do you imagine that your views and his will continue to be that far apart?"

"Probably."

"So that makes it hard for there to be some common, `religious' point of view."

"Impossible. At this point."

"Would you say it's an established fact that there's been a reluctance on the part of society to care about AIDS because of its homosexual affiliation."

"I do. And also the intravenous addict population. The addict population and the gay population are about the lowest people on the totem pole."

"That's generally true among religious people, would you say?"

"It does depend. You can't generalize. I've been very proud of our people. I'll give you a story --

"Ten years ago, I was getting a tremendous amount of flack on ordaining a gay woman. Ten years later, one of our priests stood up in the Diocesan Convention, a thousand people strong from over the diocese, our annual convention. He stood to speak to a resolution saying that we should minister to people with AIDS and have compassion, and that AIDS was not God's judgment against homosexuality. He'd never spoken at a convention before. I knew he had AIDS, himself. When he stood I thought, oh my God, what's he going to say?

"He got up there and spoke with such passion to the rest of the convention. About how people with AIDS are rejected, and some doctors turn them away, and it can even be hard to get them buried. He was encouraging people to have compassion. And he added, `I think I can say this with some authority because . . . I have AIDS.'

"At which the entire convention gave him a standing ovation. People clustered around him, and hugged him. Loved him. That was quite a change from ten years ago, back when we couldn't even deal with a lesbian being ordained. He was dead within a year."

He tells me about a Cathedral service yesterday -- the dedication of a remembrance book containing the names of persons who die of AIDS. The book was placed under the stained glass window portraying Saint Luke, reputed to be a physician.

"Various persons who led the service took turns reading the names. There were already 500 names in the book. There was absolute silence in this huge, dark cathedral. Candles were glittering everywhere, and 1,000 people were listening. It was incredible, a wonderful feeling of acceptance.

"The head of Dignity, a Roman Catholic organization for gays, came up with tears in his eyes and said, `Thank God, someone had a service like this.' The president of the gay synagogue was there. We were, all of us, crying, hand shaking, hugging, comforting one another on people we have lost. I wish you had been there."

We are silent for a moment.

"You mentioned communion," I say. "Have you encountered concerns about the sharing the communion cup?"

"Oh, yes. I sent a letter about a month ago saying that the medical profession states there is no danger with that. However, if people are nervous, they could just receive the bread and they would still be receiving the full benefit of the sacrament."

"I recently interviewed somebody with AIDS," I say, "who felt that God was punishing him for his previous promiscuity. Have you encountered people with AIDS who think they're being punished by God?"

"Sure," he says. "It's almost inevitable. Because of the long, long history of the Church's attitude. And sex, of all the sins, is the easiest in our culture to feel guilty about. From the little boy masturbating to whatever.

"I think there's always been guilt just behind every sexual act. Because basically what's in the Bible is, you only have sex to have children. Even enjoying it isn't very 'nice.'

"So people feel guilt about sexuality anyhow. And homosexuality, particularly. And permissive homosexuality, particularly-particularly. Then if you get AIDS it's very hard, even if you're a screaming atheist, not to feel some sense of God's judgment -- `it got me. They tried to kid me and say I shouldn't feel guilty about my homosexuality, but look what happened!'"

"What do you tell such a person?"

"I think you have to just keep talking about God's love for them. And, to believe in God's forgiveness. Certainly God does not operate, under my theology, by taking certain sins and sending lightning bolts down. How about the Mylai Massacre? Why weren't they given at least herpes, as I like to say? Why would this ONE SIN be singled out with this terrible disease? It's illogical. It doesn't make sense."

"You have reached a pinnacle in your career," I say. "You're in a lofty place in the world of religion that most people would never reach. What are your goals now?"

"To try to do as good a job as I can. I have no ambitions for any other position. This is it. Like everyone else, I have pride. I like to have people think I'm great, who doesn't? But I hope at my best and sincerest that I can do my utmost to alleviate suffering ... and have people understand that God is a loving, forgiving God, not some tyrant.

"I care about bringing about more compassion and justice in our society. I think our country is being led away from its best self. The fact that New York City can have thousands of homeless people when it is the richest city in the world is just wrong. Just flat out WRONG, and there's no excuse for it. These are the kinds of things I'm concerned about."

My last question. I gaze around the huge office, at the several couches forming a conversation center on one side of the room, then to his desk at the other, with a guest chair by its side. The entire ambience is set up to encourage conversation, communication between people.

"What would you like to be sure people hear about AIDS?" Again, he closes his eyes to be sure of saying what he wants.

"First, what we've already said, that AIDS is not God's judgment on the gay community.

"Second, that AIDS can only be communicated with intimate sexual contact, using a needle for an intravenous injection by someone who already has the virus, or receiving a blood transfusion of an infected person. Although blood is now being screened in such a way, that's a very slight danger indeed. You cannot get AIDS by drinking from the same cup, or hugging somebody, touching somebody, taking care of somebody, by seeing somebody, by eating from the same plate.

"Since that information is widely becoming available, the panic and fear about AIDS is founded on ignorance. People should be ashamed of themselves. For example, panic about a little child with AIDS attending school but being of no danger to anyone else -- that kind of needless alarm just shouldn't happen.

"Third, unless we STOP the panic and fear which is going abroad because of AIDS, then we will be discriminating against more and more people unjustly, which is against America's ideals. That would be against humanity, against the Bible, and against the decency for which America usually stands. I say that with as much PASSION as I can.

"I hope everybody who receives this message will take it to heart."

228

Chapter 21:
Two Observers: Needles

Here are conversations with two people who are observers to needle exchanges that potentially transmit the AIDS virus. Thomas is a taxi driver who has extensive personal experience with tatoos. "Debby" is a friend in prison who's noticed the way that hypodermic needles are shared within the "security" of prison walls.

Thomas the Taxi Driver

I've just been visiting a close friend in a Bronx hospital. My friend has a terrible cancer. His condition isn't AIDS-related, but I see the parallel, anyway: Steve is only thirty-four years old, is an extremely talented advertising copywriter, and is estimated to have only a few months more to live.

After my visit, I hail a taxi to return to Manhattan. I've brought along my little computer and am finishing up a story when the driver asks what I'm doing. In turn, I ask him for his knowledge and feelings about AIDS:

"AIDS? I am terrified. I don't know how many different ways you can contract it. I'm sure there must be many more ways than what they're talking about. Now they find out women can get it, too." He wears dark wrap-around sunglasses. A pack of Newport cigarettes is wedged under his shirt sleeve. He's a poor man's "Miami Vice." He tells me he is straight, has never had a gay experience in his life, and has been married for six years.

He and his wife have some gay male friends. He wonders if you can contact AIDS "from saliva or semen or any fluid that's fallen onto something like a bedsheet or a pillowcase. Like when you visit a friend and sit on his bed, can you get it that way? Or does it have to be direct contact. Now they've even found it in tears. What does that mean?"

He's known of AIDS for almost two years. But he's been seriously concerned for only three or four months.

"When I first heard about AIDS, it sounded so isolated. Now it doesn't seem that way. At first it was just from transfusions. Now it's sounds really widespread, not just homosexuals. If it can pass on to us, the general population -- that'll make it the Black Plague of the 80's."

He's never been "unfaithful" to his wife. "Not once. I think less about it now than before. I used to imagine it lots, with all the women I meet in this job. Now I don't let it cross my mind. Too dangerous. I'm just glad I'm married. I have my wife when I have the urge, instead of the poor single guys who've got to go out to look for it."

As for gays he says, "whatever they want to do is fine. They're entitled to their own freedom. If Falwell says this disease is God's punishment of homosexuals — that's just his own trip. He says *everything* that happens is God's doing anyway, so what's new?"

I ask Thomas what made him become so much more alert to the disease in the past few months. "Rock Hudson -- he made me think it wasn't just isolated to the people I thought would get it. He's your average American male star. I was thinking just junkies, and unclean people. Rock Hudson is clean, and here he gets AIDS too!"

I've been noticing the tatoos on both of my driver's arms, and on his hand. A scorpion. A dagger. A Sun. . . Skull. . . . other designs. He wears a large scorpion ring. "Yes, that's right -- I'm a Scorpio. The tatoos are souvenirs, from when I visit different states. Each visit, a new tatoo."

I ask if his wife has ever objected to all the tatoos. His reply makes me realize my question was sexist: she gets them, too. What's the attraction? "Tatoos are something you hang on to. They're permanent. I've lost a lot of things in my life -- but tatoos will be with me till I die."

It is not a painful process, he says, just a mild scratching. "You have to make sure they're sterilized, though. No exposed needles. You get worried about hepatitis. I always look to see if the place is clean. With a sterilization machine. Sometimes they tell you, `I haven't gotten new needles, they'll be in next week, but these will be fine to start with. Sit down.' I say no to that, but some people go along with it. You can buy tatooing kits to do it yourself. They're self-contained, all the equipment you need. Sometimes guys share them, like in prisons."

I tell him that, as I hear him describe it, tatooing sounds like more of a way AIDS can spread than sitting on a gay friend's pillow.

"You're probably right," he says. "I've had people come up to me, admiring my tatoos. They'll say, `I just started doing it myself, last month. Let me know if you'd like a new tatoo.' Who knows what their conditions are like?

"Tatooing is only supposed to penetrate two layers of skin. But I've seen some guys with bad scars because the needle's gone so deep. I mean real, big indentations into the skin.   A lot of tatooing is done in prison. People do it themselves. A lot of the Spanish population in New York, for example -- they get a few used needles and India ink.

"You get the needles in the mail. But many of these people can't afford to buy two or three dozen. They'll just use one or two, and try to sterilize them over and over by burning the end with a match. Or dipping one in alcohol.

"Tatooing's illegal in New York City, but there are at least eighteen parlors in Greenwich Village.   They're in people's homes. That's how they get away with it.

"I never thought about it before, but maybe it's true.   It could be one more way to get AIDS."

"Debby" in Prison

She is a friend in trouble.   She is in prison, in a county jail, awaiting the trial she hopes will prove her innocent.   She phoned one night and said she might have a few observations I'd be interested in. She always speaks, on the prison telephone, very discreetly.

Now I sit across from her, separated by panes of thick, glass strength.   Two ancient telephones are our only connection.   Her voice is tiny, remarkably disconnected from her image in the human acquarium across from me. I could be watching a movie, an exhibit at the Fair.

We sit on low prison toadstools. On either side of my friend are other prisoners.   They shout on their phones to the visitors at my right and left. "Look how thick the glass is," she says. "Put your finger next to mine."   We're kept apart by the deep wall of smudge. "Talk right into this thing, Mike. Don't cup your hand; I still want to see your face."

"So," I say. "You are a woman who is in prison."

"Yes," she says.   "Unfortunately." It's good to see her laugh. "I'm here for a non-violent crime. It's my first brush with the American prison system. I haven't come to trial yet, and I hope I will be acquitted. It's a terrible experience being here, and a real eye opener.   What I'm seeing is blowing me away."

"What are you observing that is relevant to AIDS?"

"I think it's only a matter of time before it explodes inside the prison system, based on what I'm seeing here and what I hear about the men's side.   There are drugs used inside the prison.   There are needles being shared.   On the women's side, I have first-hand observation of that, and it frightens me to death.   I think that people have masks over their eyes when it comes to sharing needles and using heroin in jail."

"How do they get needles in jail?"

"Well . . . it's hard for me to say."   She makes a face through the cloudy glass.   Her eyes veer right and left with emphasis at fellow

prisoners on adjoining stools.   She's already told me that my arrival in
coat and tie will make me look like a narcotics officer to the other
prisoners.   "I can't say everything" -- she doesn't say the words, she
mouths them.   "I didn't count on being observed," the tiny voice says
from miles away. I see a powerful black woman in uniform staring at me
from across a warren of cubicles.

"Let me just assure you," she begins again. "It's here and it's
plentiful.   I was talking to the psychiatrist about all this the other day.
He's at least someone I can talk to intellectually. He was telling me he's
seen different drugs be in vogue during the past ten year's he's worked
here.   They use drugs almost like a bartering system. They use 'em for
money, to buy commissary goods, to buy phone time."

"And basically," I say, "the kind of drugs you're talking about are
heroin?"   I do in fact cup my hand around the mouth to hide my words.

"Yes, and sometimes downer pills that can be gotten from the
Infirmary."

"You're sure you've seen people using the same needles?   Right in
prison?"

"Oh, yes. Absolutely.   You know, Mike, I did have six junkies
in my cell.   A couple of them have been transferred out, but they sit right
in front of my bed.   They use the same exact needle that's been in here for
EIGHT MONTHS. I've never seen them clean it. It has appalled me to
see them pass it from arm to arm.   The needle gets clogged up with
chunks.   And I see them literally suck their own blood up into the
syringe, and then plunge it into their veins. Then pass it to the next
person to do the same."

"There's never any discussion of what we would call 'hygeine?'"

"No. None whatsoever.   I can't broach that subject because I'm an
outsider.   It's done by my bed because my bed is hidden from view. I
can't understand why they want to do that. They talk about AIDS. They
know it exists. They know some of the dangers, in a peripheral way.
But when it comes to personal pleasure and gratification, everyone's
wearing blindfolds."

"Let me ask you, there's some theory that prostitutes are especially
vulnerable to having the virus because of their number of contacts. Have
you seen prostitutes in jail sharing the needle?"

"Yeah and that's a good point to touch upon. Most of the people
in here who are drug abusers ARE also prostitutes.   So we're talking
double-indemnity from the get go.   That's how they support their drug
habit. They turn tricks on the street and they buy heroin. So they're
sitting on a double time bomb — that is precisely the case with some of
the people in the room where I'm assigned right now.

"It's very interesting, the whole ritual that goes on behind the shooting up and sharing of the needles. It's a real social scene. They watch out for each other. They have unspoken trysts, and cameraderie. One will keep the syringe, one will keep the needle, one will keep the dope until they all get together.

"Mike, I can tell you now because there's a little more noise in here: the trustees have their people bring it in. The trustees have a lot more privileges here. In the whole time I've been here, every trustee has been a junkie. And the psychiatrist told me that the deputies JOKE about the heroin problem. When they're at parties, they have discussions about it. They know it exists. They're not about to chase it down, not about to follow it up. They don't observe it closely. They see people 'kicking.' They know who's on methadone one week and who suddenly 'doesn't need it' the next week.

"The weekenders bring it in too, the women who come in to spend the weekend. The search is not that great."

"A trustee is someone allowed to leave his cell?"

"Yeah, essentially the trustee is to help the deputy in the chores that concern the prisoners. We have a kitchen trustee who brings, you know, the meals. And an office trustee who cleans the office. We have a laundry trustee who collects the bedding. Those people who are in special favor with the deputies and they have a lot more freedom and a lot more access."

"And they're supposed to be trust-ed?"

"I think that's a joke," she says. "They're just favorites, chosen by the deputies."

"Do you also hear things from the men's side?"

"Yes. We have a system of communication called 'Jail Mail.' You send a 'kite' which means you write a letter and you stick it up on your bars, and it disappears and gets delivered to the men's side. So there is a lot of communication. The trustees do it, and the letters generally get delivered. A fair amount of news crosses the border."

"What do you know about AIDS on the men's side?"

"There's a parallel scene over there, but in a lot bigger amounts. You'll understand, though, that I've avoided getting too many of the details. In fact, I've been encouraged here on the women's side to get into the scene. I had one of the junkies in my room say to me, right after she pulled the needle -- " My friend gestures her eyes to her left. The attractive black woman, thin, trim, is the woman who made the offer. "'Oh have some! You'll love it!' It's frightening. There are pregnant women in here, exposing themselves to the risk in the very same way."

I decide to end this part of conversation, so our limited visit won't be spent in discussing only AIDS. I ask Debby if there's anything more she'd like to say. She unfolds a bedraggled piece of notepaper and holds it up to the glass. I read through the glassy fog:

"I know a little about AIDS. I know enough to understand that AIDS causes a person, often a young person in the prime of life, to die an excruciatingly painful and lingering death. I've observed the jail ritual of injecting heroin. Heroin addicts here take refuge in the escape the drug provides.

"I wish there way to reach these people! To burn into their brains the fact that the 'escape' is really a deadly trap that leads to AIDS.
Perhaps repeat heroin offenders should be assigned to community service on hospital AIDS wards. Maybe it would make a difference. Or maybe heroin should be legalized and dispensed by the government, the way it is in England. That might do away with the filthy conditions under which addicts now share their dope."

As an afterthought, I ask her, "where do they get the money? How can they afford drugs in prison anyway?"

"Friends," says the little phone voice with a clear hint of irony. "Friends."

Chapter 22:
Dr. Grossman in November —
Four Patients

As CHRONICLE *began to be a reality, Dr. Grossman mentioned its progress to various of his patients, looking specifically for a range of situations that could be described in this document. This chapter describes three patients I encountered in a hospital visit with him one November afternoon, and a fourth patient, Alan, whose apartment I visited.*

By now the disease was no longer an anonymous spectre to me. It was devastation and suffering happening to real people I had met, along with thousands of others, people I would picture in interviews still to come with scientists trying to find a way out . . . .

Hospital Visit

Wednesday afternoon. We emerge up the stairs from his office, and he stops me at the street corner. Yes, I remember the *POST* headline: "AIDS PATIENT IN HOSPITAL SUICIDE, Jumps 17 floors from his room." In addition to reporting the man's "DEATH LEAP" the paper mentioned two other men -- one with AIDS -- who had tied themselves together with silk rope and jumped from a thirty-fifth floor window.

Yes, I remember the story. Aside from wondering how many newspapers the page one banner had helped to sell, I'd thought about what it means to have a disease so frightening it seems easier to kill yourself than endure it.

He points up at the window three blocks north of us.

"One of the patients we'll be visiting is just down the hall from where the suicide case was," he tells me. "The man's hand was still holding the chair he'd used to break through the window. He evidently just followed the chair right down."

On the way upstairs, we see a patient of Dr. Grossman's, a man with ARC. On the surface, the man looks radiant with health.

We'll be visiting three patients today.   Dr. Grossman prepares me
for the first one   "'Donald' is a thirty-year old black fellow who's been in
NYU since September," he says.   "He has a diagnosis of AIDS manifested
as cryptosporidiosis, a SEVERE amoeba that causes life-threatening
diarrhea.   Hard to believe.   The diarrhea is so intense, it actually threatens
the patient's life.   They die of dehydration.

"His weight from a usual 115 went down to 87.   Now he's back
up to 100, all from TPN, Total Parenteral Nutrition, which he gets via an
in-dwelling catheter in his chest, surgically implanted.   He will, for the
rest of his life, be nourished by IV fluids.   They'll be provided him in his
own home and administered by his mother."

I wait in the hallway while Dr. Grossman secures permission for
me to visit.   I see the large plastic box -- like a fisherman's tackle box -
- for used needles, broken glass, etc.   "SHARPSAFE" is the brand name.
The box is a one way trip for dangerous objects; it is never emptied or re-
used, just thrown away.

I enter and meet Donald.   He sits in a chair against the wall, a
bottle of nurturing liquid hanging above him, a long clear tube reaching
down to his chest.   I am now getting used to the sight of people
connected to globes above their heads, like the word-ovals that hang above
cartoon characters.

Dr. Grossman is friendly and funny.   I feel him working to create
lightness.   But Donald's words are lifeless.   If I am honest, I realize I
might not find it so rewarding to work with him.   He seems to give very
little back in response to each question.   The doctor keeps pressing
energetically for contact. Subtly, I begin to sense that Donald appreciates
him even as he is taciturn.

Donald's mother enters the room.   A shy woman, darker-skinned
than Donald, with a drab dress and brown leather slippers.   Dr. Grossman
starts explaining to her, soothingly, how she'll be able to administer
Donald's feedings herself.   She'll receive special training.

"You don't have to feel he's totally tied to this thing, honey," he
says to her.   When he calls her "honey," I watch to see if she feels any
disrespect.   Instead she takes the term as it's given -- with warmth.

"I'll do anything to make Donald better," she says simply.

A nurse comes in to change bottles.   I study her actions and I
realize how intimidating this process must look to Donald's mother; it
certainly doesn't look easy to me.   Tiny lightbulb signals are on the metal
plate of the gadget --

- o   Air in line
- o   Battery
- o   Occlusion
- o   Infusion

236

Dr. Grossman puts his hand gently on Donald's shoulder. "Tell Mike what happened the day that fellow jumped," he says. Donald smiles faintly.

"That day I said something I will never say again the rest of my life." His mother laughs. "There's this nurse here. I kid around with her. We saw the news about the man who jumped out the window. We saw it on TV. I said to her, `next, that will be me.'

"All of a sudden, there were a dozen psychiatrists watching me. I was on Sucide Watch. When I went to the bathroom I had to keep the door open. They wouldn't leave me alone, although I told them I was only kidding. I won't ever do that again!"

I can imagine a second AIDS patient jumping through this hospital's window. I'm not a bit surprised at their vigilance. You don't make hijack jokes when you pass the inspector at the airport.

Donald tells me he was doing paralegal work before he got AIDS. He was born in Brooklyn. I ask where his mother is from.

"Charleston, South Carolina," she says.

"No kidding! I'm from Beaufort," I tell her. "I miss grits and boiled peanuts like crazy up here, you know what I mean?" Her smile is so big and proud it is almost a medal. Suddenly she no longer seems shy.

"I bring Donald boiled peanuts all the time," she says. It is an achievement. It is something a mother can do in the face of sickness. "If you ever come visit him at our place, I'll be only too glad to boil you some."

Later, I ask if Donald is generally so taciturn.

"He's not like he used to be," Dr. Grossman tells me. "He's normally an articulate, smiling boy. There is more than a little dullness in him now. It's either just too much hospital or -- worse. Most AIDS patients eventually get neurologic problems."

We are headed for the second patient.

~ ~ ~ ~ ~

Intensive Care. A warren of glass windows. Dr. Grossman leads us to a cubicle in which one wall almost swarms with equipment. Wires, lights, machinery, sacks of liquid and tubes -- all linked to each other, passing through one man's body like some new form of intelligence.

A parasite, I think to myself. An electro-biochemical creature that lives off the twisted figure -- the broken sacrifice in a crib. Eventually, of course, I realize: the man is living *because* of this throbbing, electronic wall. The man is the unwilling parasite.

The man: I am unable to do justice to his condition.

Two people are in the glass room with him. One of them is a

young woman, perhaps a nurse in training or a hospital volunteer. She darts quickly around the "U" between the bed and the three remaining walls. One of the wall-monster's displays flashes, and she hurriedly adjusts something on it, or on the man's body. She moves a tube. She swathes liquid on a leg to minimize a leak.

With startling speed and loudness, one of the largest sections of the creature on the wall -- a kind of medical jukebox -- gives us amplified burps, like a pinball machine in a cavern. (It's "exquisitely sensitive," Dr. Grossman tells me. "It's alert for the slightest changes.")

A medical resident stands at the foot of the bed. He stands stiffly as we enter the room. Dr. Grossman introduces us, and asks him to summarize the man's condition in non-technical terms for Mr. Greenly.

"Patient is a forty-one-year-old homosexual," the young man tells me. "He had two previous episodes of pneumocystis pneumonia because of AIDS. Recently he was experiencing increasing shortness of breath. We tried various antibiotics with little response. Now we're using an experimental drug. He is slightly less febrile."

As we're talking, Dr. Grossman moves around the other doctor to the side of the bed. The patient's body is twisted, stretched out in front of us. The resident explains something to me about too much carbon dioxide in the man's respiratory system. He is explaining why the man's cheeks and neck are so swollen, which I can see despite the tape across his face that flattens them down.

I don't understand all that the resident tells me. What I understand is that the creature on display before me is in another world now. Dr. Grossman entwines his own fingers onto the man's lifeless hand. The man's eyes continue to stare without change into the space where Dr. Grossman has now positioned himself.

"Harry, can you hear me?" That is not his real name.

"It's Ron Grossman." I notice the clarity with which Ron says his name, the push he gives his words to help them reach the other side.

"If you can hear me, Harry, just squeeze my hand." There is no movement of the fingers. They are merely an extension of a twisted figure. The nurse who swabs and tends him moves her own gloved hand, or gauze over various parts of his surface. He is a piece of geography.

A large tube goes directly down into his penis. Other tubes are inserted on either side of his groin. I hear the resident in the background of my consciousness. ("That tube is the Bactrim, that one is the DFO. Further up on his body, you'll see . . . ")

Further up on his body I see more tubes. And a twisted blue hose, like the end of a vacuum cleaner, dominating the man's face, his mouth, his nose. It is connected to the juke box that knows one tune only, the loud electronic burp. That is the song of Harry's room.

238

The man is forty-one years old, the resident had said. I am forty-one. Ron Grossman is my doctor. I picture myself in that bed, and Ron inviting me to squeeze his hand. Can I hear him at all, even without the power to move?

Listen to you, Mike.   Your shallow concern for the embarrassment you would feel. How ashamed and lacking in dignity to have Ron lean over the side of the crib to your twisted, swollen self in your nakedness under the tubing. You feel self-conscious, imagining your genitals exposed and painfully linked to machinery as the nurse cleans around you, just like swabbing up a coffee spill.   But what about the agony that brought you into this glass room?   What about the fact that your life would simply be over?

We leave at last. Here is the summary I asked Dr. Grossman to give me:

"He is 'Harry,' born and raised in the South, by the way.   A major figure with a national publication.   Been in the hospital since 10/11/85. With his third case of pneumocystis which originally looked like he was handling pretty well.   He went sour only this past week with the development of a disease that looks just like mumps. Tremendous swelling in the saliva glands and both sides of the face. I talked with him Friday night at ten o'clock, and it sounded like he was gargling as he spoke.

"By Saturday morning he was intubated. Tube in his trachia, to breathe for him.   What you saw today is a severely deteriorated patient who requires respiratory support on that machine. And every manner of other kind of support.   Had you ever seen anything like that?"

"No," I say.

"I should think not.   That was the state of the art.   When you hear about the whole business of machines and tubes and bottles, which is rather abstractly talked about, in terms of writing a Living Will and the whole legislation about the patient being able to say, 'Enough!' even if he can no longer speak -- that's what it's all about.

"There are no other kinds of tubes and wires this man could have have. He has them all."

We don't say much to each other at the elevator, Dr. Grossman and I. Each of us stays quietly with his own thoughts and feelings.

"Who are we seeing now?" I finally ask.

~ ~ ~ ~ ~

"Michael, in this whole AIDS mess, we're about to see one of the few bright spots.   One of those times you feel you could do something to make a real, positive difference to the patient's future.

"'Eugene' is a teacher of special education in the New York public school system. He had a very, very rare situation -- hypersplenism. His spleen became programmed to remove many different kinds of blood cells from his blood stream.

"That's because his body's response to the AIDS virus was to create an OVER-active portion of the immune system. Normally the spleen's purpose is to do away only with cells no longer useful to the body. In Eugene's case, though, the AIDS virus caused his immune system to target cells that shouldn't have been destroyed.

"This was the fifth episode in which his spleen took too many cells out of the blood stream and brought him near death. A combination of anemia, fever, and low white count. In an emergency procedure, his spleen was removed six days ago, followed by an extraordinary bounce in all of his counts. He looks, I think you'll agree, quite normal.

"Now, since that operation, his future's very different. We've been able to buy him a guaranteed period of good health. We can't predict what diseases he still may get, but for now he's genuinely free of the problem AIDS manifested."

We come to Eugene's room. He is pale and his lips are chapped, but he looks surprisingly healthy for a person so recently in surgery. I notice Dr. Grossman touches his shoulder as he says hello. Eugene puts a robe over his pajamas and we stroll to a sun room down the hall. He says the various seizures of hypersplenism were "like being hit by a truck. All I could do was lie flat on my back. I had a fever. I had a dry, retching cough."

He learned he had ARC in September of 1984. On February 1, 1985 -- he remembers the date exactly -- he saw his first KS lesion. He has since noticed two others. The marks themselves, though, were not the source of his pain.

He'd been resisting the spleen operation with the thought that a visit to L'Institut Pasteur might offer a solution, even a "cure." "If you'll be visiting them in Paris," he says, "ask them how long before they have real, hard data."

I ask for his thoughts on why he got AIDS. "It's a punishment," he says. "I come from an Irish Catholic family. I have a wonderful lover, a really special man. But he travels a lot, and I thought I could have it all. I used to go down to the Mineshaft," he says. "I've seen five people fist-fucked by one guy, one right after another. I think AIDS is a kind of punishment."

The Mineshaft is a notorious gay bar, lately much in New York news. Mayor Koch recently closed it as a health hazard. A wide variety of on-site sex had been allowed.

"I used to spend time there, often, when my lover was away. I got high, I was inebriated. I didn't always pay attention . . . I did everything. Now I just keep saying, 'I'm sorry. I'm so sorry.' I apologize all the time. He's right in there with me, though. He's an exceptional man."

Eugene shows me the scar where his spleen was removed; thick, gray tubing holds the skin in place, in addition to black cord stitched back and forth across the jagged line.

"What's been the impact of your illness on your family?" I ask.

"Something good, actually. It's brought us closer. My father and I used to be cool to each other. Now we can hug." Eugene's lover, also a man in his thirties, strolls into the day room. After introductions, Dr. Grossman and I conclude the visit.

~ ~ ~ ~ ~

"Let me ask you, Ron," I say. We are walking briskly back to his office. "It's the first week in November, 1985. What's your perspective today on your experience treating patients with AIDS?"

"Michael, I imagine that even without AIDS, almost every doctor reaches a point where the major emotional impact of really seriously ill people is blunted -- both by having seen it so many times, and by the knowledge of what the outcome holds. You learn not to hold out false hope for recovery when you know it just isn't there.

"Also, it's essential to preserve the finite amount of emotional energy we all have. Therefore when you realize that maybe you're over-investing in feeling bad, sad, disappointed, hurt, frustrated . . . ultimately you see you're cutting into your own emotional wellbeing. You're not doing patients any favors by letting yourself get down. You saw what I looked like when I came out of Intensive Care.

"Bottom line, any doctor who's had a lot of experience simply holds up. Because you've got to."

We're back at his office. He is rushing to another appointment, checking on messages, putting paperwork in his briefcase.

"As for AIDS," he says, "compared to a year ago, and certainly compared to two or three -- each individual patient is generally doing better, living longer, living slightly more comfortably. Perhaps experiencing a little less pain. But -- the longer range view of this illness remains absolutely as bleak, dismal, and nearly hopeless for the individual patient as it was at the very beginning of the epidemic."

"You mean, for the person who at this moment has the disease?" I ask.

"Yes, that's right. The prognosis today is no different, not yet. It's just the pathway that's different."

"What is your sense of its spread to heterosexuals?" I am headed out the door with him now, as he's hailing a cab.

"Inevitable. But slow."

"Is education helping, would you say?"

"Not yet. Not enough."

He is off. I look down the blocks ahead and again see the window where a man and his chair crashed through to the concrete below. What new man or woman has on this very day learned that he or she has AIDS? What researcher in what laboratory feels excitement at this moment, suspects an advance, a step forward, to a treatment that will change the AIDS prognosis?

I do not want to walk past the hospital again just now. But it's chilly, and I want to go home.

~ ~ ~ ~ ~

(NOVEMBER - A WEEK LATER) I'm leaving for Paris in just a few days to visit the Pasteur Institute. My schedule is tight and oppressive when Dr. Grossman phones me.

"You're not likely to encounter someone as physically devastated as Alan who can still talk with you," he's willing to meet you. Are you free today?"

I will not say no. I've already heard at the Gay Men's Health Crisis about the times when a volunteer must accept a buddy's withdrawal from the world . . . one has to reconcile the client's need for peace with one's own need for appreciation and response. I've never personally encountered anyone like Alan, however. Nor have I yet been to San Francisco to learn first-hand about the Shanti organization and its approach to death and dying. I thank Ron for the offer and agree to visit Alan.

I arrive at the basement of a West-Side brownstone. I step down past a barred metal door that Alan's Red Cross aide has left open for me. It's like entering a cave. My eyes adjust to the dark hallway and spot the door to Alan's apartment, also left ajar. I knock and swing open the door. I hear a moan of "hello," and step further inside.

He has dark black hair which looks almost glued to the skull of his face. The skin below his eyes appears shadowed. The eyes themselves have no life. They passively watch me as I enter the room and thank him for seeing me. I set up my tape recorder, arrange a chair, and tell him about this series of interviews. I realize after a minute that I'm talking too much. I'm embarrassed by the sound of my own inauthentic chipperness.

I calm myself and face the man more squarely. I've been avoiding, I realize it now, I've been avoiding my own pity for him. He may not want it, and he may not want to know about it, but I realize that I'm feeling pity anyway. So much of a dying skeleton does Alan appear, in fact, that it's hard to imagine he was once a person, a regular human being.

We begin to talk. I'm in a one-room apartment, with the refrigerator a few paces from the bed. "Now," I say, still sounding too much like a happy schoolmarm, "let's start by having you tell me about yourself. Try to talk up as loud as you can, okay?"

"Um-hmmm." It is the low moan of distant wind through the treetops.

"Where did you grow up?"

"Mobile, Alabama." I can hear the trace of a Southern accent.

"And how old are you?"

"I'm thirty-nine." Every syllable seems painful. He tells me he can't remember whether he came to New York City six, or was it seven, years ago. He lived in Alabama, then Florida, then San Francisco for twelve years before moving to New York with a friend.

The door opens and a shabby looking man in a sports jacket and open shirt comes into the room. "Hi, I'm Mike Greenly," I say.

"Hi." His voice is a bullfrog's. So deep and so hoarse that he may have a "condition" of some kind, I am thinking. "I'm the attendant," he says. I believe I can smell alcohol from across the room. (Later when I stand with the man out on the sidewalk, I am certain of it.)

"Nice to meet you," I say. He gets something from the refrigerator and says he'll be outside if I need him. Alan resumes talking. He worked in a brokerage firm once, then in a department store training program, then as a waiter.

"Why did you leave the department store training program?" I ask.

"They just didn't like what I was doing," he says. I laugh out loud at the simplicity of it. He can't remember anything more specific. He remembers, though, that he was diagnosed for AIDS in April of 1984. He previously had bronchitis and had recovered, "but never really felt back on top of things." In April, the congestion was back again, he'd lost weight, and he was "a typical AIDS case. I had pneumocystis pneumonia and they put me in the hospital."

As a result of a shot he received in his hip to treat the pneumonia, something happened to the sciatic nerve of his leg. One leg is now disabled, and Alan can't walk. Also, as a result of some work done with tubing down into his lungs, "they messed up my nose. I have no cartilage between the two sides of my nose. My friends said I should have sued, but I didn't have the money for a lawyer." He lifts the bedsheet to reveal his legs. The bottom half of one leg seems to be almost pure bone, just a flesh colored twig. "There's no meat at all," he says, "just a bit of muscle."

I ask him about the reactions of his friends to his getting AIDS. "My best friend has Kaposi," he says. "Mostly they reacted very nice. They've all been very supportive."

"Do you have any thoughts about how you got it?"

"Just being very promiscuous, I guess. I don't regret anything I've done sexually. I enjoyed doing it. I did it excessively at times. I would go to the baths a lot, have sex with maybe a dozen people a night and perhaps several times a week. Or go to the 'glory holes' at book stores." Alan was recently a bartender, and would often arrive at the baths at five in the morning, when they were still very crowded.

"Mainly I did marijuana," he says when I ask about drugs, "but I did other things too."

"Poppers?" I ask, about the amyl nitrate stimulant.

"Yeah."

"LSD?"

"Yeah."

"Cocaine?"

"Yeah."

"How do you feel about the discussion going on now about whether to close the baths? What do you think?"

"I hear friends discuss it, but it doesn't matter to me. Not much matters to me. I think it'd be better if they left them open. I might have done some things different, used a condom, if someone had really told me about all this."

His mother is dead of cancer. His father is a retired government worker. A few weeks after his first stay at the hospital, Alan phoned his father in Alabama to reveal that he has AIDS, and that he is gay. At first, his father wouldn't speak to him for days. "Now we're closer." The father has visited New York once since Alan got sick, about seven months ago.

The Red Cross attendant stays for twelve hours a day, he tells me. The other twelve hours, Alan is alone. I see a bedpan next to the bed. I imagine this apartment at midnight, with Alan alone and stranded in the hospital bed.

"His ignorance amazes me," Alan mentions about the attendant. I ask him for an example.

"Well for one thing, he thought Las Vegas was a state. And when you want something from the grocery store, you have to describe every detail. Most times when he comes back, it's not what you wanted. I like him, and I'm glad he's here, but his ignorance gets to me. It's like, `please bring me some Dannon yogurt.' He'll come back and say, `I couldn't find the yogurt.' You know -- there's only a few places to look for yogurt. You check all the places that are cold." Someone else, delivering those same lines, could be very funny. Alan, however, talks in a monotone and is simply stating facts.

I ask about his general outlook these days. "I'm surprised I'm still alive," he says. "I've accepted death. I'm real tired of being sick. I'm just waiting to die. I've accepted it and I'm ready for it."

Is there anything he would like to say to readers?

"Not really. The whole thing is, I don't really care. I'm at that point where it's not going to affect me. It's like, so what?"

"Why did you say you would see me, when Dr. Grossman told you what I was doing?"

"I don't know," he says simply. I laugh in surprise at the utter honesty of his indifference.

"I just thought it might be interesting. I know I must sound cold and uncaring, but that's the way I feel now. I don't have interest in anything any more. I don't read. I don't watch TV. Even when he doesn't bring back the yogurt I ask for, or when he can't find a cinnammon bun, I think to myself -- what's the difference? I'm just waiting to die."

~ ~ ~ ~ ~

(DECEMBER) I'm in Dr. Grossman's office, on the way to make a house call with him. "Isn't that a handsome fellow?" he asks me. He shows me a photograph of a muscular man in the woods. He's wearing hiking shorts and squinting in the sunlight. He is bare-chested and appears to be in robust health.

"Yes," I say.

"That's Alan."

"Wow." I stare at the picture again. Only vaguely can I see the resemblance, mostly in the cheekbones. The transformation is astonishing and horrible.

"It's too bad your tape recorder can't record your facial expression, Michael," he tells me. "'Wow,' indeed."

"I just heard from a visiting nurse," he continues, "that somehow -- they don't know who did it -- someone stole Alan's watch, his gold ring from his hand, his turntable, and his SONY walkman. Alan is still hanging on, and still wishing he weren't."

We leave for the house call.

Chapter 23:
Fifty-Two Hours in Paris:
Part 1

It seemed impossible to write this book without a visit to the Pasteur Institute where I'd heard the AIDS virus was first discovered. So I cashed in a "free" airline ticket -- my reward from Pan Am for many nights on the road as a marketing consultant. I decided to spend a concentrated weekend learning something of how AIDS looked from the other side of the ocean.

I am a Francophile and my French is passable. You'll find no descriptions of the Eiffel Tower, however. I saw it once, over the treetops.

This chapter contains interviews with several Pasteur scientists and a visit to the most important volunteer support organization for People with AIDS in France, "AIDES."

Night Flight to Paris

I skip dinner on the plane. It's after midnight in Paris, and I'll be staying only fifty-two hours. Best to try to sleep, adjust to Paris time, even though I don't sleep easily on planes.

When I awake, the Parisienne fashion coordinator next to me tells me that her friend lost his lover fifteen days ago. The *pauvre garcon* was treated for AIDS at L'Institut Pasteur, but it was too late. Might her friend have breakfast with me? Assuredly not. The French do not like to talk of illness. Babies are born with AIDS now in France. Blood problems. But we do not discuss this as freely as you Americans. Perhaps we avoid the unpleasant, *mais voila.*

We land. I have a headache. I've gotten through customs and into a taxi. My driver tells me with pride about the power of French research. Did I notice Italians at the airport? They arrive all the time because French cancer research is outstanding. Yes, any cab driver will know L'Institut Pasteur.

My appointment is 11:30. A one-hour nap might help.

FRIDAY: Jean-Michel Claverie

I arrive late at the guard house of Institute Pasteur. I am led hastily into the antique laboratory where Monsieur Pasteur made history. Natural stone base, pink brick, white trim, and a black slate roof: it is so picturesque, it could almost grace a wedding cake.

"Later, you can see the museum," the secretary says breathlessly as we race into the building. "You will luncheon with one of the research heads. For now, Monsieur Claverie awaits you; we are hurrying."

The brown tile stairs are enormously slippery.   They curve dangerously around an elevator that doesn't work. I am amazed Monsieur Pasteur did not break his neck traveling up and down this staircase.

Jean-Michel Claverie is blond, husky, thirty-five years old. We sit on facing couches, far across from his computers.

"I do theoretical molecular biology," he tells me in English. "I study DNA and protein sequences and structures." At the level at which he and his computers support the identification of molecules, he estimates there are perhaps 100 people in the world who are his equivalent.

"There is a 'club,'" he says. He adds with courtesy, "Most of the members are in your country."

It requires effort to adjust his conversation to a non-technical level. Finally I understand that his work was essential to the Institute's achievements in identifying the "sequence" of the AIDS virus. In French, the disease is called "*Le SIDA -- Syndrome d'Immuno-Déficience Acquis.*"

"We were the first lab to assemble the sequence of the virus," he says, as if that explains everything. But what is a "sequence?" It is a way of describing the exact genetic construction of the DNA molecule in an organism. He shows me a sequence: pages of dense text. Row after row after row on every page. The pages are blackened with tiny letters, as though with highly trained ants with little room for the parade.

The letters describe the succession of the four different rungs on the "ladder," the "double helix" of a DNA molecule. Each virus species has its own, unique pattern, each as uniquely identifiable as a fingerprint. The AIDS virus, for example, is written as a sequence of some 9,000 letters. Every DNA sequence uses only four letters of the alphabet: A,T,G,C. The letters represent "nucleotides," tiny molecular building blocks. A wispy fragment of genetic sequence looks like this:

```
TTTATGGGGC GGCGAAAATT CGTCGCATCC CGTCAGGCGA GCCAGATGTT TCTGTGCTGG
CAGAAAGAGT GCGCAAAACG GGGGAACTGC GACTGGATAG GCTCCGGTCG TATGGCCATC
```

The letters densely cover page after page. I realize I could have used more sleep.

"If you want to understand how the virus relates to other viruses, you need the exact sequence of the virus's genes," Jean-Michel says. "You can then compare it to others."

He shows me his lab's application of a process that didn't exist ten years ago. On a light box connected to a computer are photographs of "gels" onto which bits of DNA molecules (from a specially prepared brine) collect into patterns. This "electrophoresis" technique uses particular enzymes and electric current to help elicit the identification.

"It's very complex," he tells me dryly. I will be meeting Dr. Wain Hobson, who led the Pasteur team in cloning the AIDS virus and determining its sequence. "That has been a big competition," Jean-Michel says. First the virus had to be isolated. Pasteur Laboratories was the first in the world. Next, when the virus was found, came the competition to formally identify it.

"Gallo in the U.S. and us in Pasteur. There were actually three independent determinations of basically the same virus. All were published within about two weeks -- one in *SCIENCE*, one in *NATURE*, one in *CELL*." There were very minute differences in the sequence from each country, reflecting the normal ability of a virus to mutate over time and geography.

"I always pictured a competition to be simply looking under a microscope and being the first to spy a new organism," I admit. "I see that's not really the point."

"No longer," he says.

"What is the prize for the kinds of competition Pasteur and other labs are involved in? Is it fame? Is it money?"

"Money can come from products that result, of course. But, especially, it's more influence in the scientific community." There wasn't money made directly from publishing those pages of "T,G,C,A."

"What is the value of influence? How does it express itself?"

"People listen to your opinions more. You can affect the development of new ideas. You have more impact on grant committees. People ask you to conferences. You can more easily attract the best people to come and work for you."

So it's a cycle -- you attract the best people, which helps you win the competitions, which helps you get the best people again. The result for the public is ultimately better health.

"All subjects are not as important for the media as *le SIDA* is now," he says. "At the very beginning the virus was not well received by basic scientists. It was considered biomedical which has less interest for them. Basic scientists have a view against biomedical researchers, who are doctors. Those doctors are often considered as having a standard of research which is not as high as ours in pure science. So that's one prejudice some of us had against AIDS as a medical topic.

"Also, the basic scientists felt the media was too present, too much hysteria."

"Then tell me," I say.   "What finally made the virus more important in the perception of the 'basic' scientists?"

"For some, they began to realize the benefit they could take out for their careers and institutions. Even though the scientists found the media always too present, they began to see the importance that could result.

"Also, in the beginning, the real size of the epidemic wasn't known. It was just 'all those homosexuals on Castro Street, and who cares about them?'" Jean-Michel earlier spent three years in California. He seems pleased to be able to mention San Francisco geography in conversation.

"But then they were realizing the virus was very important in the Congo, in Africa. They saw the disease could happen frequently in heterosexual people. They were learning it is a worldwide epidemic. People were getting scared. Then the state decides to do more, and research can get more money." He folds his arms to wait for my followup.

"So -- your Castro Street reference -- it is accurate to say that since there is some prejudice against homosexuals, and since scientists are after all human, some scientists were affected by those same attitudes concerning AIDS?"

"Well, yes, but I can only say 'to a certain extent' and 'among some.'   There is something else for you to consider: a lot more people now die of malaria every year than have died of AIDS. But that is not victims in San Francisco.   That is not rich people.   That is Africa. Malaria is ignored, too, just as AIDS was in the beginning.   Partly prejudice maybe, and also there is not so much money in Africa."

I thank him sincerely for making the point.   When have I ever thought about malaria?

MALARIA.   Englishmen in pith helmets arguing foolishly with Tarzan.   In the hut, a young woman is suffering — fever and chills.   A tarantula waits in the shadow of the partly closed shutters.   Can the medicine reach her? Tarzan will fetch it through the tree tops.   In my mind, the medicine has existed for decades, and malaria is a dead disease. Dead with movies that filled my boyhood.   I am startled to think it's a current problem and is largely ignored as AIDS once was.

"Have you personally known anyone who's had AIDS?" I ask. "Anyone who was close to you?"

"No."

"Do you ever yourself observe people with AIDS up close?

"Not here. This is a laboratory for reports." He mentions another thought instead.   "Another way AIDS' importance grew: when it was realized people were getting AIDS from blood transfusions. Then people saw the huge market for diagnostic tests for blood samples. This is a major market.

"The innocents saw people could die for reasons more than

misbehavior." His voice goes high and squeaky in imitation: "'my goodness, I don't want to get AIDS when I get a transfusion! We must have some diagnostic test!'

"Now the big fight is a money fight for the patenting of blood tests, a diagnostic kit is to test for the virus and protect the blood. That kit will make a lot of money for someone. But who will get the patent, the French or the Americans? A big question. We will have to see."

FRIDAY: Dr. Wain Hobson, Dr. Caroline Chaine

I cross the street with Jean-Michel to another picturesque building of similar architecture. I'm becoming acclimated to the half-French we're speaking, and I seem to be over my earlier fatigue. I'm grateful, now, for having reread some newspaper articles as background.

In particular, I'd studied a series published this summer in the *New York Native*. That is a feisty gay newspaper which became an AIDS database for many journalists. The paper reported on the disease in depth when most media were skimming the surface. In between naps on the plane, I'd read a five part series by Darrell Yates Rist. It's called "Going to Paris to Live" and is being published by Irvington in New York. For the remainder of my time in Paris, I am enriched by what Darrell wrote of the Americans who sought help in Paris, and of what they found.

As I enter the office of Caroline Chaine, the Secretariat General for PRESSE at Pasteur, I've already learned that:

- Pasteur Institute was the first to isolate the AIDS virus itself.

- The virus belongs to a particular category: retrovirus. Jean-Michel has explained that the true difference between a virus and retrovirus is simply how each multiplies (or "replicates").

- A virus can enter a cell directly and replicate itself. But a *retrovirus* requires a more complicated strategy since it can't directly reproduce its own gene. A retrovirus needs help from a special enzyme called "reverse transcriptase." HPA-23 is perhaps a way to block that very help.

- HPA-23 has been used before on other viruses. The drug was never conceived as a "cure" for AIDS, but at least its prior usage gave assurance that it wasn't toxic. The Pasteur Institute has been researching its use with AIDS . . . . that's why Rock Hudson visited Paris.

- It was thought HPA-23 might stop the AIDS retrovirus from multiplying. It it couldn't fully cure the disease, maybe it could at least halt its progress. How? By specifically blocking the reverse transcriptase enzyme the retrovirus needs for its own replication.

Could HPA-23 stop AIDS in its tracks? It would be like temporarily removing gasoline from a vehicle. How long can the retrovirus be shut off from multiplying? What about side effects over time? Might a virus that is not allowed to multiply eventually just die by itself? If so, how long would it take to die?

There are not yet answers to those questions.

Dr. Wain Hobson -- whom I eventually call Simon -- was the project leader in identifying the virus after it was discovered. He is a young Englishman, married to a French citizen, and is more sarcastic and uninhibited than the normal British stereotype.

Dr. Chaine -- Caroline -- wears a black leather skirt and bright blue eye shadow that matches a bright blue hair ribbon. She is savvy and cordial.

Before long, I am enjoying being with them both. Grandly I volunteer to buy us sandwiches. Simon leads me to a nearby shop, about ninety-two times more charming than a New York delicatessen. He and I have hamburgers, which sit neatly in the showcase next to petit-fours and chocolate. We wait as they are popped into a microwave.

I learn that Pasteur Institute operates on $40 million a year, of which half is government funded. The remainder comes from private donations and royalties from Pasteur products. The Institute has some 2,000 employees of whom 500 are scientists.

"How good is $40 million," I ask Simon while diet vegetables are eased into French bread for Caroline. "In terms of the need to know things, how much knowledge does $40 million provide?"

"Whoah!" he says. "You can't ask it that way. Out of all there is to know about human genetics, we may have only 0.01% so far! So you can't say, `hell, let's just learn it all at once and spend 300 trillion dollars this year.' $40 million is actually substantial."

"What about AIDS," I ask. "How much is going into that?"

"Well," he says, "your government is spending $200 million while France is spending only $2 million. Even allowing for AIDS being ten time more important, numerically, with you than with us, we are still not spending very much on it as a country.

"You're looking at the New World versus the Old World," he says when we are back in Caroline's office. "One feels the Old World totally screwed up on the microchip revolution. All the microchip stuff came from California and Japan, even though Europeans as a whole outnumbered the United States. AIDS spending is just another example."

All my interviews at Pasteur Institute make me feel like a delegate from the Super Power country.

"How many AIDS cases do you have in France?" I ask.

"420 cases," says Caroline.

"And how much media attention does it get in France."

"A lot," they say together.

"It's special," Simon adds, "since the virus was discovered in France. The French press has a special awareness because of that, although France, Britain, Germany are all very conscious of AIDS now."

While we are making international comparisons, Simon summarizes with some reluctance the blood test patent issue. He does not want, he says, to see it cast as a Franco-American struggle when it is really a finite technical and legal issue.

"The French put down a patent. Bob Gallo put down a patent subsequently. But Gallo's patent was granted before the French one. That is the state of affairs and it is best left to legal experts for discussion." It's not at all the first time I've heard of this controversy between the Pasteur Institute in France and Dr. Gallo of America's National Institute of Health.

"We want that they recognize the anteriority of our discovery," says Caroline, "and the . . . " She is struggling for the proper English ending to the sentence.

"Financial and commercial ramifications of that recognition," Simon finishes for her.

"Exactly."

"But please," Simon tells me. "It's not a problem between the two governments, as some journalists have cast it. It's a problem, perhaps, between two groups only. Not Franco-American."

"Well, I certainly don't want to create international incidents," I say, "but let me ask you . . . when I've asked people, 'how come, since the French discovered the virus first, there's not more official recognition of them in the United States?' One answer I've heard is, 'they didn't do all the paper work and testing they needed to.' Does that make any sense?"

"Some sense," says Caroline. "It's true that our first publication in *SCIENCE* in May of 1983 was less detailed than Dr. Gallo's, one year later. But all the main characteristics of the virus were right in our paper. It was easier for Gallo -- after having been the 'referee' for our paper with SCIENCE magazine, and after having listened to various reports made by the Pasteur Team during the following year. That made it easier for him to say more in April 84. In science, when you discover something -- when you discover a new virus -- of course one year later you know much more about it than when you saw it the first time."

"By the time Gallo published those papers," Simon interjects, "he knew very well what Pasteur had done, and where the virus was going, what to look for. It was easier! The description, the outline, the type of virus -- people started to have a feel for it.

"Montagnier went against the grain with what he said. He got it in the neck. He had a credibility problem. No one believed him because he went against the dogma. It was the Old World versus the New World. Before Bob Gallo published, it was clear from the data from the Paris group . . . ."

Dr. Luc Montagnier heads the team working on AIDS. He is out of the country this weekend. He discovered the virus along with Dr. Francoise Barre-Sinoussi and Dr. Jean-Claude Chermann. I am absolutely determined to see one of these three leaders of the discovery team, although as yet I have been granted no appointment.

"But what do you mean, can you summarize, 'he went against the grain?' How?"

"The dogma was, the line was being pushed at that point, was that the AIDS virus was an HTLV virus. A leukemia virus." I know now that the "HTLV" viruses bear Dr. Gallo's stamp, like a steer with the brand of its home ranch.

"There were cogent reasons for that theory," he continues. "Yes. But Montagnier's virus didn't fit it. Therefore he was actually a bit ostracized. And in fact, that cogent theory of the virus being HTLV . . . was WRONG! Back then though, they thought the Paris group had mud on their faces for not fitting in with the dogma."

"What are you working on now?" I ask him.

"We want to see the virus from Africa," Simon replies, "to see its genetic makeup. And the possibility of making a vaccine. We're interested in developing sequence technology even further."

One virus can have many strains, he explains. Just as there can be Hong Kong flu, Philadelphia Flu, etc. "It seems likely that the virus really came from Africa," he says, "so you must look closely at the strain from that continent. To see how different it is, and in what ways."

"Do you have any insight into why, in Africa, it seems to be so much more a heterosexually-oriented disease?"

"It's very, very simple. We know how the virus works. It's a blood-borne disease. So who's it going to hit in the West? It's going to hit blood transfusion people, drug addicts, hemophiliacs, homosexuals. They are the first wave because they are exposed, or are in some way immuno-suppressed. Sperm can be immuno-suppressive, and homosexuals can sometimes contract other infections which render them slightly immuno-suppressed.

"Those groups are the first line of attack. They are naturally the first ones to get it. We see AIDS will slowly evolve to the point it will be more and more a disease of man in general and not of a subset. If you look at the latest figures from the CDC, you'll see that it's reaching a growing percentage of people who don't fit the original risk groups. A move toward more diverse distribution of the virus."

"As for Africa, the reason it's more homogeneous there is simply because homosexuality hardly exists for it to have struck first. There it's simply AIDS among sexually promiscuous people, like the relatively wealthy men who have the money to buy prostitutes.

"Mind you, we're not talking tribal Africa. There's very little disease from tribes we're looking at. We're talking about cities, where there are hospitals and where we can see these people. When we say 'Africa,' we mustn't get into our old colonial pictures that they're a bunch of bloody Zulus with grass skirts and banging drums. OK, they're poor with crummy shanty towns. But they have skyscrapers too."

"In general in Africa," Caroline adds, "even aside from prostitutes, sexual promiscuity is wider spread. And hygiene is not as good."

"We don't like to talk of the dirt of this disease, do we?" says Simon. "We talk about monkeys scratching and licking and so on. Don't tell me that doesn't go on in human sex. And any way of contact -- a lesion with a lesion -- can spread the disease. Look at prostitutes, for example. Prostitutes have multiple partners. Therefore their vaginas have got to be much more irritated and have many more sores. It's OBVIOUS whether we like to talk about it or not. Similarly among highly promiscuous people."

What do Caroline and Simon think about Jean-Michel's comments on malaria and how very many people are dying of it?

"Of course!" Caroline says. "It's true."

"Of course," he says.

"But Jean-Michel says they're poor people and unseen," I continue, "and thus not so likely to receive assistance -- just as gays were ignored by some at the beginning of AIDS. What do you think?" Caroline starts to disagree with their being ignored, but Simon interrupts her.

"*Mais non, mais non*, it's absolutely true," he says. "Listen! I was at the vaccine meeting in Cold Spring Harbor. And the guy from Rockefeller who heads the Great Neglected Disease Program said it was considered by companies not worthwhile to make a malaria vaccine. But it *is* worthwhile to make a vaccine against cat leukemia virus. Because these ladies who keep twenty persian cats, they don't care if they fork out $50 a cat to have them vaccinated against the disease, which is the number two killer of cats after the car. It's a Western thing. There's money in these California ladies. It is therefore economically worth the companies' while to make a vaccine against cat leukemia virus and NOT malaria.

"Yet there's no comparison in the impact, the economic impact of malaria in the Third World, economic impact to *homo sapiens* instead of *genus felis*. And let's face it, there are a ton of African diseases that we're not even concerned about."

Caroline explains that one of the reasons Pasteur Institute got involved with AIDS had nothing to do with how many people had the disease or with their various lifestyles. A commercial firm associated with the Institute makes hepatitis vaccine, she says. For a time, there were allegations that people could get AIDS from that vaccine. It became important for Pasteur to prove with research that the hepatitis vaccine was safe. The commercial need to protect sales of hepatitis vaccine thus helped to start the AIDS project.

"AIDS had to be tackled in its own right, though" Simon adds. "It's an important disease that gets into the blood supply. We've got to get rid of it straight away."

"But at that time," she replies, "since nobody knew what the AIDS virus even was, we couldn't really know the true importance of the disease." Always things go back to the significance of discovering the virus in the first place. I must find a way to speak with Dr. Chermann or Dr. Barre, just to hear about that discovery.

Caroline, as the press officer, knows that I have offered any kind of flexibility I can. Montagnier will be out of the country for a while, but maybe the others are returning? Could I invite one of them to lunch tomorrow? Or just stop by the lab? Midnight? 5 a.m.?

It's hard to say. They are difficult to reach.

Wain leaves, late for a conference. I ask Caroline what she can tell me about Rock Hudson's treatment in France.

"When Rock Hudson came over, it was in July '85. In fact he had received a treatment in France the year before but that was a secret. In July he fainted in his hotel, and the day after they announce he has AIDS, and the day after that they admit the Pasteur treatment. But we would never have said anything at all about it; it was up to him to admit it."

"There was a time when lots of Americans were coming over."
"Yes."
"Is that over?"
"Yes."
"Why did it stop?"

"It stopped because this drug, HPA-23, was authorized in the United States. So now they don't need to come. The Americans arrived in February '85, because there was an article in *Lancet*, a medical paper. It was a report of two patients treated with HPA-23, and one of them had a remission for sixteen months. So dozens of patients arrived, and we got hundreds of letters.

"Now we have contracted with the firm of Rhone-Poulenc for clinical tests in France. They have the authorization of the FDA for treatment in the United States."

"I understand HPA-23 is not a cure," I say. "I understand that. But what have you seen?"

"It's true," she says, "that Dr. Willy Rozenbaum who treats a lot of his patients with HPA-23 says he has seen remission for three years so far."

"Continuous treatment?"

"No. You have treatment and then it stops, and then you start again."

"What is the side effect of HPA-23?"

"The main side effect is on platelets. Coagulation. You become vulnerable like a hemophiliac, but even much more cautious."

"Have you personally seen people with AIDS?"

"Yes."

"So you know how terrible the disease is?"

"Yes." She says it a way that lets me feel it. She really does know.

"So you know -- if given a choice between having to be 'cautious' versus having the disease . . . ."

"That is not a choice!" she says.

As I put on my jacket, I put in one more pitch for Caroline to help me get an interview with one of the discoverers of the virus. She will leave a note on Chermann's desk. I should call his lab at 6:00 tonight and see.

She sends me on a tour of the Pasteur museum. Almost all the photographs of Monsieur Pasteur are stern. I'm shown a film about the Institute, and I am impressed.

Now I stroll one block across to Pasteur square. I cross the street near the Pasteur laundry and the Pasteur pharmacy. As soon as I've given a taxi driver the name of my hotel, I close my eyes.

FRIDAY: The "AIDES" Organization

I am groggy after a nap at the hotel. It is almost 6:00, and I've a 5:30 appointment with Daniel Defert. He's the founder of a volunteer organization which -- in one year -- has become nationally recognized as the effective champion of support and counsel for people with AIDS, and of public education for society as a whole.

Daniel said he'll be working at the group's headquarters this evening. I needn't feel worried about arriving precisely on time, he said. But I *always* worry about punctuality, just like my father. So I dress as quickly as I can and wait impatiently for a cab in front of the hotel.

The Friday night traffic moves like dough. My fidgeting on the sidewalk is clearly distressing the doorman. Finally I scramble into a cab and realize I forgot to call Dr. Chermann to ask again for the interview. The taxi driver will do his best to hurry, he says. In fact, he gets lost.

"Our headquarters are in a small and dirty office, up some dirty stairs, in a a dirty building," Daniel had said to me. The description is accurate. Dim lights over each creaky landing flick off automatically to save electricity. You must find and push a button at every landing. I remember in a movie, on a staircase like this one, a killer with a razor in the shadows.

You really could approach this more cooly, I tell myself. You are in Paris, beautiful Paris, for a weekend. Slow your brain.

I open the unmarked door at almost 7:00. Inside, the walls are painted in flourescent pastels; the lighting is harsh. A woman and three or four men crowd around a table with several telephones, pamphlets, and mail.

"I search for Daniel Defert," I say in French. "I have an appointment."

"He is in the other office with an American already," someone tells me. It's as though they believe the other visitor is Mike Greenly. I notice my private dismay. Up until now, I've been enjoying being the only foreigner around.

"May I use the phone while I wait?" I call Dr. Chermann's office.

Yes, the doctor is back from Australia today, but he is not at the lab tonight. We do not know if he received your request for an interview. In any case, he will be elsewhere in a conference tomorrow morning and not available. As for Saturday afternoon, one cannot say. Yes, we will take a message.

A man of about my age, with a friendly smile, has been listening to the conversation. He is a biologist from Marseille. He has come to Paris to attend a conference tomorrow, where Dr. Chermann will be speaking. Perhaps I would like to attend, if I can get permission?

Excitedly I phone the lab again. Ah, but the conference is not available to the public, and certainly not to reporters.

But it is a book I am writing. It will include the Pasteur Institute. This is not some sensationalist expose. I am serious. I will be discreet.

One cannot say, Monsieur. You can try waiting at the gates tomorrow. *Au revoir, monsieur.*

Daniel Defert enters the office. Here is what I know of him:

He was, for twenty years, the lover of one of the greatest philosophers of modern France, Michel Foucault. Among Foucault's particular interests were the effects of institutions on minorities. His work was highly respected and is acknowledged for its influence on French society. When Foucault died in July of 1984, Daniel became intensely interested in making a difference for people with AIDS.

I'm told Defert's politics are "leftist," though I am not sure what that means in a French context. From our phone conversations, I know he is smart and has a quick sense of humor. He is sharp-edged and warm at the same time.

I am introduced to the other American, who is leaving. After some discussion, it seems the best way for me to get a picture of the AIDES organization is to briefly interview some of the people working there tonight.

Everyone seems quite fascinated with my portable computer. An extra chair is brought to the table. Daniel sits on my left. My first subject is on my right. Others, including a few newcomers, sit or stand around the room as I conduct the interview. It is like a friendly court of inquiry. One man offers to obtain a coca cola, and I accept. He is pleased to have suggested an American beverage.

I begin a discussion with Girard, the biologist from Marseille. He is about to open a Marseille affiliate of AIDES. Daniel and others from Paris will assist, but it will be an independent organization. "AIDES" is not an acronym, he says. It stands for:

Aides aux malades, aide à la recherche,
information du public sur le Syndrome
Immuno-Déficitaire Acquis, le SIDA

help for the sick, support for research,
public information on acquired immune
deficiency syndrome, AIDS

French people -- to whom AIDS is "SIDA" -- will view the name as "HELPS." The organization stresses its concern with the disease itself, irrespective of the PWA's own sexual orientation. I discover that particular sensitivity when I begin to inquire about the organization's membership — gay and straight. Daniel becomes upset with my question.

"What kind of freedom is it where people have to indicate their sexual affinities," he asks with irritation. I receive a stream of information as Girard looks on, protected from my unfortunate *faux pas*.

The AIDES organization has received top support from the French government. It began life totally on volunteer funding, but these offices are only temporary -- too small and not appropriate. Conditions will change partly because the organization has nothing to do with personal sexuality.

The French population is trusting the "safe sex" guidelines that AIDES independently publishes with far more success than a government tract would receive. Even the government realizes that and will help the organization for the public good. Again, complete independence from personal sexual preference makes a difference.

AIDES directors are possibly of varied sexual preferences from each other. Daniel conscientiously chooses not to know or inquire about each individual. He has received the question many times from television or radio reporters about a particular PWA's sexual interests. Always, he protects the individual, because sexual orientation is not the issue. (He slams his hand on the table.)

The issue is the virus. Daniel will help French media obtain interviews only when they promise to refrain from asking such questions. As a result, France has been learning that this is everyone's disease.

I take a deep breath and a humble sip of coca cola. I am suitably chastised, a barbarian from an overly direct point of view. Gently, I pick up the thread of conversation.

Daniel interrupts. "You come from a different culture," he says, trying to excuse my lack of knowledge of his view of things. "I do not know your background. I do not know from looking at you, for example, if you are of German heritage, or Dutch, or -- ?"

Now, in mock indignation, I slam my own hand, smack, onto the table. "I refuse to answer such a question!" I shout. "My ethnic background has nothing to do with my ability as a journalist!"

I am applauded from the other end of the table. "Superb!" someone cheers to me. We all laugh amidst the clapping. I have understood Daniel's message: our differences don't matter, what matters is that we fight a human disease as caring human beings.

I learn from Girard that Marseille has one and a half million citizens, and has seen ninety cases of full AIDS so far. The general public is quite aware of the disease, and is concerned about it. People talk about AIDS every night at dinner with the daily news. There is a need for reassurance and education.

The AIDES organization will surely be useful for Marseilles. The first hour that the AIDES MARSEILLE phone line had opened, the volunteers began hearing from a variety of people, including a man writing his thesis on the disease in that city. Soon there will be radio announcements telling people about the free information available by phone.

We talk, as a group, about the information AIDES is giving. At first, they simply translated pamphlets from U.S. organizations like the Gay Men's Health Crisis. France has had the advantage of learning from two years of prior U.S. experience.

But the translation received poor feedback from French readers. It was too overt, too direct, too explicit. AIDES has since created a simpler brochure for the French public with only one real purpose: to encourage the use of condoms ("*préservatifs*.")

Frederick, a medical doctor, now takes the rickety witness chair. He has a refined and formal manner. He tells me he's vice president of

AIDES. He received his medical training in Paris and also in Africa. He had two patients with the disease in 1981 -- at first he didn't know what was their sickness. Each patient died within four or five months, and he began to learn the danger and fascination of this disease.

Now, with AIDES, he's responsible for liaison with other medical doctors in Paris. He calls on them to be sure they're current with *le SIDA*. The doctors know they will ultimately have patients with the disease, and they appreciate receiving the perspective of an informed physician.

It is nearly 8:30 and Dominique will be leaving the office soon. If I want to talk with her, now is the time. She works as a psychiatric nurse and also spends long hours in her volunteer work for AIDES. She screens and trains volunteers and helps to supervise interactions with PWA's.

She is a large woman with very serious countenance. She has been typing letters intently since I arrived. She asks me, please, to talk only in French. When occasionally we exchange a joke, the laugh that brightens her huge, dark eyes is a pleasure.

She has worked as a nurse for ten years. During all that time, she has been struck by an observation: when a person is sick enough to be admitted to the hospital, one's personal identity can get lost. One becomes a "patient" with a disease. Something of that identity loss happens to people with *le SIDA* -- the disease becomes bigger than the human. Her volunteer work for AIDES lets her do something for the human balance.

She has also observed how often terminal patients are treated as "dying." She believes they should be treated as "living" until the moment of actual death. Again, the issue is general, but it's accentuated with this disease.

When a friend died one year ago, she determined to make a difference for others. The organization at the moment has twenty-five volunteers working specifically with PWA groups, and about 100 volunteers altogether. The need is growing rapidly.

What do her friends think of her volunteer work? Some of her gay male friends think she is overly devoted; they'd like to spend more time with her. Her straight friends think she is crazy (she says this with her husky laugh) but probably admire her.

She volunteers that she is heterosexual; I most certainly did not inquire. She finds that some of the qualities she would most wish to find in a heterosexual man -- tenderness, a lack of competitiveness-- she more often finds in her gay male friends. Some of her heterosexual boyfriends are wonderful and exciting to be with, she says, until it becomes time to really talk.

Recently she broke up with a man who wanted her to live with him. He has considerable wealth and couldn't perceive that he was treating her as just another worthy "object." Finally he gave her an ultimatim: choose him or the AIDES organization. He didn't realize what an easy choice that would be for her, she says with a smile.

As she now prepares to leave, she mentions one of the major cultural differences she perceives in treating AIDS patients in the U.S. versus France. In her country, she says, people never have to worry about having their hospital costs paid for; it's understood that they will be. That assurance relieves a great amount of stress.

Now I am given a demonstration of France's Mini-Tel system: government installed computer terminals, little TV screens that are linked to the telephone. Not only is the phone directory accessed in this way, but the government has encouraged citizens to link to each other in a number of ways as the system expands through France.

The AIDES organization has its own section on the menus I am now shown on the TV screen. Daniel explains that the first week of having the AIDES program available to homes with Mini-Tel, 500 calls and messages came through with virtually no publicity. Mostly the requests came from from young people.

Daniel is planning to use this electronic bulletin board to provide basic information from AIDES, like the "Safe Sex" guidelines, plus the latest developments in treatment and news of the disease.

"That's terrific," I tell him.

"Yes," he says proudly.

Later, at nearly midnight in a nearby restaurant with Daniel and a number of the volunteers, I offer my check and become the first citizen of another country to join AIDES. Girard agrees to meet me in the morning for the biologists' conference. I bid everyone, *bon soir*.

SATURDAY MORNING

Girard has locked himself out of the apartment he's borrowed in Paris. I must go to the conference myself and hope I gain entry somehow. Fortunately a doctor from a village in the south of France, introduces me as "Doctor Mike from New York" and I'm in.

The conference itself is an overview of AIDS. I don't learn anything really new. Although I don't understand all the technical French terms, the grizzly medical photos are universal. AIDS' targets do vary from one country to another. For example, there are more drug addicts as a percent of total .cases in Italy and Spain than in some of the other countries. (Just as there are more of them in the urban east coast of America versus the west.)

After the conference, I approach Dr. Chermann. Would he meet with me, please? Today?

"You are writing the book about *le SIDA*?"

"*Oui, mais* -- it's about people, really."

"I will see you."   A woman compliments him on the panel he'd organized for the biologists, and says something irritable about the Americans.

"*Attention*," he said. "*Voiçi un journalist Américain.*"

"I don't care," she says to me. "You are not recognizing properly the contributions of this country."

"We are all human," I say which, while sincere, seems to pacify her more than it deserves.

Chermann will see me, at his lab this afternoon.

Chapter 24:
Paris: Part 2
Dr. Jean-Claude CHERMANN

When I started this chronicle of "the human side of AIDS" I didn't realize I'd become so involved in the human side of scientists. Now I realize, it was inevitable. My interview with Dr. Mathilde Krim made a deep impression on me in the early months of this project. As I more and more experienced the real horror of AIDS and its effects on the people I was meeting, I began to hunger for a balance to the pain, a reason for solid hope, and an experience of people who were actively working on finding solutions.

I imagine you will perceive that I was totally charmed by and respectful of Jean-Claude Chermann. You will therefore understand why, in the interests of being fair, it wasn't long after I landed back in New York that I phoned Dr. Robert Gallo's office for an interview.

But that is a separate chapter.

It is Saturday afternoon. I've been in Paris for thirty hours and am leaving tomorrow morning. Now I wait in Chermann's office.

My tape recorder rests on a rolling hill of papers. Looking down from his bulletin board are photographs of chimpanzees, doctors, and his family. There is also a large poster of Monsieur Pasteur himself. He holds something in a beaker and stares into its heart. Pasteur's beaker glows with light.

Jean-Claude Chermann is a *"Chef de Laboratoire "* of the Pasteur Institute. With Luc Montagnier and Francoise Barre-Sinoussi, he led the first team in the world to discover the AIDS virus.

"It is a crazy life," he says apologetically as he enters the room. *"Ma femme ne me vois jamais."*

I am writing for technical readers, I explain. Could he simply tell me what he felt, as a human being, when he was discovering the AIDS virus?

"En français ou en anglais?" he invites. It is clear that his

English is far better than my French. But after speaking French all morning, I sound quite strange to myself right now. I enunciate my words as though talking to a deaf man.

"First, tell me how you got involved with AIDS at all," I say. "How long have you been at Pasteur Institute?"

"The second question is more easy. I am in Pasteur Institute for now twenty-three years. I started as a twenty-three year old, and now I forty-six." His dark black hair has touches of gray above his ears. "We were involved in AIDS because we were here, teaching retrovirology. We know the retrovirology for a long time. I am a retrovirologist now since 1967."

"That is your speciality?"

"Yes. In Pasteur we have three goals. One is research, that is the most important. Second is to teach. Third is to lead with our production. Okay?" I take "production" to mean actual output, including commercial medications and procedures growing out of the Institute's research.

"I was teaching retrovirology. Some of my previous student was involved with AIDS. Gallo said in 1982, 'maybe it should be a retrovirus.'" Dr. Robert Gallo has been a constant topic with every medical person or scientist I've encountered here.

"One of our students, Francoise Brun, whom you have seen here today, and also Willie Rosenbaum, both bring us a lymph node of a homosexual at risk with lymphadenopathy. But we don't know at this time that lymphadenopathy means pre-AIDS. They came and they said, `we want you to search about retrovirus.' I was not interested." He makes this last point with drama -- the discoverer of the AIDS virus was almost not interested in pursuing it.

"I am very serious. I will tell you why. Because everybody was thinking it was an HTLV-I virus. I say I'm not interested to look at an HTLV-I, because if it is, then Gallo and everybody . . . ."

"In other words," I ask when his sentence trails off, "if the problem with the patient's lymph node was the HTLV-I virus, then that exploration had already been 'done' by Dr. Gallo? It was 'his' retrovirus already?"

"Yeah. Absolutely. I am just speaking my feeling in human," he says. It may not sound noble to be disinterested in a pursuit for such a competitive reason, but that is the truth.

"*Oui, c'est ça que je veux,*" I say. Your real feelings.

"But, we said okay to those associates anyway -- we will do for your pleasure, to show that we can do, but we are involved in something more important than lymphadenopathy: looking for probably a retrovirus in human breast cancer.

"But, okay, we do the culture of the lymph node. And, after two weeks of cultivation, we see a peak of production of virus." His hand traces a peak two feet higher than the folders on his desk.

"And we say, okay, that is a retrovirus, perhaps an HTLV-I."

"You just assumed that, yes?"

"Yeah. We were expecting that, we thought was normal. But two or three days after, we start to see the peak going down." His hand veers down to the paperweight.

"And we say, now it is NOT look like HTLV-I. We try to find something more to help us, to re-infect and to work with. We took the lymphocyte from a friend. We were crazy. Today he has not the right to go in my lab. Because the virus has adapted to his own lymphocyte now. If my friend today stick himself in our lab, he will be surely infected with AIDS.

"We also obtained some other problem lymphocyte from maternity wards. We were able to re-infect and grow again the virus. That was the first thing." You must be able to re-create a virus in order to study it, and Pasteur Labs had achieved that. But how to learn more about whatever it was, Virus X?

"We clearly knew it was not HTLV-I so this time it start to interest me."

"Because you sensed it was something new?"

"Absolutely. You have to understand what we are. We are French. That means nobody knows where is France in the States. Maybe some people know that we are a small country." His thumb and forefinger make a gesture, about the size of a French after-dinner mint. A little mint, however tasty, all too easily overlooked in a huge U.S.platter.

"What can we do in France, in comparison to what they do in the States -- ?" He shrugs. "At this time, a lot of isolation of HTLV-I in AIDS has been done in the States."

"So, people thought HTLV-I and AIDS were linked?"

"Absolutely! And, if you want, because it was coming from the States, we were thinking here too, they must be right."

"So -- honestly -- you were excited about the idea that, perhaps, as a French man . . . "

"No, no, no. Not yet. My first impression was, it will be an HTLV-I and I am not going just to verify what they are do in the States. But when it starts not to be that, we decide that if it could be responsible for AIDS, we have to also find a virus that can be more in a *pre*-AIDS patient than in an AIDS patient. And, secondly, we have to find a virus that kills the same way."

I have understood for some time now, that it is in the earlier stages of AIDS that a patient's blood carries the most AIDS virus. Many full-AIDS patients have the virus already depleted. So Dr. Chermann needed to start earlier in the disease cycle. What could he isolate from the blood of someone who would ultimately develop AIDS?

"For that we start with a lymphadenopathy. We don't know for sure if it will be AIDS or not, because we look now for pre-AIDS, Okay?"

"Yes."

"And it was true! We find a virus that was killing the same. And also, we said the virus we find must kill the specific cells that disappear in AIDS. We find that the virus was killing a sub-population of the T-4 cells. All these things was going on. At this time when we find that, it was January '83.

"So in the middle of February, I called Bob Gallo. I said, `we have a virus. But we need to distinguish this virus from HTLV-I.'

"I will tell you, between parentheses, that I know Gallo for seventeen years. He's a good friend. We meet each other each time I'm going in the States or when he comes in Paris. And I said, `I have something, I don't know what it is. It looks like a retrovirus. It has a reverse transcriptase and so on. We need to receive some of your reagent, to control if it is an HTLV-I or not.'

"Gallo sends it immediately. Clearly we see there is no relationship between HTLV-I and this new virus. Except we do find a cluster of activity between the HTLV-I cells and the serum of our patient. So maybe our patient is DOUBLE infected, with both Gallo's virus and the new one?

"But we still do know: we have found a new retrovirus. At this time we decide to announce it — a new, human T-lymphotropic retrovirus. At this time, HTLV-I was called `human T-leukemia.' Do you understand?"

I am realizing the importance of these letters. Gallo's virus was

> **H**uman,
> affecting **T**-cells,
> relating to **L**eukemia,
> and was a retro- **V**irus

hence, HTLV-I and, later on, HTLV-II. Chermann is saying that what the Pasteur team had discovered was also human, was also affecting T cells (relevant to AIDS), was a new retrovirus, and was cultured from *lymph* problems not from leukemia.

"Leukemia" and "lymphotropic" both begin with the same letter. If part of what scientists struggle for is the honor of naming a virus, then the chance for public confusion and disagreement was perhaps accentuated by that coincidence.

"Okay," he says. "We publish with Gallo. That means Gallo was our referee. Gallo accepted our paper in *SCIENCE*.. The title of the paper was, `Isolation of a T-Lymphotropic Retrovirus in a Patient at Risk for Acquiring Immune Deficiency Syndrome.' So we were announcing a new human retrovirus in a pre-AIDS patient."

He flips rapidly through a notebook to show me the title page, to prove its existence. "You see? This was May '83 that we described this virus. One year*before* May '84 when Madame Heckler tells the American public about the virus being discovered." The U.S. Secretary of Health and Human Services had held a press conference to announce that Dr. Gallo had both identified the AIDS virus and was producing it in large quantities. "Another miracle to the long honor roll of American medicine and science," she had said — unfairly, some said, denying the French of the credit they were due.

"When your paper was first published in 1983," I ask, "how were you feeling?"

"We feel happy we find something new. Different from HTLV-I. We say it clearly!

"But the initials were the same as Gallo's," he continues. "One month after, we *change* the name to 'Lymphadenopathy Associated Virus, LAV.' I will tell you more later about the decision, changing that name.

"For now, we still did not yet call it the AIDS virus. We were cautious. We are scientists, you know. We had isolated a retrovirus, yes. But it was ONE isolation, from only ONE pre-AIDS patient, Okay? We do call it 'new,' but we cannot yet say, `the cause of AIDS.' We knew it fits very well with AIDS, so we start immediately to isolate the virus from AIDS patients. That would be the second step."

"But I have a question about your first step," I interrupt him. "Whether the virus causes AIDS or not, isn't it significant to find a new virus in a human being?"

"Yeah!"

"Well . . . did other scientists congratulate you?"

"No. Absolutely not. Because it was coming from France. And not confirmed by the states."

"*Et, ça c'est important?*"

"*Ah, ça c'est très important,*" he says. "In this paper, the morphology of the virus that we described by electron microscopy was different from all that was known.... people made complaints. They called *SCIENCE* and Gallo without telling us. They say we make a big mistake, that the virus is not a new retrovirus. People were angry against Gallo in accepting our paper too rapidly. Gallo told me all that.

"I say to him, `you know that I am working with retrovirus for seventeen years. You have to believe me.'

"He says, `but there is a lot of reaction. You have to prove . . . .
It's only one isolate you have so far.

"So we start to isolate the virus from a lot of AIDS patients.
Africans. Haitians. From the spring of '83 when the paper was published
to February of '84, nobody believe us!   But we have more and more
evidence that it was the AIDS virus really.

"We went to all the best Congress in the world, all the
conventions of scientists." He is standing now. He sprays the room with
an imaginary machine gun. "Tcht-tcht-tcht-tcht!" His "gun" shoots and
sweeps past me to the window.

"We were completely shot down everywhere. We were kill by the
Americans and other scientists. They were all believing HTLV-I and
HTLV-II, and not believing our reasons for a new virus.

"That was a bad feeling for all the lab.   When we first started, I
took all my people and said, `We found a virus together. We don't know
what it is. We don't know what danger it means for us. We have nothing
to be protected, it is unknown. Would you like to stop, or continue?'

"Everybody said, 'continue!'

"We all continue.   At science meetings, it was generally ten
presentations of American, ten minutes each one.   Only five or ten
minutes total for French. In ten minutes we have to convince people!"

He momentarily switches to French as he remembers the rejection
and skepticism.

"Each time we went to a convention, we telephone back, always
with bad news. Nobody believe us."

"*Vous ètiez découragé, ou non?*" I ask.

"No, not at all. We were not discouraged, we did not doubt our
findings, because we kept coming up with the same results. We isolated a
new virus. We isolated, isolated -- new, every time. We could not
understand WHY should we be able to isolate it, and not also the
Americans or anybody else! Everyone else was working on *le SIDA*, too,
just like us. But everyone else was finding HTLV-I, while we find LAV.

"Why? It was impossible here to contaminate. I have one room
for HTLV-I, one room for HTLV-II, one room for simian AIDS, and
another room for LAV. It's impossible to contaminate one with the other!

"I said, `Okay, they are publishing their HTLV-I in Haitians.
Essex, Gallo, all of them. We were looking also in a Haitian for HTLV-
I, but we found only LAV instead. Impossible!' I must find HTLV-I in
my lab to believe in myself. I have to know I can find it.

"Now -- we know why the problem!" He is triumphant.

"Why?"

"Because people was *double*-infected." He sits to explain to me
calmly the answer to the mystery.

"They find HTLV-I in 33% of AIDS patients. So lots of people were double-infected, with both that virus and LAV. If I was in Italy, I'd find it too because lots of Italians have both viruses. In France, not so much the both.

"Back then, nobody knew this reason, I decided to call a lot of friends. I said I must absolutely find people with HTLV-I. I must isolate it in my lab to prove I am capable. We got one, from hospital St. Louis. They sent us a young woman from the Caribbean islands." I imagine the hospital sent a vial of blood with Madame's name on it. For Chermann, that's as tangible as sending in the woman herself.

"And -- we isolate HTLV-I!" He cheers and raises his hands to the sky in celebration. He stands once again and paces between his desk and the wall.

"When HTLV-I was present, we showed we could find it! Now we were sure that we had also found the AIDS virus, something quite separate. COMPLETELY SURE! That's when we formally changed the name — end of June '83. That's when we called it 'LAV.'

"Nobody was understanding what we were doing. They were asking us for serology for HTLV-I or HTLV-II. Now we call it 'LAV' to make it clear to the other scientists: `this has nothing to do with other virus. Please forget it! If you want to ask us for something, please ask about 'LAV' and not 'HTLV.'"

He snatches a photograph down from the bulletin board. Three men, one woman, all on bikes. "In November, I say to Bob Gallo -- I make four kilometre bicycle with him -- I said, `Bob, you're crazy. I tried to convince you that WE have the virus. The virus is killing T-4 cells. Please grow the virus yourself, and have a look.' I say this while we do four kilometres." He pants a bit, out of breath on the bike.

"I say, 'I don't want to speak any more with you now. Our next meeting will be end of January '84 in Park City, Utah. At that meeting, I will convince you, giving all the data about AIDS.'

"I did not communicate any more then." He puts his hand firmly on the phone, shoving it away lest he is tempted to phone Dr. Gallo with still more proof of his AIDS discovery.

"We arrive in Utah. Bob Gallo was the chairman of the meeting. Nobody was believing any more about retrovirus and AIDS. They were looking instead at hepatitis and other virus for maybe involvement with AIDS. I arrive at this meeting. The French arrive." I imagine the Marsaillaise from an invisible orchestra. In his head too, perhaps it plays as the French delegation enters a conference in the U.S. state of Utah. Secretly they must smile at the proof they are about to reveal.

"Gallo makes the keynote Sunday night about HTLV-I, HTLV-II, and so on," he tells me. "The following day the session start. I was supposed to speak before the break. But . . . ." He recites for me, in order, the names of every speaker who preceded him. He can probably even remember which necktie he wore that morning, or exactly what he ate for breakfast. It was to be the day, at last, when he could finally be vindicated to peers.

"They were taking longer, longer, longer. No time for me to speak!" His pacing is agitated now; it is hard to be contained behind a desk when you want to shout.

"The time is — tk-tk-tk-tk. Finally a colleague gets angry and insists that time is made for Chermann to speak. "Gallo took Haseltine like that -- and put me there." He imitates the Harvard researcher being pulled away from the podium, as now he, the Frenchman himself, steps into the spotlight.

"And I present ALL the data! We give the manuscript. All of it." On a sudden thought he leaps over to his bookcase and pulls out a summary of conference reports from Utah.

"One thing I am disappointed in the Americans, they are not serious," he says. "Here is my paper, just as I presented it. There was no HTLV-III from Gallo at that meeting. But here it is, an HTLV-III paper, into the book!"

It takes me a while to understand. The French team, unrecognized and disbelieved, announced their "scoop" in Utah. Dr. Gallo subsequently announced the discovery of the AIDS virus himself, naming it as the latest in his own "HTLV" series. In fairness, Chermann is saying -- practically hopping in front of me now -- if Gallo couldn't present such findings at the Utah meeting, then they do not belong in the official record of the sessions. A kind of pro-American favoritism dwells within the pages.

"We gave our manuscript in January, at the conference. But Gallo give the manuscript after May '84," he says. "That is not good, not fair. Margaret Heckler had already made the announcement about us. It is not right to accept manuscript long after conference."

"Do you think Gallo should have called the virus he isolated 'LAV?' I ask.

"Sure! When somebody find a virus, you cannot change a name. For that we get very angry.

"But first, at the Utah conference, Gallo was very surprised. I make the presentation, and usually Gallo had been fighting me in previous presentations." He imitates Dr. Gallo interrupting and challenging from the audience.

"This time, he was the Chairman. And I was at the podium. This time, when somebody ask a question, he goes -- " Chermann coos with conciliation. Dr. Gallo realized, evidently, that something special was being announced by the French. "He was not fighting with me. It was the first time he was not fighting with me. And the people recognized it. He was trying to answer in my place."

"To help you?"

"In my opinion, for the first time he was convinced at this presentation. He don't want that I speak too much, because if I speak too much he has no time to do more and more research himself. I don't know, that is my own opinion.

"I am speaking just human now, as you ask. For me at that time, I thought it was very nice that he was speaking for me. But I will tell you something. The Americans in this room was very surprised at my presentation. Because all I say was fitting very well with AIDS."

"After that, was a cocktail." He leans against the bookcase, a Frenchman alone at a party far from home. "And somebody came to me, a young girl from Beth Israel Medical Hospital in New York. She said, `YOU have the AIDS virus! Congratulations!'"

"I said, `yes, I know.'

"She told me, 'we were looking for another virus, a hepatitis virus, whatever. But now I'm sure that it's a retrovirus, and that your LAV is the cause of AIDS.'"

He stands tall now, almost glowing like the poster of Pasteur just over his head. "For me it was something extraordinary," he says. "That somebody like that came . . . ." He repeats her phrase, to hear it once again: "`YOU have the AIDS virus!'

"I called the phone, called here at Pasteur. Saying to my people, `we win! we win!'" He pronounces it "ween." I am thoroughly charmed by his pleasure as he re-experiences it.

"`People is believing.'" Now he can let himself sit.

"The second thing, I will tell you something, is the CDC. They did not stay for my presentation. So they send us thirty serum to Paris: ten normal, ten lymphadenophy, ten AIDS. And we decode each one! They sent them blind and were impressed we were accurate every time. Now, for the first time, somebody could say, `that one is like this, this one is like that.'

"Usually there is lots of press to announce news after these conferences, but this time, there was not much news after the meeting. They did not call the press as much as normal. But, at least, at this Utah meeting, the scientists believe us finally. Same thing at CDC later. They verify we were right.

"We did not ourselves do something for press. Madame Heckler found out about our discovery, but not from us. Malcolm Martine, who knew, told a journalist, and that is how the story got out. We got the credit in New York from James Mason of the CDC. We did not ask for it loud; we were keeping quiet. We were naive, completely naive. We have become less naive now.

"After the Heckler announcement, 100 press men came in. `Why are you coming today?' I ask them. `We found the virus one year ago.' But the reason they came was that the United States recognized us. America has to confirm you before you get credit."

"And today?" I ask.

"Today is different. Today there is no honest scientist that doesn't know we found the virus first. Everybody knows it."

"Including Gallo?"

"I think so. But he says we were not well defined, we were not correlated well. Anyway, now in Atlanta, a lot of people want to have their picture standing next to us. Some TV people put their microphone next to two Frenchman talking, just to hear them speaking French." The idea of the French language being recorded for the American TV audience obviously pleases him.

"We have a big problem now," he says. "I think something is not fair in the States. We put a patent in for our blood test in December '83. The Americans put in their blood test for patent in April '84. We have months ahead in priority."

"This is a blood test to see if someone has an antibody to the AIDS virus?" I ask.

"Yes. A kit that can be used around the world to see if someone has it. But the patent has been given to the American and not the French, even though we were earlier in the asking."

"Why do you think that is?"

"I don't know. Maybe *protectionnisme* ? I really don't know. But now we have to pay royalty on American blood test. That is not fair, you know. December '83."

"What will you do?"

"Some legal things, I think."

"Do you think you have a good chance of winning?"

"Maybe many, many years from now." He laughs ruefully.

"What are you working on now?" I ask him.

"Well for us, you know, the AIDS virus is over. Do not misunderstand me. But now we have the virus, and the work to be done is clear. Vaccine, for example. But my curiosity is, why the virus happen in Africa and U.S. simultaneously." I gaze up at what I believe are, in fact, African chimpanzees. In Africa, it happen to heterosexuals first. In America, homosexuals. The disease has to do with virus, not sexuality. Now the path for AIDS is clear, the things that must be done are known. There will be knowledge gained for all immune system. Pasteur work exploring many new things now."

"*Je vous invite à dire quelque chose*," I say. What would you like to tell the readers of your story?

"I say now, when you do your work, whatever it is . . . when you do your best and you test yourself and you know you are right . . . I say even if nobody believe you, must have courage in yourself.

"Believe you can do, despite what other may say. That is my message. Believe you can do."

We shake hands warmly.

~ ~ ~ ~ ~

Now, on the plane going home, I regret not having asked for a reprint of his paper, the discovery of the virus. I will do so from "the States."

I am jammed into my seat with recorder and computer on my tray. On this single occasion, I will ask for milk with the meal. I will raise high my cup, 33,000 feet above sea level. The clear plastic vial will be filled like a beaker from the lab. Maybe the pasteurized liquid will glow.

"*A Monsier le docteur Chermann et tous ses associés. A vôtre santé, monsieur. Félicitations.*" I raise my cup of milk.

Chapter 25:
Dr. Robert Gallo

He is an important and influential medical scientist as Director of the Laboratory of Tumor Cell Biology at the National Cancer Institute. NCI is a part of our National Institute of Health, and Dr. Gallo is one of the NIH scientists actively involved with the study of AIDS and what to do about it.

I found my talk with him valuable for the perspective it gave me on what it took to find and then begin to conquer the AIDS retrovirus, and also for a better appreciation of Dr. Gallo himself.

(DECEMBER, 1985)   I'd read angry, if relentless, reports in the *New York Native*   implying that Dr. Gallo was more concerned with getting credit vis-a-vis the French than with building on their discoveries and solving the problem of AIDS more quickly.   An August issue of*TIME*   had mentioned the "smoldering rivalry" between the French and American research teams.   Only weeks before, I'd had a delightful and charming interview with Jean-Claude Chermann.   I've always felt a special support for the underdog, and it was easy for me to relate to Pasteur in precisely that way.

So I was prepared to dislike Bob Gallo.   Some of the doctors and scientists I'd had contact with did perceive (admittedly sometimes from afar) that he'd seemed ungracious to the French achievement.   Some had an impression of the man as arrogant, abrasive, overly sure of himself.

Others, however, were very clear: Dr. Gallo has made absolutely brilliant contributions to his field, and there is an excellent and compelling reason he's received so many awards: he deserves them.   Dr. Bob Sandhaus, a friend and a reader of these interviews via his computer, had spoken with gratitude of Dr. Gallo's generosity to him as a young researcher.

Bob Gallo is a controversial and multi-faceted man, that much was clear.   What would *my* experience of him be like?   In our first phone conversation, he did seem full of himself.

"You do not have to go to Paris, my friend. I am the father of the human retrovirus." This man needs a press agent, I thought. He told me about the award that was bringing him to New York -- prestige and a financial consideration. I could understand why he might not have time to see me, could I not?

Nonetheless, the interview was scheduled. I phoned from the lobby of his hotel that morning. "How much time do you want?" he asked. "That's too much. I can only give you a half-hour. No, don't come up here. I'll come to the lobby. There are couches near the cashier."

Actually, we were together for several hours.

~ ~ ~ ~ ~

He is a large man and he has a staunch, bullish manner. I can see how the combination might be intimidating but, in fact, he's not insufferable as I expected. He tells me about his childhood. He read inspirational books about the lives of doctors and scientists, and those stories genuinely influenced him. As we talk, he becomes increasingly personal. He tells me he's always worked hard, maybe harder than others, because he's always felt a private doubt about his own worthiness. I know that he's done some extremely important work on leukemia; soon he tells me that his sister died of the disease when he was a teenager.

During this discussion, I feel no emotional "hook" or connection with him. He's not gracious or vulnerable or inspiring or warm like various other scientists I'm now encountering. None of it: he's an armored tank. But you're not here to become his nephew, I remind myself. You don't need a "warm and fuzzy" connection to simply be fair. Get him to talk about Chermann and the discovery of the virus.

"In a way," he says, "that is a story a hundred other people could tell you about. It doesn't need me. It seems awkward for me to tell you, but here it is: We were alone. Period. We developed the techniques to find these viruses. Period. The Pasteur Group you spoke with were not involved in all those years."

We're off to a definite start!

"In 1975, we discovered what you've just heard a lot about in the news. Interleukin-2. IL-2. Under Steve Rosenberg, Cancer. If you read *NEWSWEEK*, we have honorable mention in discovering it. We gave it to Steve to use in the way that he's using it. He pioneered that use of it, no question about it. Why I mention it now is, that was *essential* to growing T-cells, to isolating every human retrovirus, HTLV-I, HTLV-II, and HTLV-III, the virus that causes AIDS. What the French call 'LAV.'

"So the technology, the field of human retrovirology, was opened by us. The discovery of how to grow human T-cells was by us. How you detect these viruses, by us. The discovery of the first human retrovirus, HTLV-1, by us, in 1979. The link to a cause of a human cancer, by us. And also, subsequently, by the Japanese. The discovery of the second category of human retrovirus, which is probably causing another kind of human leukemia, by us, in 1981. This is called HTLV-II. And now we come to AIDS, right?"

He has cited a string of accomplishments with hardly a breath. Of course he is self-assured, I am thinking. That's quite a list for anyone to be proud of.

"You could say, `what does all this have to do with AIDS?' Well, AIDS is caused by a retrovirus, a human retrovirus that chiefly goes into the T-cell, the same cell which the leukemia-causing retrovirus, HTLV-I and HTLV-II also invade. In 1982, I formally proposed that AIDS was caused by a retrovirus. By their own admission, in a lecture in Italy in September of 1984, Chermann said they got the idea from us. He had not been working on any human retrovirus. They initiated his work in January, 1983.

"Chermann . . . I think he's a decent guy, a decent scientist. But his position in the field of human retrovirology was here." He gestures about one foot above the couch. "Mine was here." About three and a half feet. "Apples and oranges, that's what you have to understand.

"In '82, no one except Max Essex at Harvard, me, and our co-workers believed a retrovirus was causing AIDS when I proposed it. No one believed in its likelihood. There wasn't a nickel funded for retrovirology in the world in 1982, except in my lab and Max Essex's, all alone in America. Pasteur got involved in January '83.

"I certainly believed -- and Montagnier sometimes turns this against me -- that the virus would be closer to HTLV-I, our first retrovirus, than turned out to be the case. So okay, we were only ninety-five percent right. But no one else had an idea that was even close to believing that a retrovirus was really the cause of AIDS."

Who gets the credit, I think. It's like the game of CLUE I used to play in my childhood. Who committed the murder. In what room of the mansion? And with what weapon. You have to be right on all THREE questions. A partial answer isn't enough. "Colonel Mustard did it, in the Ballroom, with the Lead Pipe!"

The issues of scientific credit aren't played on such a tidy gameboard. But Dr. Robert Gallo did correctly call the murder weapon: "A Retrovirus." He had already linked a retrovirus to the cause of leukemia. The leukemia retrovirus also infects the T-4 cell -- similar to the process of AIDS infection -- and that parallel was one of the clues that led him to suggest a retrovirus as the AIDS cause.

"Here's another reason," he says. "Guess how leukemic retroviruses are transmitted. Blood and sex, also just like AIDS. And by congenital infection, again just like AIDS. Guess where they come from. Africa. They can impair the immune system as well as cause cancer.

"Put yourself in my place, Mike. Knowing all that information, and having Max Essex of Harvard telling you that the cat leukemia virus, a retrovirus that causes leukemia, can actually cause AIDS in a cat if you simply make a minor change in it -- you can see why, to us, there was a good and logical chance of our being accurate about the cause of human AIDS. But the scientific world wasn't thinking that way. The world at large wasn't thinking that way. America wasn't thinking that way. We did!

"What I'm trying to tell you is, and I've got more to tell you, in a discovery, IDEA should count for something. Not for everything. Not for ninety percent. But shouldn't we give it five percent, anyway?"

I nod. Shouldn't I be willing to give him that amount of credit for pointing the way to a retrovirus? It's almost ten o'clock in the morning here. Four o'clock in the afternoon in Paris. I think of Jean-Claude Chermann and cajole him mentally . . . "*Allons-nous. Donnons cinq pour cent au docteur Gallo.*"

"It's called a 'hypothesis,'" Gallo tells me with a hint of condescension. "It's a HUNDRED percent from us for the hypothesis.

"Secondly, the technique to isolate these viruses is identical to the technique for isolating HTLV-I and HTLV-II. What the Pasteur group used is what we use for HTLV-III."

"All right," I say cautiously.

"Does that count for anything?"

"Yesssss." I am feeling wary about how I'm spending these percentages of credit. "You mean how to find it?"

"To initiate growth of the patient's T-cells, one needs a growth factor called T-cell growth factor or IL-2 as it is now often termed. You can't grow the T-cells without the growth factor. Doesn't that count for anything?"

Hmm. You're going to have to be able to grow cells to do anything about them. So surely, yes, that was a valuable help. Here was a growth technique "From the labs of Robert Gallo." I suppose that surely deserves some credit. "Yes, okay."

"You can't write all this in a newspaper in only a paragraph or one column, can you? It's more complicated than that."

"You're saying, things build on each other in science."

"Obviously! If a guy on stage says, 'I predict this!' and you're in the audience, you might say to yourself, `well, he's predicting that direction openly. He's not saying I can't work on it, too. Thanks for the idea, buddy!'    Secondly, if he says to you from the stage, `hey, and I've got the tools you need to do it, too -- at least what you need to start off with. You don't have to use any tools different that what I've already provided you. They're right here on the table . . . .'"

"`Okay, great!'" I say as his competitor in the imaginary audience might say. "`Gimme those tools.'"

"Well Pasteur also got the growth factor from me," he says. "You know what Montagnier says?" Here he gives me a perfect imitation of a deep-voiced Frenchman speaking English: "`Well, yes we got the growth factor from Dr. Gal-LO, but we only used it for practice!   When the real experiments came, we got it from a French compa-NEE.'

"It doesn't matter, but we did supply him with the growth factor, the same growth factor we referred to earlier called T-cell growth factor, IL-2. The same technique for HTLV-I and HTLV-II. That counts a little, right?   Now I digress for one second. To give you an example of good will -- this doesn't count for anything but it at least tells you the atmosphere."

He tells me that Dr. Barre-Sinousi, who worked on the AIDS team with Chermann, was in Dr. Gallo's lab for six weeks in 1982, "learning lymphocyte culture.   Doesn't count for anything, but nice to know." One of Montagnier's technicians studied in Gallo's lab for a year. "I don't have anybody training over there. It DOESN'T count, okay, but it would be nice if they'd occasionally mention it.   One can get a little P.O.'d about these things that never come up.

"Now we get to the next step. It doesn't count either, because we didn't publish these results until later, but you should know about it. We had this virus *before* they began ever working in the field. I can prove we had the virus in our lab in December of 1982. "

If he could really *prove* his lab had the virus, I think, even if he didn't publish the results, it could be a very relevant point in a patent struggle or a courtroom. "When I was at Pasteur Institute," I tell him, "they mentioned they should get a patent on a blood test, because in fact they were first.   Their application was legitimately submitted before yours."

"They didn't have a blood test."

"But I understand they're doing litigation, because they think they should get some patent money."

"They're not doing litigation.   They're THINKING of doing litigation. And if they do litigation, they're going to fall in the sewer."

"Oh," I say, depicting the analogy in my mind.

"I promise," he says.

"Okay," I say.

"I promise. I hope the issue goes away. They don't really want to do that. They want the money to be shared."

"You think a compromise is possible?"

"That's what they'd like. They want to say, `look, you made great contributions, we did too. Recognize our contribution.'

"I say, `look, I recognize it. It's all over the place!' I don't know how they can get more recognition from me or by anybody else. What more do they want from me? Unbelieveable! These guys make an observation and then the talk of their credit for it goes on and on and on."

His voice drones like a stuck record. I can't help laughing at his gusto as he portrays himself being hounded by Pasteur for recognition.

"What I'm trying to tell you is, we helped Chermann get into the field of human retrovirology freely."

"Got it," I say.

"So: idea, us. Technology, us. Now the next step in the history. When they found something, how would they know it was really a new retrovirus? How would they know it wasn't HTLV-I or HTLV-II? Those are retroviruses too. They have to have reagents. Take a moment and look at their original paper. Take a look at the acknowledgements. The acknowledgement is to me, for providing them reagents to help them.

"They also often talk about nomenclature," he says.

"Yes. I got the impression that, naming the AIDS virus 'HTLV-III' made it seem too much like part of your family of retroviruses."

"Go back and read their paper. They called it an 'HTLV' themselves. We'd all agreed that 'L' was to stand for 'Lymphotrophic' not 'Leukemia' in the future. This was the third category of human T-Lymphotropic retrovirus. Their paper was a case report of *one patient* with a lymph node enlargement. Most importantly, when they published that paper, they couldn't yet permanently produce the virus in a cell line. They couldn't grow it yet. And they couldn't prove it causes AIDS.

"When they submitted their paper to *SCIENCE* , I was a reviewer. Several other scientists had felt negative about the paper. To get it accepted by the journal, I got two other people in my lab to sign a letter on its behalf. I phoned *SCIENCE* , myself, recommending that it be published.

"We had preliminary data in our own lab. I didn't feel confident enough in it to publish, so I have to give the Pasteur group in Paris full credit for the having the balls, for having the guts . . . they published the first paper of the right virus at a time when they didn't know for sure it really *was* the right virus. Unequivocally, though, I give them that credit. In Heckler's first press conference, I said -- we didn't know it for sure then, but I said that the virus my lab had just *proved* causes AIDS, the virus we'd developed the first blood test for, could *also* be the virus the Pasteur Institute had reported on last year.

"They didn't have credibility in 1983 for knowing the origin of AIDS. Let's not have such short memories. The world didn't know the cause of AIDS in 1983. Anybody who tells you they did, go back and read the newspapers. You show me where their paper received any notoriety. You show me one scientist who believed that these results showed the cause of AIDS. That paper when it came out was attacked by people on our committee of twenty -- that's the NIH committe devoted to finding the cause for AIDS. They are people you should talk to some day. They said to me, `why didn't you apply the same standards to the Pasteur group as you apply to yourself?' I said, `because they deserve to get into the field. Because the field needs more stimulation. We need more people involved, and because they have little to lose."

"Chermann told me he published the paper," I say, "and then encountered a lot of derision from scientists who didn't believe he'd found the cause of AIDS."

"Stop it, just stop it. Chermann never thought he had the cause of AIDS in '83. He had no data on the cause of AIDS. It requires *proving*. You can't just pop out a picture of a virus and say, `that's the cause of AIDS.'"

"No," I have to agree, "but he had a hunch of it, a belief. They were trying in their lab to prove it true themselves, and meanwhile no one believed them."

"This is, I think, enormously self-serving. It is not a matter of 'belief.' This isn't a religion you know. It's a matter of DEMONSTRATING to your colleagues what the cause of AIDS is. I thought a retrovirus was the cause of AIDS before Chermann ever got into human retrovirology. Okay? The one he found, well, you greet that first report with justifiable skepticism when the person provides you only with a single case report on a virus he can't yet characterize. Or a virus he can't yet even grow. A virus he can't yet link to the cause of AIDS.

"So what are you talking about, 'believe?' Believe on the basis of what? That he has brown hair? You can tell me you believe zinc causes multiple sclerosis, and you may be right, but I don't believe you. You've got to *demonstrate* it. That's what life is about. You may believe you're going to write a good book. Demonstrate it to me. Please!

"The point is, they didn't demonstrate a cause of anything. They identified a virus that *we* later proved was the cause of AIDS. The overwhelming data that anybody ever had for the cause of AIDS is the next step in the story. You must understand that science works by peer review in the literature. Go to the publications, not the bullshit. Not `I said so-and-so at some meeting.' I've got a lot of things I said at meetings! I'm not going to publish a picture of a virus that's new and say, `hey, I got a picture of it, once or twice. That's AIDS.'

It is noisy here in the hotel lobby, but I'm as privately engrossed in his words and my thoughts as if we were meeting in private. I know the crime was done with the Lead Pipe, but was it Colonel Mustard or Miss Scarlet? The Conservatory or the Library? A partial answer is not good enough. Dr. Gallo is forcing me to appreciate rigorous scientific standards.

I had left Paris convinced that the French had found the AIDS virus first. And, in fact, they had. Or at least they officially reported it first. But they had built their work on Gallo's and they were not yet able to PROVE their virus caused AIDS. The final paragraph of their paper states, "The role of this virus in the etiology of AIDS remains to be determined." Its summary says the virus "may" be involved in AIDS. "May."

Dr. Gallo is now describing the problem that next faced researchers. The AIDS T-cells were dying before they properly could be characterized. You cannot do further research unless cells survive long enough to permit you to work with them. While Gallo talks, I think the anguished frustration of families, friends, and lovers during all these efforts. I think about the editor of the *New York Native* , who for so long found himself covering and championing a nationally invisible topic. And, of course, I think about people with AIDS. Them, most of all.

But meanwhile, there is a "system," an established system. There is discipline. Committees, review boards, standards. And there are real human beings craving personal credit for their own devoted work. There was also a practical and specific need for a "reagent" -- to help cells live in order to research them.

"The first mass production of the virus -- that is, a permanent cell line infected with and producing the virus without being killed -- was developed by my co workers and myself. This in turn led us to the develop the first reagents made against this virus. And the first monoclonal antibodies. And the first nucleic acid molecular probes. And the first hyper-immune sera. *All by us, Mike!* That's a simple fact. We were not in any way holding back on the progress to fight the disease.

"I was with Chermann in February of '84 when he told me that you can't make antibody to this virus, it doesn't happen. `It doesn't happen,' he says, while I'm sitting there since November of '83 and we're mass producing the virus that we knew was the cause of the disease. I strongly suspected it could also be what they had found. That is the one thing they could rightly claim: it is true, and I admit it. I didn't play as generous as I could have. True.

"In retrospect, if I had to do it over again, would I have given them more acknowledgement in our earliest papers on HTLV-III prior to publishing? Would I have worked to show that what we proved caused AIDS was also the same virus they had described in their 1983 case report? Maybe so. But I felt like, I've got a lab of hungry people too. I'm proving this thing causes AIDS. We've solved the mass production. I'm not gonna mass produce theirs for them, too, and prove it's the same virus. Let them do it!

"That was my attitude. In retrospect, yes, we could have done it for them. Then all this would never have been an issue. On the other hand, I guess a lot of people would then say to me, `If you're going to do all that for them, why don't you just go over and work for the Pasteur Institute?!'"

I hear my own sigh amidst the confusion in the lobby. If there were two companies -- cosmetics companies -- no one would expect cooperation between the two. NO, I will not send you my formula for lipstick that's fresh for a month. NO, you can't sell my hypnotic, aphrodisiac cologne. But these were not "companies." They are major centers of research against a deadly epidemic. Of course the way I would like it is if *anything* that could help anybody's health were shared for the greater worldwide good.

But who am I kidding? I know about organizations, and funding, and politics, and marketing, and human vanity. It would be comfortable and easy for me to simply fault Dr. Gallo without thinking. I came to this noisy couch quite prejudiced against him. There are people in the gay community who attack him, there are members of the scientific community who envy him or snipe at him. But he is also, I can see it now in truth, deservedly praised for his outstanding accomplishments. And perhaps he is too automatically seen as the Goliath against a Pasteur David.

Things are not as clearcut as I had thought and the abrasive, brilliant man on the couch beside me has personally contributed much toward solutions that will save the lives of PWA's. You do not have to be "nice" to help humanity. No, he has not acted purely with altruism. But, as I've been hearing from others, he's been generous, too. "Whenever I've been asked for anything -- from cell line virus, whatever, help from others centers -- I've given it.

"What we published in the spring of '84 was this," he continues. "I got up and said, `We know the cause of AIDS with certainty.' No one on earth had done that before. Number two, I said, `we have a blood test that will protect our blood banks.' No one had said or done that before. Number three, I didn't refer to just one isolate . . . but to forty-eight isolations! You don't get them in one day. That takes time. We had -

systematically ... results that went back long before our spring of '84 publication date. Data going *back* is what I'm trying to tell you. Number four, we published antibody data in human serum that unequivocally linked the virus to the disease. We characterized the viral proteins. We made antibodies to the viral proteins. We had developed a blood test.

"The Pasteur group says they put in a patent application for a blood test months before you," I remind him.

"Absolutely," he says. The tank advances. "You will find that I won't lie, and I give them more than their credit due. But if you're an inquisitive reporter, Mike, why isn't their patent approved in Europe already? Why isn't it approved anywhere? I think they actually want to join in with ours, because there are serious scientific flaws in theirs.

"Here's what they patented: a case report. They state the virus cannot be grown in the cell line in the patent. I don't think you have to be a specialist, Mike. You can't have a blood test for the world if you can't mass produce the virus to test against. It's ludicrous. We have succeeded in putting in immortalized tissue culture cell lines that mass produce the virus without themselves being harmed."

"You know, the test that they published detected only 20% of AIDS blood sera that was infected. That's because they couldn't mass produce the virus in order to produce a sufficient amount of viral protein for reagents -- so how can that patent get approved?"

"If I understand you correctly," I say, "you're implying that if you choose to allow Pasteur to have a co-patent with you, it's only because you choose to and not because you have to, given their product's drawbacks."

"Of course. I believe so. But they've played such hard politics, we don't want to look like we're just caving in to pressure. Although at least it would end this controversy overnight."

He feels angry and degraded at the charges against him, he says. He is not a homophobe. He is not a Reagan stooge. He was advised by friends in the first place not to get involved with AIDS research, that it'd be a volatile media issue. He was already, his friends had said, the father of human retrovirology -- let others take his past contributions further. It has certainly been a struggle. Nonetheless, he hints, I may actually see surprising solutions to the controversy between his group and Pasteur, maybe even before this book is published.

That's fine, I say. This book is intended to be about the people involved in confronting the issues, not the day-to-day shifts of fact.

We talk about a vaccine. He expects and he hopes that his lab and others will be able to predict during 1986 when a vaccine should be ready. The AIDS virus mutates into many forms, but he is working with sub-units that each mutation has in common. He assures me that we will also soon be seeing major steps forward in the treatment of people with AIDS.

What would he like to say to the public? He's at an exasperated loss. "I have no great words of wisdom. 'Don't believe everything you hear,' I guess.

"I'll tell you what a lot of scientists say to me. This is perhaps the only pleasure at all I've gotten out of AIDS: never in the history of biomedicine has science moved so rapidly. I believe that my co-workers and I can look in the mirror and say, 'how did that happen?' and we can feel good about the answer. You see, it happened from a lot of contributions that came from a lot of places. But , really, people who know the field well would say that, as much as from anyone else, it happened because of our lab. And that makes me feel good."

The interview is finished. I ask him how it feels to have such a controversial reputation. It hurts, he says. "I am, in fact, sensitive, believe it or not." I wonder whether to give him feedback on how abrasive he was when we spoke to him on the phone. I decide to tell him, and he apologizes. He shows me a thick sheaf of messages from his jacket pocket. "Understand this," he says. "The pressure I'm under is genuine and awful. I do the best I can."

I thank him for his time and I most sincerely wish him well in his research.

Chapter 26:
Married Bisexuals — Part 1

When I interviewed"Wade" the L.A. Hustler, I began to realize the potentially huge significance of a mostly invisible breed: the "bisexual" male (especially) who could receive the AIDS virus in sexual contact with another male, and then pass it on into his heterosexual household. One reads about women who've received the virus from bisexual lovers, but there has generally not been so much reported about bisexual men themselves. Their significance, I believe, far outweighs their coverage in the media.

I think there are various reasons why this coverage has been sparse. The most practical is this: married men who covertly engage in homosexual practices lead the most closeted of lifestyles. It is hard enough for a husband to admit he sees a female prostitute, or has an illicit heterosexual liaison. It is much, much harder to admit his liaison has been with a man.

After considerable "networking" to obtain these various interviews, I'm convinced that married bisexuals are more prevalent in our society than most of us realize. My contact with these men -- including those who flatly REFUSED to be interviewed, even anonymously -- has made me wonder about the men who would NOT be married today if they hadn't originally felt obliged to be. What kinds of inner tensions do they live with every day, conscious and unconscious? What are the consequences of a life lived in secret? What kind of conduit might these lifestyles provide to the AIDS virus?

The three men presented in this chapter has each handled his sexual preference in a different way.

"Manny" - His Wife Knows

I interview him in Manhattan, in the apartment of his South African lover. Manny is in his late forties, and lives with his wife and son on Staten Island.

As a boy, he went to parochial schools and decided at the age of twelve to become a Franciscan Brother. In 1953 he entered a Franciscan Juniorate, a boys' religious training high school. He entered Postulancy and then received the Habit of Saint Francis, becoming a Novitiate. In 1959 he took temporary vows. He understands, as he talks to me, that I have no real knowledge of these Catholic terms. ("But some of your readers will," he says. "It's proprietary talk.")

"All during this time," he says, "I recognized that I was gay. I was definitely, decidedly attracted to people of the same sex. That was very clear to me. I didn't feel comfortable about it, I just hoped it would go away. I always thought of these sorts of things as sinful. When I went into the Franciscan Brothers, I was very resolved to 'do right' and put aside these sexual thoughts. The temptations were always there. Whenever I saw someone I was attracted to, I would have that longing, that lust. But I'd then put it out of my mind."

He started teaching high school in 1959, while going to college. He taught virtually every grade from sixth grade through graduate school. The course he teaches at the present time is to professors at the City University. He speaks with the precise articulateness of a professor at a radio microphone. His whole life has been teaching, he says, and even though he's now been promoted to an administrative capacity, he maintains one course so he can still be teaching something.

"Back then," he says, "I was not allowed to have sex, and I was not even supposed to entertain thoughts of it in my mind. I was working hard, going to school, throwing myself into my work, and living in a community of Franciscan Brothers.

"When I was twenty-six years old, I had my first homosexual experience. It was with another Brother. We went to a party at a Friary that was neither his nor mine. We had something to drink, and were the last to leave. We went to my room, and I heard myself saying, `how about a game of strip poker before you go to bed?' He was a very goodlooking fellow, and we had sex that was, to me at the time, the hottest thing in the world. Next day, we both got up and went to Confession. We both traveled the train together to 31st Street and confessed our sin to a priest. That was the first and last time I ever had sex as a Franciscan Brother."

"What did the priest say, the one you confessed to?"

"He was quite taken aback. Both of us went in, one right after the other. He was kindly, and reminded us that we did profess to have vows of chastity. Not celibacy, but chastity, which is a little bit stronger than celibacy. We were not to commit any acts or even any thoughts of impurity."

The years went by, and once again Manny had no sexual

experiences.   "But something in my life was profoundly uneasy," he says.   "I began to see that thinking about things sexual was not something I had to be ashamed or afraid of, that sexuality was part of life to be embraced and even celebrated."

He requested permission to apply for his doctorate in English Linguistics -- that explains the precision of his language, I decide -- and it was finally granted.   He went off to graduate school in Indiana, which "gave me the opportunity to step back, to really look at how my life was. I went out there, mind you, without the slightest thought of leaving the community."

By 1970, as a result of what felt like natural evolution, he wrote his Superior General for a Letter of Dispensation from the vows.   The man was shocked, and thought Manny must be going through a severe depression. He flew to Indiana to hear for himself that Manny wanted to leave the Brothers.   "The sex part of it wasn't even in the picture then. It just felt like time to move on after eighteen years with the Brothers."

He returned to New York and the City University system.   He knew he had feelings about being gay and, with the help of a friend, began to explore places for sexual encounters -- bathhouses, bars, trucks on the edge of the West Side highway.

"I wouldn't say I was promiscuously sleazy" -- he pronounces the words so clearly that they do, in fact, sound, sleazy -- "but I would say I did my share of 'tricking,' maybe once every couple of months or so.

Ultimately I met a young man and we had a kind of fling for a few months, then someone else.   And at the same time, I was dating women.

"In my heart of hearts, I could not say to myself, 'I am homosexual.' Instead I advised myself something like, 'here I've spent all this time with the Franciscan Brothers. I really need a good healthy dose of heterosexuality. I'm sure that if I decide to get married, if I meet the right women, that all this will fall away, like a butterfly emerging from a cocoon.'"

"The forays you had with men were always sexual."

"Oh yes."

"When you were seeing women, were your experiences also sexual?"

"No, they were not.   There were a few times when things got very close to it, but it was never anything more than masturbation with a woman until I met Kathleen.   She and I didn't have sex before we were married, but we went together from March till December of 1973.

"That August, I went on a trip to the Orient, and an incident on the plane had a profound effect on my life.   I was in a plane in front of three, middle-aged gay men from the Village.   One was a butcher, another was an antique dealer.   I found their conversation appalling.   I found it shallow. It was nothing I could identify with. They would scream and screech and carry on and titter. I asked myself, is that what I want? Is this what it means to be homosexual? The only homosexuals I knew were those I'd related to at a purely physical level. It was on that trip that I decided: Kathleen was a wonderful person, a kind soul, and someone I could have sexual feelings for. I decided that when I got back home, I'd propose. And I did.

"When we were about to get married, that December, I went to Confession. The priest suggested I think it over, maybe I should get into counseling. I thought, no, I don't want to stay where I've been. But -- I don't think I was married more than four months, when I went back to the baths!

"I went through one depression after another, right after I was married. Only people who have themselves really gone through depressions can understand. I didn't know what was bringing it about. I just didn't want to see anyone or do anything. When the bell rang, I didn't want to face whoever it was at the door. I couldn't even answer the telephone. I'd just watch the quiz shows on television.

"Kathleen, of course, was upset. We'd had very intense sexual experiences for the first few months of our marriage, and then it all gradually dwindled. I continued, however, to have sex with her right up to the time I told her I was gay, which was four years ago.

"While I was married, I think I was always depressed -- for seven years. I'd spent the better part of my life denying who I was. You know, back as a Monk, even to have been suspected as a homosexual, I'd have been thrown out with no questions asked. So, in the marriage, I just gradually learned to suppress my feelings and live a secret, double life."

"What happened in 1981 that made you tell Kathleen about yourself?"

"1981 was a very important year. I had heard about a group that called itself the 'Forum.' It was a group of fathers who are homosexual. How could such a thing exist, this Fathers' Forum? I thought I was the only one in the world! Danny was born in 1978. That just made me feel even more alienated -- here I was with a son, and I had these feelings, and I was still going to the baths and pretending with Kathleen. We were having sex maybe once a month.

"With the men I was seeing, I was mainly having oral sex. The two times I did have anal sex in baths, I contracted gonorrhea. That was a tough one to explain.

"Eventually, though, I found this Fathers' Forum. I saw a newsletter on the bulletin board of a bathhouse and it had the president's phone number. I called him and we spoke for a half an hour. Just to be able to talk to someone else who understood was a profound help,

Michael.   I agreed to go to a meeting -- I made up some kind of excuse for Kathleen.

"There I was in a room with all these gay fathers, about forty of them.   They had refreshments and small discussion groups with sharing on various topics.   It was remarkable.   I remember a father from Long Island who was fearful that his son was gay.   He thought that was terrible. I asked him, `What's so bad?   We're gay ourselves, aren't we?'   But he just couldn't accept it in his son, and he never came back to the group.

"I began to look around the room and see people who seemed 'normal,' not like that hysterical trio on the plane and not like the 'tricks' from the baths.   I even saw someone I worked with at the college.   He came over and was cordial and said, 'yes, I'm gay too.'   I began to feel comfortable.   In the small group sharing I said, `please, let me talk.    I'm just burning to talk.    I don't know what's happening to my life, and I need help.'    I cried and sobbed.    They looked at me and said, `we know, we know how you feel.'   Nothing in my life compared to that night, to what I felt from the discovery of others like me.   I knew my life had changed.

"A few days later, Kathleen said -- Kathleen is very sensitive -- she said, `you know, you look like something's on your mind.'   So I told her.   Eventually I explained it all -- that I was actively gay, and I wanted to have a relationship with another man.   She understood.   I met someone at Identity House, a counseling service here.   We had a relationship for a year and a half.   That was my first homosexual relationship that I can say was really a relationship.   Prior to that, I was just one of those married men, secretly going to bathhouses."

"It was four years ago that you had your first serious relationship with another man?"

"Yes.   He was married himself, though he had no children.   It lasted a year and a half.   I've been in my current relationship about a year."

"What is your own sense of personal vulnerability to AIDS?   Or of Kathleen's vulnerability, through you?"

"Frankly, I'm not very worried.   I last had sex with Kathleen about four years ago.   In my relationships, I've had a variety of sexual experiences, including passive anal sex which I know is a high risk activity without a condom.   I know it's possible for me to be infected, of course, but the fact is, I'm very in tune with my own body and psyche. Honestly, I believe if I were sick inside, I'd be feeling it.   Even something microscopic traveling in my blood stream.   I think I'd have a sense of unease I really don't feel now.   I feel healthy."

"How does Kathleen relate to your lifestyle today?"

"Acceptant, but with difficulty.   She doesn't cheer me on, you know.   I've given her the opportunity to leave me; I'd understand if she did.   I've given her the opportunity to have a relationship with another man. She's thinking about it. I told her I would help her in any way I possibly could, but I don't think she's ready for it. It's not easy for her, but she has learned more about what it is to be a homosexual than I had in my whole life preceding, and I came out at the age of forty-two. She has made incredible progress that I wish I personally could have made long ago."

"You are now, as I understand it, sexually monogamous in your relationship with Henry?"

"Yes."

"I know you're now an active leader, Manny, in a variety of organizations, including several groups for gay married fathers. So you see a variety of married men who are gay or bisexual. What overall observations do you have from the men you see?"

"I became very active because I wanted to repay the organizations for the support I got when I needed it. The married men I've observed over these past few years are terrified of AIDS. In some cases, they would prefer to go back into the closet, to withdraw, to rethink the whole thing rather than to think about the possibility of contracting AIDS. Many of the women whose husbands are out to them are equally frightened that they might contract it, particularly if their husbands were in non-monogamous sexual relationships. Of course, I guess there are women whose husbands see female prostitutes and they must also be worried, too, if they know about it."

"What is your sense of how many men that you've encountered have told their wives about their personal sexual attractions?"

"Mostly, with the groups I deal with, I'd say two-thirds are out to their wives. But it's my very strong opinion that the overwhelming number of gay men in the United States are actually married men who simply don't do much about it, ever. Or men who act out their personal impulses only on rare occasions when they have the opportunity. Plenty of them go through life repressing their feelings, denying them. They can get migraines from that, or other symptoms. I practice hypnotherapy as a sideline, you know, and I truly see cases like that. Important feelings that are repressed and denied really can manifest themselves in other ways, even physical ways."

"You are positing," I say, "that there are a terrific number of people in heterosexual marriages who are currently functioning sexually with their wives, and who secretly -- if they could tell the truth about their primary sexual attractions -- would say, `well, it's really other men that most excite me.'

"Yes, I am. I absolutely am."

"So you're saying that a fair number of readers of your words, right now, may have a friend or a relative or a neighbor who definitely appears to have a settled relationship with his wife, and be very happy in his thoroughly heterosexual lifestyle . . . but who privately may experience stronger sexual attractions to other men?"

"I see it all the time. I know it's true. I just believe the vast majority of homosexuals are people you will never see on Christopher Street, and never see as part of any gay organization. They are hidden, and they intend to stay that way, whether it troubles them or not. In my private practice, I see married men who never do anything about their private desires beyond buying an illicit magazine and masturbating. They're simply afraid to go any further. Or they furtively go out to a gay porno movie. There are a lot of hidden people out there. It's the absolute truth.

"A good number of gay married men don't want to think about AIDS at all. And don't want to be confronting their own hidden gay impulses. I heard once from a married man with children who goes to the baths three or four times a month. He called me in a panic because he had back trouble, and he was afraid it was AIDS. I suggested that he might not have to be so frightened if his symptom was a back ache, and that he should consider joining one of the groups for gay married fathers for information and support. He went crazy when I said that.

"`Gay?' he said. `I'm not gay!'

"`I'm sorry,' I said. `I thought you went to the gay baths three or four times a month.'

"`I do,' he said, `but I'm not gay. I only go to the baths because I'm oversexed. If I were to have a relationship with a prostitute, it would pose a threat to my marriage.'"

"What would you personally most wish to communicate to the public?"

"I think a lot of people may end up reading what you write about this topic, Mike. And among those people will be some married men with their own secret attraction to other men. They have to know, I'd want to tell them, that . . . we are not alone. There are vast numbers of us. We often experience conflicts and ambiguities. They just have to know that there are others around who've gone through the feelings they're going through now. There are other people available who can be a source of solace and support if ever they take the initial step to reach out for it. That has to be known."

Lester - An Unhappy Marriage, His Wife Does Not Know

He's a psychologist for the New York City school system and a private clinic. For the first time he recently attended the Fathers' Forum in Manhattan. He is forty years old and has lived in the New York area all his life. He has a master's degree in psychology, and another master's

291

degree in special education. He is pursuing a doctorate to advance his career.

"I went through most of my adolescence, right up through college, never seriously thinking of sexuality. Whether it was naivete or my own inhibitions, I don't know. I figured, whatever those feelings are -- that attraction I felt for men -- it would ultimately go away. I never wanted to believe I had that kind of interest. I never wanted to attach a label to it.

"In my mid-twenties, after a lot of suppression, I discovered 'cruising' places. I didn't have any gay friends, and I was lonely and withdrawn. I'm sure a lot of my social problems were sexually related. I found the 'Heights,' a long walkway on the edge of Brooklyn Heights. It was about nine or ten at night. After each experience, I was disgusted with myself. Those experiences began before I met my wife.

"She was my grandmother's student nurse. She's thirty-six and she's truly just beautiful. She was totally unintimidating as a woman. She offered all the nurturance I needed and she was totally unthreatening. With her, I was able to have heterosexual sex. I felt safe. I was almost like a child, thrilled with the fact that I could really be attracted to a female. We got married twelve years ago.

"The first three years were wonderful. Then, progressively, things got worse. I had my sexual conflicts and professional frustrations. She started to grow and had her own frustrations to worry about. She got stronger and more independent, and she became less nurturing of me. She was less and less that Super-Nurturing Woman I'd been dependent on. She had an abortion, fourteen months after our first girl was born. I know she really wanted to have the child, but I'd already begun feel the sexual pressure again. I just couldn't see it, a second child. I'm sure that abortion had psychological repercussions for her.

"I wasn't actually sure about getting married in the first place. I was worried, because I knew I had internal sexual conflicts. But I thought somehow, she'd balance things for me, make everything better. I thought I could just repress enough. I thought the hidden, sexual part of me could do without. But it wasn't true. I found myself getting volatile and moody, I got impatient.

"Even in the first three years, when we had a good sex life, there were times I could feel an inkling. I'd procrastinate going to bed till she was asleep. Sometimes I'd sneak out, late at night, and go look for sex."

"How long was it, after you were married," I ask him, "before you had your first homosexual experience again?"

"One week."

"The first week?!"

"She was a student nurse. She worked a late shift. It was convenient, I could go cruising before picking up her up. I was cheating from the very beginning. It didn't interfere then with our sex life, hers and mine. But by the third year, I was already finding reasons to have less and less sex with her. We'd see each other less and I was cheating more than ever. I would sometimes be silent in the car when I picked her up. I just couldn't bring myself to talk about things. It was clear we were both unhappy.

"Lester, that was many years ago. You've been staying together all this time?"

"I've gone through so many years of hating myself," he replies. "Blaming myself for everything. I went into the marriage thinking, I'm betraying her, I'm deceiving her. And -- she grew in her own way and was no longer the 'goodie-goodie' nurturing person I wanted her to be forever. She started to be a person with her own needs, so we had conflicts quite aside from sexuality. Two people growing, but not growing in the same way. She became more in touch with the fact that she had needs too.

"I had four years of psychoanalysis, and now I'm completing two years with someone else. I've been learning a lot about myself. My sister -- she doesn't know anything about my gayness either -- she can't understand why I stay in the marriage. She's right, of course. It's been a long enduring pattern. I'd say this pattern I've described to you, going to Brooklyn Heights and cruising the promenade, and staying in a marriage that's unhappy -- it's all continued, you see, year after year after year.

"Finally, four years ago, I actually met someone I began to see on a regular basis. I began to see him once a week. He was married too, but we'd have a night out with each other regularly. The one thing I wouldn't permit with him -- I just couldn't get into anal intercourse, even though he tried and tried. He was very persistent. It happened once. One other person tried it, too, but that was also pretty unsuccessful. With AIDS now, it's been on my mind more and more. What kind of sexual experiences had he had, with people aside from me? Did he have the virus? Is it inside me? Meanwhile, I've started going to bars, but mostly socially."

"How long have you been going to bars?"

"Three weeks." He laughs at the brief timespan. "You're talking to an adolescent now, Mike. A forty-year-old adolescent."

"When is the last time you had sex with your wife?"

"Over four years ago. A few weeks ago, I saw a Gay Hotline ad in the Village Voice. That's how I found the fathers' group.

"What's going to happen to me now? I don't know. You understand, I'm telling you not just what my wife doesn't know, or my sister . . . but what my neighbors don't know, the people at work don't know. Nobody. Nobody knows anything. Only now am I beginning to meet other gay men who can be friends and who I can share with. It's all new to me."

"Lester, you're in a really bad relationship now with your wife, right?"

"I hate admitting it, still, but yes."

"What does your wife think about you?"

"I don't know."

"You've never talked with her about your feelings for men?"

"No. Never. I think she'd be overwhelmed. She's not a prejudiced person, she doesn't label people. She's not bigoted. But I think it'd be a personal letdown."

"What do you imagine is the way out for both of you?"

"I guess it's a matter of my growing emotionally. I could be losing a wonderful woman, a wonderful family situation. I don't know what's right, but I tend to think a separation would be best."

"Honestly, Lester, it's hard for me to understand your saying you could be losing 'a wonderful situation' when you're both so unhappy."

"I know, I know. I guess I wish it were still like the past. I'm in pain, and I know I have to do something. But you want to hold on to those institutions, whatever it is. Those things that everyone expects you to do. To be 'normal.' Right now, actually, I feel more normal about myself than I ever have. I'm meeting a lot of 'normal' people now, even though they're gay, and I'm liking myself better than ever.

"The only thing is, the AIDS virus. I know it's not like something that incubates for only a few days or weeks like chicken pox. It takes a lot longer, and that worries me. Right now, though, the sexual part of life is less important to me than the comfort of just being with other gay people, just socializing with people like me. I know now that I like relationships. Maybe someday I can have one with a man. I'm not twenty anymore, so I can't wait forever."

"What would you like readers to know, Lester?"

"I know I've lived an emotionally dependent life. I've been dependent on others, first my parents, then my wife. Now I'm trying to go from my wife to me, myself. I'm going to try to live more honestly. I'm a good father. I'm a good son. I'd like to become my real, true self as much as I can.

"I'd like people to know that not being able to be yourself . . . it really takes a lot out of you. It really hurts."

Walter - Happily Married. Wife Doesn't Know

The only place I could conveniently see him was in Las Vegas, at "Comdex," the largest personal computer show of the year.

"Call whenever you arrive," he said. "I'll take a nap. You've got to catch me before the madness starts, or we just can't talk at all." My plane was hours late, and it was after two in the morning before he knocked at my door.

He has just turned thirty-six. His sales career began in electronics retailing. When home computers first began to flourish, he found the opportunity irresistible. He's now been married thirteen years, having met his wife on a blind date a mutual classmate arranged. He was twenty-two when they met.

"By that age, had you had previous sexual experience?"

"Yes. With a male cousin who lived in the house with me. I was thirteen, I guess, when it first happened. I started to date girls heavily when I was fifteen. The only sexual experience I had was heavy petting. When I look back, I wonder if I was supposed to try more things. Would I have been classified as 'abnormal' for not trying actual intercourse? I did get aroused though. Meanwhile, I was also still having experiences with my cousin. Today, you know, he's married and has two kids. We never talk about those experiences we shared.

"Oh! There were, come to think of it, actually several other male cousins at various times I fooled around with as a teenager. It would just happen in the right circumstances. Each of them now is married, and I've never discussed those experiences with any of them. Who knows what's going on in their lives, I have no idea.

"So I graduated high school and got a sales job. I was living with my family, paying them fifteen dollars a week and setting money aside. I was very business-oriented and that was financially practical for a while.

"I used to buy the*Village Voice* and respond to the 'Roommates Wanted' ads. I'd have telephone conversations, pretending I was interested in rooming with people. The phone calls excited me, but I never did go meet them in person. Physically, I had no sexual relations with men or women until right before I got married, at the age of twenty-three. Finally I did meet one man I saw sexually for a year and a half. Eventually he found a full-time lover. I got married during that time.

"You've been married thirteen years. Does it happen to you, today, that you see a man on the street, in a sales meeting, in a business lunch, at 'Comdex' -- and feel physically attracted to him?"

"Yes. Certainly yes. There are men that I see in my regular business day that I would love to go to bed with. Just as you hear guys joking about women they see during the day."

"And what about you and women? Do you also feel attractions to them?"

"I have never been to bed with another woman than my wife. If I let myself, yes I could. I have not let that happen. I mean, I use the excuse, 'I go to bed with other men because I can't get that experience in my marriage.' If I let myself go to bed with other women, then that's cheating. That's my rationalization."

"Now, Walter. You call it a 'rationalization.' What that implies is, you don't accept it or believe it yourself."

He clears his throat. "Probably true." He laughs softly.

"So. Let's get below that, already. What is the real truth?"

"Um, the real truth is, I'm a warm loving person needs to be loved. And I find that I get it from a man, more than I've experienced from a woman. If I let myself experience other women, I might find -- I don't know. But I know I like a manly man. I'm attracted to that. I'm not at all attracted to feminine type men. But I am more attracted to men than women.

"How is your sexual experience with your wife?"

"I remember my first night on my honeymoon, I was terrified. Would I or would I not be able to perform? Turns out, I had no problem. As time went on, there were times I had problems, but only because I worried about it. I was more concerned with how I was performing than just letting myself perform. We were having sex once a week, I guess.

"Over more time, however, our sex became better because I became less inhibited. I said, `this feels good. So I'm going to stop worrying about it.' Neither my wife nor I had previously had penetration with the opposite sex. In that sense, we were both virgins when we married each other. Our sex now is better than ever. I travel a lot, of course, and we hardly ever have sex during the week. It's infrequent, like once every two or three weeks. But when we do have it, it's really good and could sometimes even be several times that day. Either of us might initiate it. I have no problem getting aroused. It mostly happens when the kids are not around now. I have three kids.

"So you have a mutually comfortable sex life, you and your wife?"

"Yes, we do. Anne says to me that she's glad we're comfortable and compatible with each other. She's pleased with the frequency with which we have sex. She doesn't feel the need for more. It's genuinely comfortable and happy for both of us, just as things are."

"And meanwhile? What about you and men?"

"Well meanwhile, I've gotten aggressively more active. I am still aroused by men. Part of it, I guess, is the challenge. Since I've gotten married, I've met some guys I've become quite close with. Married ones. There's a park area in Queens I've sometimes gone too. School teachers, all kinds of people. I met a married man there, two kids. We're now genuinely close friends. We talk all the time.

"I also placed an ad of my own, again in the Village Voice. You know what? One ad, it was something like `MARRIED MAN, BISEXUAL, SEEKS SAME', that one ad got me 146 responses! I sat there with stacks of mail, sorting them, grouping them. I made, in effect, a kind of computer database out of them. I met a lot of men that way. Doctors. All kinds of people. Ultimately I even met a Rabbi, through someone else.

"Mostly, what I'd like though is someone steady. Not everyone wants that, but I like to express tenderness and affection in my sexuality. I'd like someone I could see on a regular basis. I had that for a while with a married doctor. But I guess I got too intense for him, though we're still friends. At any rate, I have such a different awareness of the world now, meeting all these other people who are married but also like men."

"Of course," I say, "you've had a totally self-selecting population. People who were reading the Voice, people who were looking in the 'Personals,' people who were willing to respond to your ad."

"Sure!" he replies. "I'm not saying that everyone out there's bisexual. Of course not. But I think many people have a lot more potential than they realize. Of course, right next to my 'MARRIED BISEXUAL' ad are all kinds of ads that are purely heterosexual. There are plenty of men, I meet them all the time in my business, who are married and I would guess have only heterosexual sex on the side. There are men who are only heterosexual and only with their wives, plenty of men, I know that.

"But I now know so much more about the population as a whole. Of course, I've swapped perspecives with the various married men I've myself encountered sexually. There are all kinds of us. I'm sure there are all kinds of women, too, I just don't get to hear those stories so much in my circumstances."

"What about AIDS?" I ask. "Do you worry about that?"

"Yes, I do. I haven't been so actively involved with anal sex, but I have. I am now pretty much following the 'safe sex' guidelines. Sometimes I think they make them overly strict to avoid lawsuits. I don't exchange body fluids like I used to, though I do when I kiss. That doesn't seem to be so much of a risk, from what I can tell. If I were having anal sex today, I'd use a condom. My oral sex ends different now, so as not to intake body fluids.

"So I do worry, yes. But I am being more careful now. And I'm hoping they'll find a vaccine. I'm sure my lifestyle is revolting to some of the people who'll read about it. I can only tell you, as the person who lives it, I'm a caring, warm father and husband. I don't believe my external sexual interests cause problems for anyone. My wife and I love each other and are happy with our own sex lives. And I'd like for the progress of scientists to help me continue being able to express my full sexuality freely. We're not all alike. I know what my own needs are."

"What would you like to say to readers of your story?"

"If your readers don't understand how many people around them feel all kinds of sexual impulses, then they probably don't know much about people. That's what I've learned. Personally I think there's something nice about it. I'm happy with the sexuality I feel. Of course, I'd like to be able to feel this way and, with the help of science, not die for it! I certainly don't want to get AIDS . . . I guess I'm counting on science to make sure I don't."

Chapter 27:
Married Bisexuals — Part 2

This chapter presents two bisexual men with exposure to the HTLV-III virus, one of whom is apparently headed toward full AIDS.

"Dana's" blood has tested positive. His wife, "Keri," knows about his bisexuality and of the fact that he now carries the virus.

"Stewart" has serious ARC symptoms which are progressively getting worse. Stewart's wife knows nothing whatsoever about his years of covert homosexuality -- nor the truth of the disease he has.

Bisexual Husband (Sero-Positive), Heterosexual Wife

DANA. He's associated with a famous member of the entertainment industry and helped create his employer's success. He no longer lives in Hollywood, but travels there often. I meet him and his wife through a doctor who knows them, and I visit their home in "Middle America." I have separate interviews with husband and wife, Dana and Keri. They are both in their early thirties.

"How would you describe your sexuality?" I ask Dana.

"Bisexual."

"And how long have you felt that way?"

"All my life. From the very beginning. The first sexual experience I had was with another boy as a child. I was seven or eight. My first female sexual experience was at thirteen. I was from a small town. In this day and age, it would have happened sooner."

In high school Dana realized that being attracted to other males "wasn't accepted." He started competing for girls with the several boys he'd been seeing sexually. After high school, he moved to a large mid-Western city and stayed at the YMCA. Some of the young men he was friendly with were male hustlers. When he had trouble finding a job, when he was hungry and out of money, he followed their example on two occasions.

"To me it was degrading, but I had to, just to eat. It was

traumatic." He'd been trying to deny his own feelings of attraction to men. But as much as he found his act of prostitution upsetting and shameful, the episode reawakened a realization of his interests. He met a "benefactor" in the entertainment business. They became friends and business associates and, eventually, sexually involved.

"It was like the opening of an old door," he says, "comfortable and wonderful. I fell in love with him." The man was married. Their affair ultimately ended and Dana moved on.

"In the full swing of the Sexual Revolution, I did anything with anybody. I was just sexual. I told my friends, `I'm a true bisexual and I won't hide it anymore.'" He was already in the entertainment business when he met Keri. She was visiting from the mid-West and was an old friend of Dana's current lover. She simply assumed Dana was "gay." When he later happened to visit her town, he phoned her for a drink. Alone together, they suddenly felt sexual chemistry. And they fell in love.

"It was extraordinary, the comfort I felt with her. Like one person instead of two. She knew of my attraction to men, and that was okay. As long as I didn't have sexual affairs with women. My roommate and Keri had been talking about getting married themselves, you know. So I had to go back to L.A. and tell my lover I was taking his fiancee away from him."

He laughs at the complication -- that hearty sound must what people call a "lusty laugh." This couple's home is an attractive surburban setting. Christmas lights flicker at the door on an artistic assemblage of branches. The house and the comfortable furnishings inside look "cozy." I wonder how many neighbors realize how different his sexual pathways have been from theirs.

Dana and Keri have been married for six years. "Sexually you name it, we've done it," he says. They've now been monogamous for two years, "because of AIDS." He remembers when he used to be afraid of hepatitis. He'd thought that disease would be "the worst thing in the world. Then, along came herpes, and I thought it would be the most horrible, horrible thing. And then AIDS. I thought, oh my Lord! This is toooo much. Something's got to give here. Two years ago we decided we'd be monogamous till this whole thing blows over."

"And if it does?" I ask him. "If there's a cure for AIDS, or a vaccine?"

"Hallelujah." His big, rolling laugh is joyful. I can appreciate the charisma of his warmth. "I'm waiting! I know how I feel about my attraction to men. I always have, I always will. It's a part of me. Today, in the supermarket line, my wife and I can appreciate the same men."

300

I ask him about his feelings since he learned he's tested positive for the AIDS virus. He brought Keri to the doctor's office to get the news of his test. "I thought it meant that for sure I 'had it,' I didn't realize it only meant I was 'exposed' to it. When I found out I didn't really have it yet -- I haven't even had symptoms of ARC -- well, I was relieved. Now I just take it as it comes.

"I've seen what AIDS does to people. I know others in the business who've gotten it. One friend of ours has gone from being a beautiful, gorgeous man to just 119 pounds with no hair, emaciated. He's had AIDS for two years."

I ask what's changed between Dana and his wife, in addition to their current monogamy. They've made no personal changes at all, and she continues to test negative he says. They've never been actively into anal sex. They are not using condoms, although they've got them on hand. "I'm not sure why we don't use them. I guess deep down inside, we hope this thing won't happen to us. We've talked about spermicides too, but haven't used them."

"It doesn't sound as though you feel any urgent need for a shield at all," I say.

"I know. It sounds so irresponsible when I say it out loud. I guess I just don't feel she's as threatened because of the physical makeup of the vagina. We have oral sex with each other, but the only way she gets semen is vaginally. We were tested last month again and again, she came up negative . . . if I were going to expose her to it, I think I would have done it already. But I'd do anything she asked me to."

KERI. Her hair is the color of chocolate, rich and flowing across her shoulders. Her dress is cut low. She radiates sensuality, the way her fingers stroke a wineglass or caress a pillow on the couch.

She sells insurance for her father's company and is unusually successful. "I've turned being a woman into an asset," she says.

"Dana describes himself as 'bisexual' and you as 'heterosexual,'" I say. "Is that true?"

"Yep. We used to have an open relationship. We'd both go to bed with other men, and it was lots of fun. We had a real good time. We changed that for AIDS. All the outside sex was fun, but it's not worth dying over!"

"What happened when you learned he had a positive test for the virus."

"I sat in the doctor's office and cried and cried. I thought, 'God, I'm gonna lose him. I've found the perfect person in the world and now I may be losing him.'"

"And how do you feel now?"

"I'm more comfortable now that everything will be fine. At least, that's how I was feeling till about two weeks ago. I just spoke with another doctor who said, 'I tend to be over-cautious, but I think you should always use condoms, you should always go by the safe sex guidelines.' He got me to worrying about it some more again. This doctor tells me that just because I'm negative doesn't mean I won't eventually turn positive, that re-exposure could be an issue. That concerns me, I didn't use to worry about that.

"I've never used a condom in my life. I went out and bought some a couple of weeks ago. I guess . . . I've realized something. I've been thinking about this ever since I heard you were coming to see us. I've been wondering about my own psychology, you know. I don't want Dana to feel I'm trying to protect myself against him. I want to BE there for him. I want to be the one that doesn't back away, no matter what happens. If I get us to use condoms, I don't want him to feel I'm putting up a barrier, I don't want to be pushing him away.

"Was it hard for you to marry a man who's bisexual?"

"Oh no, it was real easy. I was surprised to learn he liked women, though. I thought he was only gay. The first night he came to town, surprise, surprise, we spent the night on the bathroom floor. We got married six months to the day after that night."

"Keri. I saw all the churches on the way over here, I certainly get the sense this is a religious part of the country. Are you conscious of how different your way of looking at life and sexuality is from most of the people around you?"

"Sure, but that's always been so. In college I was the wildest hippie anyone ever saw. I've travelled the world by myself, and never thought I'd be living back here."

"To the people who read about you, who read your words, who wonder 'how could she be that way?' -- what would you say?"

"Gosh. I still think I'm pretty wild!" she says with a giggle. "I've always had a real drive for new experiences. I think a lot of the problem many people have in their relationships is they stifle their real sexual feelings, rather than just expressing them and getting on with it. They can then wind up having more serious affairs that could actually damage their relationships more. Myself, I'm a sexual person, and I don't feel guilty about it. I enjoy the way I am. It's AIDS that drastically changed my promiscuous habits."

"Keri? To the reader who thinks, 'Good! She was probably too promiscuous anyway," what would you say?"

"I'd say, 'well . . . maybe I was.' I've gotten a lot of positive things out of the change. I try to focus on those things when I miss the old times. I'd be lying to you if I said I didn't miss that exciting stranger now and then. There's an excitement in sex with a stranger the first time. But now I'm putting more of my energy into work. Dana is too.

"When you take a night off from each other, go out to bars, and spend the night having sex, you don't work as well the next day. I used to think I could never commit myself to one person, though, and now I realize I can. One of the best changes, I think, is that I view people a little differently now. We used to meet new people and if I was attracted, I'd be thinking, 'are we gonna do it or not?' That used to be my first and main thought with many of the new men I'd meet. Now, that's no longer a question -- so I see more in people today than just whether or not we'll have have sex."

I look over my shoulder after I say good night. They're an attractive couple. With the Christmas lights twinkling on the branches, with the fire place glowing in the darkness, with his hand around her waist, they could be an illustration on a sentimental greeting card.

"Stewart" - Married, Secretly Gay, ARC Patient

He is terrified of exposure. He works in a religiously affiliated organization and he worries about losing his job. The New England town he lives in is quite conservative. Only the fact that his doctor knows me personally has made him willing to be interviewed.

His doctor describes his condition:

"He's a fifty-eight year old married man who has ARC syndrome. He became ill about a year and a half ago with fever. It came and went. He then developed a progressive decline in his white blood cell count, with proportional decline in his lymphocyte count.

"He was known to me, privately, as being in a high risk group. His own personal lifestyle made him even riskier because he was promiscuously anal-receptive without a condom, frequenting the baths when he left town because of his job. He has explained to me that, because he was rarely able to express his personal sexual impulses here, when he went away he acted with quite a bit of abandon. He's like the married men you've written about who take advantage of bathhouses at lunchtime in New York City.

"Now he's developed ulcerations around the rectum, and some very painful bleeding. The herpes culture there was positive. It's quite severe and it takes a month to treat every time, even with super doses of medicine. I give him so much medication because of his weakened immune system. He also developed a viral pancreatitis, which caused a lot of abdomenal pain, and he was hospitalized for that. He has tested positive for the HTLV-III antibody.   Recently he developed difficulty swallowing and a sore throat.   He has white placques in the back of his throat which is the yeast infection, "thrush."   Approximately eight months ago he began to experience tenderness and tingling in his hands, a sign of his nervous system being involved.   Recently, he's had difficulty concentrating and remembering things.   He is going to great lengths to compensate for the problem at work, so he isn't discovered.

"Dealing with his medical problems has been something I could handle so far.   It's dealing with him as a person -- with his fears and anxiety, his sense of isolation, his guilt -- that has been harder.   He doesn't want to bring shame upon his children because of his lifestyle.   He has asked to be cremated with no records left behind."

~ ~ ~ ~ ~

I meet him in the doctor's office late on a weeknight.   There must have been a time, I decide, when he looked like Clark Gable or Burt Reynolds.   He's still an attractive man, though it's clear he's now lacking in strength.

Stewart has been married for thirty-five years.   Except for one experience with another man on his first night in college, he'd had no sexual experience prior to marriage.   He loves his wife very much.   Their several children are now married adults settled nearby.

How did he have his first homosexual experiences after marriage, I ask him.

"It was almost accidental.   I'd read the Kinsey report.   They were saying a large number of men have had homosexual activities.   One evening I went down to the post office.   I noticed a man in a car staring at me, driving slowly down the road and following me as I walked.   I realized I was seeing the Kinsey report come to life.   The man was there for sexual activity with other men.   I then began to notice, I began to be more conscious, of men everywhere, quietly making contacts with other men.   I was about twenty-seven years old.   Maybe women do this too, but I'm just not sensitive enough to notice it.   I hadn't been walking around attracted to other men on the sidewalk, but I now began to find I was interested."

He characterizes himself in his earliest homosexual experiences as "Here I am, do what you please."   Learning how to enjoy passive anal intercourse came several years later.   "It was painful at first, although I enjoyed giving pleasure to the men I was with.   I loved the closeness, the snuggling, the loving relationship with other men.   That's what I began to discover about myself.

"At first, for example, I just couldn't kiss another man.   Then one night I met a man at a rest area on the road. We went out into the bushes and he told me to just relax, that if I could let myself relax I'd discover it was pleasureable to kiss. I did, and it was.

"Often with other men, I wouldn't ejaculate. If it was at a bathhouse, I would sort of save myself because maybe I'd want to be with several other people that night. If I was not too far from home, I wanted to be able to go home later and have sex with my wife. I've always enjoyed sex with her, and I've never had sex with another woman. I began to have even more sex with her, however, almost taking care of my guilt. I could feel I'd done my duty in both directions -- I had taken care of her, and I'd satisfied my own needs. There's something special I get from being hugged by or kissing a man. I just can't get that from her, although I love her with all my heart."

He tells me that after discovering his sexual pleasure with men, almost thirty years went by with his secret arrangements out of town. He had occasional experiences locally, with other married men that he met at the gym. But mostly he waited for his trips. "I always washed up carefully after I sex with men at baths. I always felt protected from getting disease." Everything, in fact, was fine for three decades.

"If they knew at work I had ARC, I'd be fired, I know I'd be fired. I'd have to be out by five o'clock. If you tell me they're biased, I'll agree with you. If you tell me they should be more accepting, more understanding, I'll agree. But that's the way they are."

It's been about eleven months since he's had any sexual experience at all other than masturbation. He secretly told his wife he might have AIDS, and that's why he can't have sex with her any longer. He's also lost his former sense of sexual drive. They've agreed not to tell the children, not to take any chance that word could ever reach his employers. "I told her I don't know where or when I got it, and I wasn't lying. I don't. I didn't tell her I don't know 'how' I got it. She's very sad."

"Do you think she ever wonders or suspects your secret lifestyle? Do you ever think of sharing it with her?"

"I don't know what goes on in her mind, but I really think she wouldn't want me to tell her. She talks about how much she loves and appreciates me, and says she especially appreciates my 'high standards.' I think she doesn't want to know my full feelings. We love each other so much, but I think she just couldn't accept it, let alone my children."

He talks about having less zest and energy now than a year ago, and how foggy his mind can feel at times. All he can do is try to hide his condition and keep going.

"What would you say," I ask, "to readers who don't know how a guy can happily live with his wife for over thirty-five years and live a simultaneous sex life with men on for so much of that time?"

"I would say, `I don't know how it works either. There've been times I've tried to change myself, but I have to tell you, my attraction is very powerful. It's real. It may have been there all the time, kind of latent inside me."

He tells me he's always felt a very close relationship to God. He feels confident God accepts him personally and homosexuals in general. "The problem isn't God, it's man," he says. "I wish people were more tolerant of others."

"Is there any chance," I ask him, "if it ever came out to your community that you're gay or bisexual, is there any chance they'd be more loving and accepting of you than you imagine?"

"I think of myself as really being 'gay,'" he says. "No. I don't think so. I wish so, but I don't think so. I'm sure some of them must have brothers and sons, sisters, friends who are gay without their knowledge. People they care about. Maybe some of these very people are gay too, and maybe they're worried about my finding out about them. But people don't share these things. I have a sister I think is gay, but we've never even once talked about our personal lives."

"If you could give one message to the public, what would it be?"

"I wish they could learn to be more understanding of differences in people," he says. "That would go a long way toward helping everybody."

Chapter 28:
Charleston

I grew up in Beaufort, South Carolina -- palm trees, Spanish moss in the oaks, and only 5,000 people on the island at the time. This Thanksgiving, I went back home to be with my family and detoured to Charleston to meet two people my brother, the psychiatrist, had helped me locate. One is "Francis" who has AIDS. The other is Dr. Robert Ball who treats it. I'm happy to include their Southern perspectives in this chronicle.

"Francis"

It's early in the day after Thanksgiving, and it's 73 degrees. The young black hostess at the Francis Marion restaurant is as comfortably warm as the morning. She offers a secluded table for four. ("You can spread out all your equipment here and be right at home.")

"Coffee?" someone else asks me. "Want a danish or somethin' before your guest arrives?" The South. Still a corridor to my memories. Land of the drawling and generous hospitality I learned as a child.

Back then, the Breeze theater had a separate entrance for "Negroes." Up to the balcony for them, while the white folks sat downstairs. Now, the black and white staff at this old hotel take cooperative turns pouring coffee and welcoming new arrivals to the restaurant.

I know him right away when he enters: this is "Francis." He has asked that I use that pseudonym, to protect his job hunt. He is a slender man in his mid-forties and he looks only thirty-five. He strides to the buffet table, and I notice a slight sway to his hips.

"I was born and raised here," he says, "in a family of nine children. I was educated outside this state." He was a Lieutenant in the Navy and has a master's degree in biology. He recently completed his education in Chicago as a Physician's Assistant. All his life he had wanted to be a doctor.

"During the period of time I came through," he says, "you had to be very exceptional if you were black. They say, 'many are called, but few are chosen.' I had the calling but I was never chosen. As a black young man, I couldn't get into a *good* medical school. At least by being a Physician's Assistant, I can realize some of my personal goals."

He speaks formally, as though at a podium. His tone becomes slightly more distant as a round-cheeked, older black woman pours his tea. I'm sure to some people, he seems pretentious. My impression, however, is that he's merely trying his best to be the most he can be.

"You don't sound like a typical person from Charleston," I say.

"It is a matter of education," he says. "Once you've been exposed to English diction, and if you learn something from it and if you care, there are changes."

I remember that my father, now a college professor of psychology, once worked in my grandfather's building supply company. "Sho' ees!" he would say to the black laborers who came for nails and cement. "We gonna get 'em good!" I used to squirm in embarrassment, though in truth I think they loved my dad and his good-hearted zest. But the willowy black man across from me now, gesturing roundly in the air with his tea cup, would surely and rightly have been as indignant as I was mortified.

"My dad was a strict disciplinarian," he tells me. "You'd have to be very articulate to answer his questions. You'd have to speak precisely to the points as warranted."

"What was his occupation?"

"Dad was just an industrial laborer at one of the steel mills here."

(I notice with a pang his word, "just.") "I understand you're gay," I say. He nods. "At what age did you know that?"

"I believe I knew that fact as a pre-schooler. Some reason, some how, I felt attracted . . . it never took a name or a form till I got to elementary school. But I knew there was something different about me. As I was growing up, being a 'sissy' was not tolerated. Even in the black community today, homosexuality is something that is frowned on, ostracized, and completely alien. Therefore, closet living was something I was comfortable with from an early age. `I've got a secret, and nobody's going to know.'

"I was always neater than the others, I was always smarter than the others. But I was teased for being different. So I did all the male 'honcho' things. I got into sports and I excelled in order to camouflage myself."

"When did you have your first sexual encounter?"

"I was forced at an early age. I was thirteen. It was an older neighbor next door, about seventeen or eighteen. It was anal. I knew then that I was marked. I disliked it passionately, but I didn't know who to go to, what to do, how to discuss this episode. It was a skeleton in my closet and I told no one."

"When did you first tell someone else what had happened?"

"Not until age thirty." Seventeen years of secrecy — that, in itself, can have repercussions in a personality.

"Because before then, even in college, I wanted 'to be a man.' I really wanted that. But there were times in my relationships with girls when it seemed I never measured up. Or if things were getting too intimate, I myself would find a reason to end the relationship. I fled the closeness.

"I'd had great difficulties with an older brother growing up. He is five years older than I am. He'd say 'you're a faggot,' 'you're a sissy.' Now I realize that he recognized something back then. He knew I'd be up for ridicule and have a difficult time, and he didn't want that for me. For the longest time I hated him.

"When it was discovered that I had cancer, five years ago, he came and lived with me for several weeks. That was in Chicago. That was the first time I really saw his concern and caring. He said, 'it doesn't matter about your lifestyle. I just want you alive and well.' He really cared. Our relationship now is more open and closer, as brothers should be.

"In 1968, I had a pathologically confirmed non-Hodgkins lymphoma. Cancer. Stage 3-B, which means above and below the diaphragm. I can use that early disease as a smokescreen for my AIDS condition. I get work more easily if people know I fought a bout with that particular kind of cancer and then got over it. It's held responsible for my new difficulties and they don't have to know about the AIDS beneath the story."

"Your doctor says you have a very positive attitude toward your illness," I say.

"Oh, yes. That is my family influence. My parents are very devout Christians. Methodists. That means, 'regardless of the situation, it will work out.' There was no such thing as 'failure' in my family. Everything had to be upbeat, outgoing, and constructive.

"So, chemotherapy helped shrink my original lymphadenopathy. Now that original disease helps me to hide the new one. That's positive, isn't it?"

"How did you learn you had AIDS?"

"I had just finished the medical training program. I became ill with fevers and night sweats. This was in January of 1985. At first, people thought it was just a relapse of the earlier problem.
But then they realized, it was AIDS.

"There is one doctor who has advanced the thought that as early as 1980, I had AIDS. I simply thought back then my problems were a resurgence of the early lymphoma. But if it really was AIDS in 1980, then I've now survived five years!"

He tells me he used to experience a variety of sexual activities with other men until the AIDS diagnosis early this year. Now he has no sexual contacts at all. "In fact," he says, "I've never had a 'relationship' per se. I've had opportunities, but I always shied away. Frankly I've seen and heard of tragic ends, of skeletons that come back to haunt you if you get involved."

I imagine a Tennessee Williams character who has already read ahead in the script to the end of his own doomed role. 'What if I stay offstage?' he might think. As Francis describes keeping his "skeleton" hidden in the dark, I feel a sadness I don't acknowledge to him.

"My reputation was of the utmost importance to me," he says. "I was extremely closeted and avoided any overt manifestations of the fact that I was gay. In so doing, perhaps I did avoid possible relationships. Perhaps I paid a price. But for so long in my life, in my past life anyway, being gay was something frightening, not something good."

"And today?"

"I have a totally different approach to life now. It just doesn't matter. It wasn't my conscious choice to be this way. It's the way I am. But I still hold back. I never approach someone else in a bar, for example, for fear of rejection. He must always approach me first."

There are two gay clubs in Charleston, he tells me. He belongs to neither because he's heard of "membership lists getting into lawyers' hands." He reads gay publications infrequently. "They are about romances, and I don't have one, or national community news, which I don't care about."

He lives with his family, now that he's back in Charleston. Except for the one discussion with his brother during the illness, he's never told his family he is gay. And he has avoided telling them anything about AIDS.

"At first when I was told I had AIDS, I thought I'd almost stopped breathing. When are they going to bring the needle to put me to sleep forever? Because, from a professional standpoint, I understood the ramifications of the disease, and of my continuing series of fevers and sweats and weakness.

"At this particular moment, however, I have no symptoms at all. No lymphoma, no fevers. The doctors are truly pleased. Of course, I don't know when it will come back. But in the meantime, I'm going about as normal an activity as possible, except of course -- sex. I don't want to risk the chance. Abstinence, to the price of life, cannot be compared.

"I am looking for work as a physician's assistant, though I'm a little worried about what illnesses I myself might get if I'm involved with pediatric work and if my immune system is weakened. But I need certification first anyway, so I expect to teach in the forthcoming year. I have located a physician who knows of my condition, and I believe he will be willing to hire me after certification."

We pause as the round-cheeked woman brings more tea.

"For the coming year, then," I say, "you will be one of those teachers diagnosed with AIDS, that the public won't really know about. Correct?"

"Yes, that is the reason I'm so conscious of guarding my anonymity. By now, I simply understand though, that after all my trials and tribulations, I will overcome. I am going to get a job. If I do not get a job, I will start my own business. I will do something. I will be okay. I have a had a number of successes in this life, but they have not come easily.

"How other people view me has been the main barrier I have had, I would say. First as a black person, of course. I didn't want them to give them the ammunition to reject me as a gay man as well. I know that if I was white, many things would happen differently. I grew up here, and believe me the opportunities were limited.

"Even so, with what I have, I have come a long way. And I am planning to go a lot further. There were times I didn't want to be black or gay. But when I was in the depths of my physical misery, I realized then, understanding the possibility of dying, that the opinions of others didn't matter. That awareness was something positive from this disease, I know that what matters in the time I have left is how I feel about myself."

"What would you like to say to readers of your story?"

"God didn't bring me this far to leave me. Things will work out. I'm going to work them out. To your readers, I would say of course: Be Cautious. And if it does happen to you, find something to believe in. That will help you go through the difficulties. If you can keep a positive attitude, it will truly make a difference."

Dr. Robert Ball

We were originally to meet at 10:00 but by now I'm used to doctors being late. It is 11:15 by the time we choose a table amid the walls of books in the college medical library. I'm to catch a plane to New York in an hour, so we're both talking quickly.

A local nurse had said about him, "he's no barrel of laughs, but technically he's one of the best." His manner in fact is restrained and conservative.

He offers his professional biography like one tightly compressed pill: "College of Charleston, 1966; Medical University of South Carolina here, 1970; Internship, University of Alabama at Birmingham; two years

311

in the army; back here for a medical residency and Infectious Disease fellowship. Full-time faculty then, part-time faculty now. Clinical Assistant Professor of Medicine, Infectious Diseases Division."

A soldier reporting for duty. We both relax slightly, though we continue to talk like data terminals fighting a deadline.

"Where did you grow up?"

"Here in Charleston."

"How old are you?"

"Forty."

"Are you married?"

"Divorced."

"Children?"

"Two."

"Ages?"

"Seventeen and fifteen."

"Okay," I say, and take a breath. I have got to break this rhythm and forget about my plane schedule. I want to know what AIDS looks like from the point of view of a doctor in a medium-sized city in the South.

I ask him when he saw his first AIDS patient. He pulls from his jacket pocket a wrinkled set of pages. He keeps them with him all the time, he says. They summarize his AIDS patients and their major diseases and problems, "because questions about them are always coming up."

"May, 1982. That was the first one." He's now lost count of how many he's seen since then. Probably several dozen through the University, and an additional dozen in his private practice. "Understand that when these people get sick, the cost and nature of their hospitalization is such that they usually end up in multiple hospitals and with multiple doctors. It's not one on one, like when you go to your doctor for a sore throat."

He has three times as many ARC patients as AIDS patients, he tells me. "And ten times again that number of sero-positive individuals." About one third of his patients are black. He's had no IV drug users in his private practice. They've been treated in the Medical University system, since they lack personal funding or insurance. All his AIDS patients, thus far, have been gay. Most of his ARC patients have been gay except for one heterosexual in active military duty "who's come in contact with several prostitutes in recent years in large cities." Some of his patients who consider themselves "bisexual."

He keeps mentioning his "sero-positive" patients. I ask if he routinely tests his patients' blood serum of his patients for the AIDS virus?

312

"Yes."

"It's something automatic for you? For every one of your patients, you know if the antibody to the virus is present or not?"

"For all my high risk patients, yes, when they let me test them" he says. One of his biggest local concerns is that he feels there is not enough "gay responsibility" to go along with progress in gay rights. I ask him what he means by that.

"Unfortunately," he replies, "we've not been able to get all our patients to observe proper sexual practices. Nor will they all let themselves be tested for antibody, to see if they've come in contact with the virus and might be carrying it. In fact, I've had a rather alarming negative response from the professional gay community. This includes several physicians who are gay, friends and colleagues. They simply refuse to be antibody tested. College professors, too, and other white collar professional workers -- some of them refuse too."

"What is their worry?" I ask him. "Are they afraid of what will happen to the test information?"

"That is part of it," he says. "And, to a certain extent, they 'just don't want to know.' That's the response I get. Some of them simply don't want to curtail their sexual practices. Maybe a third or more are irresponsible in that way, not wanting to take the test, not wanting to change their habits."

"What is your impression," I ask him, "of their willingness to use condoms as a new practice? Has usage changed at all?"

"To some extent, yes. But as one very sexually active gay man put it, 'you just can't give good head with a condom.'" I hear a subdued split-second laugh, as he hears himself repeating the man's raw quote.

I don't react, however. I am wondering just how many adults there may be who've learned to permit themselves various forms of sexual freedom . . . and are now confronting the need to unlearn that very behavior. Not only gays, surely, and not only concerning condoms. My mind wanders to Don Boys in Indiana and his desire for a sodomy law. I pull myself back to this table in the library.

"You said most of your AIDS patients are gay. What is your own, personal attitude toward homosexuality?"

"I'm very tolerant of it."

"What is your sense of society's view, in this part of the country?"

"In this part of the country, homosexuality is still viewed with some disdain. That makes it difficult, because the public view is translated into action frequently, via the news media, via legislative action. Indeed, recently the local school board -- one member has proposed that any student with AIDS, or any employee with AIDS, or any student or employee who has ARC or even antibody positive tests should be immediately dismissed from school.

"As a response to this, the school board has formed several committees with large numbers of professional people, in an effort to develop a more responsible policy. The proposal is the initial, unfortunate reaction of the uneducated."

"Given those kinds of attitudes, then, can you understand the fear or reluctance of the gay community to risk personal exposure by taking the test?"

"True. I can. The same sort of public reaction has been found elsewhere in the country, too. Indiana, for example, with the tremendous public furor that arose over a child with AIDS who had to study at home. And New York, with parents picketing school to keep another child with AIDS out. Fortunately, we haven't had those kinds of over-reactions here yet. Charleston, at least, tends to be more low key and quiet. Life is stable and conservative community here. But at the same time, we have our share of archaic thinkers.

"Currently in South Carolina, as in most states, the test is confidential. The patient gets the results privately and determines what he wants to do with them. Unfortunately in the last several weeks, South Carolina's State Board of Health has ruled that anyone who is sero-positive will be reported to the State Bureau of Health by name. The names will go onto a master list, following Colorado's legislative edict. Ours is not a legislative move at all, though --simply an edict from the State Commisioner of Health who unfortunately has never, ever examined an AIDS patient."

He stares at me calmly and waits for my response.

"Then that's one of the very reasons gays don't want the test, isn't it? I assume that many of them wouldn't want their names reported. Yes?"

"Yes, that's exactly right. Since May and June of this year, large numbers of individuals had started to come in for the testing. Not as many as we'd like, as I said, but many. The direction was good. The test is simple and quick and because of it we uncovered ARC and AIDS patients who otherwise would have been diagnosed later in the course of their illness. If anything, we want to do more testing, not less."

"So it's ironic," I say. "You expect the Commissioner's position on reporting the names to actually discourage people."

"Exactly right." If fewer people know they have the AIDS virus, because fewer people are willing to take the test given a state "list," then the disease might actually spread *more* throughout the state.

"Do you speak up about that?" I ask him.

"Quite a bit. Unfortunately, the State Commissioner has not been responsive to the individuals working with the disease. Exactly why his decision came about, no one knows. We speculate it was political pressure just to 'do something.' If true, it would reflect again the uneducated mentality of South Carolina politicians."

The part of me that's still a Southerner at heart feels annoyance at his words. Let a Yankee talk that way and see what happens, I think. But he's the Southerner now, not me. And he's the doctor wanting to overcome any barriers that stop people from taking the AIDS test. I can empathize with his frustration.

"What is different for you about treating AIDS from all the other diseases you work with?"

"No other disease inspires such fear and frustration. Of course, the long incubation period makes it almost impossible to do case-contact tracing. The relevant contact could have taken place years ago. And we can't exclude individuals who may have received blood transfusions -- also years ago -- who may still be incubating the virus right now. The antibody to the virus takes only four to six weeks to develop, but once it's positive, the blood stays positive for life. AIDS is a disease that is fascinating and so complex. Honestly, it intrigues me. I admit I find fascinating. Unfortunately, though, the human side is very difficult. Just this week I lost another AIDS patient, a personable, bright young man who went through hell. That's the negative side, obviously. Doctor or not, you have feelings when that happens."

"What would you like to say to readers about AIDS?"

"I would urge them to educate themselves and keep medical information separate from their natural panic reactions. For example, children with AIDS should be allowed to go to school. The initial reaction is panic and fear -- 'horrors. All the other children are going to get AIDS.' But when parents understand that the disease is transferred by transfusion of blood or by *incredibly* intimate contact, then so much public fear can be allayed."

It's time, if I'm not to miss the flight to New York. We shake hands and I hurry to the airport.

Chapter 29:
Isoprinosine —
Struggle for Approval

One potential treatment for AIDS and ARC is Isoprinosine, which Dr. Grossman was helping to test. Because of that involvement, I met two people engaged in assessing or manufacturing it. My objective was to experience something of the test and approval process for an AIDS medication ... from those who actively believe this drug can help.

Here are two interviews. First, Dr. George Bekesi at Mount Sinai in New York, the scientist who determined that Isoprinosine does NOT DO DAMAGE to people who take it. Next, Dr. Alvin Glasky, president of Newport Pharmaceuticals, the company which manufactures the drug.

Dr. Glasky has a long and controversial history of struggling for his product's approval. Some say his personality and aggressiveness clashed with FDA politics. Or that his data needed to be more meticulous. Some say the drug does nothing. Others, that his lawsuit against the FDA has been held against him -- whether "fairly" or not, and despite the urgency of AIDS. How do I know?

All I can offer you is how he seemed as a human being. To me.

Dr. George Bekesi

"Are you Dr. Bekesi?" I have swung open the door to the Mount Sinai office and am asking a short round man with a plump round face and gold round glasses and large round eyes. It's pronounced "Buh-KAY-zee."

"Unfortunately, I am," he says from the desk. "Who are you, sir?"

"I'm Mike Greenly. I have an appointment with you."

"Ah! I had forgotten. You are the reason I came in early." He speaks with an accent that slows him down. I notice that even his lips purse roundly when he talks. His silver-gray hair stands on end, straight up and out. He almost reminds me of a snowman, like the ones I used to draw for Mrs. Zeigler. Except with long straight strands of hair, like a military crewcut. He sits across from me at a narrow table, his white lab coat open informally over his shirt and tie. There is something immediately approachable about him; I quickly feel friendly and relaxed.

"Where are you from?" I ask, after explaining the kind of interviews I'm doing.

"Well originally," (he says it 'OH-rig-i-nal-ly,' pronouncing every syllable carefully) "I am from Hungary. I was born in the city of Budapest, and I left my native country in '56."

"I had finished my undergraduate degree in chemical engineering in Budapest, and got my doctorate in the United States at the University of Buffalo. I never dreamed that I would be involved with human-related diseases. I considered myself a chemist. But my first position in the U.S. was working for a gentleman who was the head of the Department of Surgery. That's the opening I got, and that's how I entered the field of medical science."

"What is your exact position today?"

"My academic title is, I am professor in the Cancer Center of Mount Sinai. The center is also a department for the treatment of neoplastic diseases, which means all forms of cancer-related diseases."

"How did you get involved with AIDS?" I ask him. "Because of KS, as a cancer?"

"No, actually. It was completely different. My major concern—" he pronounces it very slowly, and the effect is to make me think about the meaning of the words as he says them -- " is EN-VIR-ON-MEN-TAL-LY IN-DUCED CAN-CER. And, immunodeficiency."

When I hear the word "environment," I still automatically think of Rachel Carson and *Silent Spring*, her famous book about the pollution of our waters. He tells me he's been involved for many, many years in work with chemicals from the environment that suppress the human immune system and often, even decades later, lead to cancer. He makes a distinction between "induced" immuno deficiency versus the "acquired" immuno deficiency that is AIDS. One is chemical, the other is viral.

He's worked with asbestos, for example, which has a twenty-plus year incubation period. And dioxin, which involves "Agent Orange." PCB, an electric machinery insulator which had been dumped into the Hudson River. And PBB, a tumor-inducer in experimental animals which was mistakenly fed to cows and then had contaminated Michigan's milk supply.

When the outbreak of AIDS started in the early 1980's, he says, our knowledge was extremely limited. The patients being reported in the medical journals were only "one patient, two patients, five patients" -- a few at a time. That is insufficient data for drawing serious conclusions to work with. A larger population was needed.

So the same field team for Michigan asbestos workers and their families placed an ad in the *Village Voice* in September of 1982. The ad offered a free service for 100 "healthy homosexual men," given the emerging risk of AIDS for that population. Each man who volunteered for a "complete epidemiological, clinical, and immunological" medical workup would receive a report of his findings.

The results were astonishing. One way or another, after the test codes were broken, "out of 100 individuals, seventy-six percent were immunologically abnormal!" To be sure, the men were not randomly selected . . . they had specifically responded to the ad. Even so, the high percentage of cases with altered immune systems, swollen lymph glands, weight loss, etc. was extraordinary.

Now that Dr. Bekesi had their blood sera on hand in his laboratory, "the question I was asking was *if* a person's immune system is abnormal, could I change it?" Because of his work with PBB's and asbestos -- and because people affected by those environmental chemicals also have their immune systems depressed -- Dr. Bekesi was accustomed to experimenting with "modulators" of the immune system.

One goal of a modulator is to reverse an immune deficiency so the patient can once again ward off disease. I picture listening to music in my car and driving further away from the station setting I've chosen. Perhaps a modulator is like turning up the volume knob of the radio. I ask Dr. Bekesi to create his own image of a modulator.

"Well maybe it's like a crutch," he says. "To support an injury until the person can heal himself." Good!

He decided to experiment on the blood samples of the 100 gay men with every modulator at his disposal from the Michigan work. Which ones might improve the lab results for the immune-depressed samples? One of the drugs he'd been using was Isoprinosine, so he included it in the test.

"It is not yet approved by the FDA, correct?"

"Correct, but we couldn't care less. I don't need to have an FDA approval for something *in vitro* , in a test tube. We already had two years of experience for what Isoprinosine could do that way for the blood lymphocytes of cancer patients, asbestos workers, and for people exposed to other environmental chemicals.

"Isoprinosine is a stimulator," he says, "although Newport was selling it as an anti-viral agent. But there is no virus with asbestos, you know. When we looked at what Isoprinosine does, we saw it stimulates not only the T-cells but also the B-cells."

"What's the difference?"

"The T-cell is the cell of immunity. It's involved with eliminating tumor cells, for example. The B-cell is the one that produces antibody against a virus. To our greatest surprise, Isoprinosine across the board improved all the functions of both those types of cells. Realize what we had done.   We'd just thrown it in there.   It was no brilliance on our part. It was 'try it, why not?'

"But we saw that Isoprinosine actually did something good.   We then immediately tested it with AIDS patients, not just with the high-risk people who didn't have AIDS yet. We saw that it could do something for the early patients who didn't have AIDS yet, but not after they had already fully developed it."

"If the person already has AIDS, then, it's too late?"

"Yes. Too late then for Isoprinosine."

"But it's good in the ARC state?"

"Yeah.   So we decided to telephone Newport Labs and tell them what we had found about their drug.   Finally we got a vice-president of research there. We told him we got good results and asked, 'do you have the approval to sell it in this country?' No, he said. They don't."

"Wait -- you're the one who first told them, 'your drug can help pre-AIDS patients?'"

"Yeah, we told them."

"Well, they must have said, 'WOW! Thanks a lot Dr. Bekesi!'"

"No, they didn't first understand what is happening.   It tooks lots and lots of telephone calls. I said to my contact at that time, 'Listen, buddy. I looked at all the agents. This is the only one which appears to work. It's worth a trial.'"

"A more formal trial, you mean? Because what you were doing was in the test tubes?"

"Yeah. I said we must have a double blind clinical trial approved by the FDA."

"As a person, as a human being -- were you excited to find something to help people in danger of getting AIDS?"

"Look. Personally, I didn't know anything about this disease. I had no involvement whatsoever.   I became a 'victim of circumstances.' But the fact is, when you are involved in cancer medicine, there are two types of people in this field. One type enters and then disappears very, very fast. I belong to the other group, individuals who are intellectually addicted to the problem. Daily, you see how people suffer and how they die. You can become obsessed that you do want to help."

"You are obsessed?"

"Yes, in a sense. It is easy to walk away, you know. You think, why do you want to have ulcer? Why do you want to spend all your time like this? It's the same thing as seeing a crime committed.   Are you going to turn away, or are you going to try to find the guilty one?

"I am in the second group. When I look at a battery of drugs tested in the lab on ARC and AIDS lymphocytes, and if one of them comes out which seems suggestive of something positive -- which is what happened with Isoprinosine -- then I feel morally obliged to try my best to get something done about it. So that's what I was doing. That's all. That's the way it is."

"Let me see . . . you told someone at Newport about your findings. Eventually they must have understood you."

"Yes."

"And must have agreed that it was important."

"Yes, in a strange way, it was important to them."

"Why 'in a strange way?'"

"Because they, like the rest of my colleagues, felt the emphasis had to be on patients with clinically diagnosed AIDS. Not pre-AIDS. You see, when I was advocating pre-AIDS in 1983, there was no idea of the size of the affected population. I said, what we have to treat is the "prodromal" individuals, the ones who don't yet have AIDS. Because they can still go in both directions, good and bad. Once you are in the AIDS condition, it might be too late to recover with an immuno-modulator.

"Look. There are 14,000 people with AIDS. And there are -- oh, a very conservative estimate in my book -- at least some million people who have the immuno-deficiency from this virus."

"Can I ask you this? If I'm a stranger coming to see you, and I have ARC, what would you advise? That I be treated with Isoprinosine?"

"If you are," he says carefully, "a person who shows under credible, laboratory conditions that you have an impact on your immuno function, then the question comes up, 'what can we give you?' In 1985, on November 27, what I know -- but it does not mean tomorrow morning! -- what I know today is this: in performing the first clinical trials, with the dosage we have used, I can say unequivocally that Isoprinosine is a *non-toxic* compound. That is very, very important: they weren't harmed by the treatment itself.

"Okay," I say, coaching him on.

"Number two, we started from a totally blind test. The results showed us that something positive was happening to some of patients, to their primary immune response. When the code was broken, six months after the study, it turned out that the primary immune response of a large proportion of people who received Isoprinosine -- was *normalized.*"

"What is 'a large proportion?'"

"From our study, to give you a number, out of twenty people tested, fourteen had their natural killer cell, that fights off disease, actively restored."

"What is the difference between the fourteen people who got better, and the six who did not?" I ask him.

"We cannot say. I do not know. This study was designated

simply to say, can they tolerate the dosage? Future research would need to show the difference. Our test was a one-shot affair, and for only one month."

"Dr. Grossman, whom I'm following for this book, is included in the New York center, isn't he?"

"Yes. My understanding is that the results obtained in ten test centers confirm what we saw here in our labs. Ours papers were published in 1983. What I understand now is that the gay community, for better or worse, is importing Isoprinosine from Mexico, from Canada, from Europe.

"I have heard," I tell him, "that some people worry Isoprinosine will go too far, will stimulate too much. What do you think?"

"No. That is wrong. It is the one modulator I know where there is no over-stimulation."

"Let me ask you, Dr. Bekesi. To a lay person, it seems like a long time since you published these findings. Yet this apparently positive drug for the pre-AIDS condition still isn't approved by the FDA. What about that?"

"Well, I am only an 'investigator.' My conscience is clear; we have reported our findings. I take the drug from off the shelf, and showed what it could do."

"But the drug still isn't approved by the FDA."

"Look, when you go for licensing, you go as a manufacturer. That means the FDA must make a conscious decision, under what conditions the licensing should be given. Should it be a prescription drug, for example. Which I hope it will be, because that obliges the individual to be under physician's care."

"And to the lay person who thinks maybe it's been a long time without approval?"

"It really is not. Do you know how long it takes for a new cancer drug? Eight to ten years! Nobody is more aware than I am of the lives of people with AIDS. That's the reason I'm fighting for this. But please remember, the whole thing only started in August of 1983."

"Well there is urgency for approval, after all," I say. "The virus is spreading into the general population, yes?"

"Yes it is. I know also, but I will not tell you, what is the magnitude for that so-called population at large."

"Why will you not tell me?"

"Because some of the findings are not published. We are not yet completed with all the data yet from our study."

"Let me ask you this." I am wanting to wheedle out of him whatever I can. "I'd like to know whether, directionally, does the spread of the AIDS virus tend to be a lot, or does it tend to be a little?"

"Oh, it's a general problem, yes, that is certain. It is not any longer being involved with sexual preference. It involves the public at large."

"But, is it spreading fast or is it spreading slow?"

"I think, contrary to what some people are saying, it is going to increase in momentum. My only vision of hope is that we can apply prophylactic treatment to prevent people from sliding into clinical condition. This is our moral obligation." He thumps the table with feeling when he says "moral obligation."

"I am not trying to say 'abandon' people with full AIDS, really I am not. But they are nonetheless a very minor population compared to what *could* be many more people with AIDS. The only way to reduce that total is prevention while we can."

"You're telling me, without giving away the secrets of your unpublished study, that to the heterosexual reader who feels, 'I don't have it, I'm not going to get it, and everyone I know is heterosexual and not homosexual anyway,' that it's closer than they might think, and that it will in fact be spreading."

"Yes, it will. That's simply the nature of the beast. Not because the affected population will spread it. It already went out into the broader population. Due to bisexuality, for example. Due to the prostitute population. It is a matter of a delayed reaction."

"If you could speak to the population at large, Dr. Bekesi -- the lay population like me -- based on all you know about AIDS, what would you say to them?"

"I don't want to get involved with the issue of sexual preference, that is not my domain. I cannot tell someone what to do, or how to do. I cannot tell even my own children, because they may or may not accept.

"But the fact is, AIDS is a lethal disease. I have seen many of my own colleagues die. I know many young physicians who are affected. I know what is the end. And the end is horrible.

"My point is, if you do have a problem, then you have to do the most to stabilize it. If you have the virus, and if there is a compound which is not detrimental to you, then prophylactic treatment with it is mandatory. You have to reduce the amount of infection and try to provide a crutch to eliminate the backlog. You also have to combine that with education about safe habits, to prevent re-infection. There is nothing available that lets you take it today and then tomorrow jump up and walk away. There is no easy walking away.

"I am trying to do my best," he says. "I am on the patient's side."

Dr. Alvin Glasky

He reminds me of my own father. Slightly overweight, balding, glasses. Except my father is laid back, convivial, and gentle while Al Glasky is more like me -- intense and driven. He is fifty-two years old and originally from Chicago.

He takes me for lunch at a place on the beach called Ruby's. An authentic, 1940's decor with burgers that sprawl out of their buns. As we return to Newport Pharmaceuticals headquarters, I ask him to tell me what motivates him. It's not money, he says. He has a house that's plenty big enough, more cars than he has time to enjoy, and comfortable support for himself, his wife, his children. It's rather, after a quest of so many years, seeing that he's right. I am about to get a sense of that quest and of the study of the human body's immune system. I eventually experience his personal sense of mission which I imagine scientists in other pharmaceutical firms also share . . . each for his own cause or theory.

I settle into a chair across from a huge desk that wraps halfway across the room. The office is enormous, capped by a large lit dome in the center of the ceiling. We're sitting close together, one bridge of the desk in between us. We're in a corner of a virtual chamber.

His undergraduate degree was pharmaceutical, he tells me, and he has a Ph.D. in biochemistry from the University of Illinois, College of Medicine. He spent some time working in a psychiatric institute, studying the biochemical basis for schizophrenia and other mental disturbances.

"I come from a middle class Jewish background," he says. "My parents were both immigrants from Russia. The ideal at that time was to have your son be a doctor." But doctors had to respond to the needs others presented them; a researcher can follow the commands of his own mind. He was the first person in his family to go to college, but he rebelled against his parents . . . he was a "doctor," all right. A Ph.D., not an M.D. "It was a subtle way of asserting myself. When I got my Ph.D., my mother said, 'for all these years of schooling, you could have been a doctor, already!'" I laugh; I can hear my own grandmother saying the same thing, and with just the same shrug.

For years, he worked at Abbott Laboratories in drug development research. "I discovered two products, both of which were too revolutionary for them to understand. One of which was a drug that affected learning behavior. It was their corporate belief that the brain was something you didn't touch, so therefore my drug for the brain didn't exist. The other product I developed was a chemical agent that seemed to work against herpes virus. But the concept of chemotherapy in 1965 was a heretical idea. 'Chemotherapy doesn't exist,' his boss had told him." Al learned it didn't exist because the boss had decided on a six million dollar building for *vaccine* as a treatment of viral diseases, not chemotherapy.

"At that point I left."

He worked at "a little chemical company for two years to build up the pharmaceutical division." He tells me the company billed $900,000 in chemical sales when he arrived. He grew his own pharmaceutical division from no sales at all to forty-five million dollars by the end of his two-year contract. He gives a short, breathy laugh which I soon discover is characteristic. He and the president had some differences of opinion, he says, so he left to form Newport in March of 1968.

It's a "small firm," in contrast to the giants. The company makes one product: Isoprinosine. It's sold in seventy-five countries around the world, often to licensees in bulk, as barrels of powder.

"So our sales are ten to twelve million. If we were a normal pharmaceutical firm, selling little pills in bottles and doing the marketing ourselves, that would be about sixty million. But we just didn't have the resources to do it that way." He developed Isoprinosine with Paul Gordon, "officially credited as the inventor of the product."

I like Al Glasky. My instincts tell me he's honest and conscientious, and I respect him. But I can see already that his own pleasure in being "right" could turn some people off. Do personal "politics" matter in the drug business, I wonder to myself. Or are things clear-cut? Can a drug be clearly shown to perform a specific function for people and therefore be approved -- facts are facts? Or do personal interactions make a difference in what reaches the public?

We discuss the fact that his former boss at Abbott didn't say, "we don't want to invest in chemotherapy, Al." Instead he said, "it doesn't exist."

"That is a form of intellectual dishonesty," he tells me. "I could accept a choice not to follow a certain path, but to pretend it just doesn't exist . . . I can't tolerate that." He is voicing a principle I take very seriously, myself.

"I think that kind of intellectual dishonesty pervades a lot of other areas that matter," he tells me. "For example, the NIH attitude toward the treatment of AIDS. They don't say 'it's a choice of this or that' . . . they just say, 'it is THIS . We decree, this is the approach of choice. This is the way we're going to fund.' And, unfortunately, the National Institute of Health has a great influence over the entire thinking of the United States. If you're at a university and you want to get funds, you've got to make sure your grant proposal is in line with what is the current dogma of the people who are giving the money."

Why does it have to be chocolate or strawberry, he asks me. Why can't we pursue both, why can't we pursue a dozen flavors to find the best combinations at different times? Only an insecure person is afraid to try something new, for fear of failure.   Abbott didn't need to choose vaccines over chemotherapy, he says; they could have done both. (In point of fact, he tells me, their vaccine building was later converted to a warehouse and they didn't go after vaccines after all.)

Similarly, he says, the NIH shouldn't have to choose between anti-viral or immune system treatments of AIDS; why can't we explore both? The anti-viral approach is sometimes called the search for the "magic bullet." You use a metaphorical "bullet" to kill the virus. The immune system approach, however, builds up the body's own ability to kill the virus itself.

"And which is isoprinosine," I say.   "Tell me about that powder you sell."

"Basically it's a new chemical compound," he says. " Aspirin is a compound, for example   Ours came out of ideas we had about how cells function.   We made a new synthetic molecule out of pre-existing parts. All chemical synthesis is done that way. No one starts with air, fire, and water any more!"

"What kind of chemical is in there," I ask him.   I almost say, "what is that stuff anyway?" but I think he understands already, I don't want to swim in technicalities.

"Inosine," he says, "is one of the two different compounds. The 'inosine' part of 'Isoprinosine.'   It's one of the nucleic acids that is part of the genetic material of the cell.   So the main point you'd want to know, I guess, is that inosine is something that is naturally found within our bodies.   The very building blocks that our bodies use to build genes and genetic material incorporate derivatives of inosine.   You have right now, each of your readers has right now, in every one of your cells, chemicals related to inosine."

"Okay."

"The other part of the molecule is, we call it an amino alcohol. It's a type of compound that contains nitrogen and oxygen and carbon. It's kind of related to a chemical substance that helps transmit information across from one nerve ending to another in our bodies."

"So you're telling me that the stuff that makes up Isoprinosine is, in fact, a combination of the same chemicals that we already naturally have in our bodies?"

"Yes, that's it. You can make them in a laboratory, also.   You set up flasks and heat them and bubbling liquids, all those images you think about.   But we're really working with material that is already naturally in each human being.   So to some extent, we think the unique safety of Isoprinosine is probably due to the fact that there's nothing really abnormal there. The body doesn't have to say, when it sees Isoprinosine, 'Well, what the hell is this?!'"

I admit that in the course of conducting these interviews, one of my secret pleasures has been to get Ph.D.'s talking to me in these kinds of terms.   Dr. Glasky's imitation of the body has a Chicago accent.

"Instead it says," he continues, telling me a story, "it says, 'Oh yeah, I remember a cousin like this guy.   I know a relative of that.'   So the point, Mike, is that the body has a way to get rid of it, without producing other more toxic things, which is normally what happens with other abnormal drugs."

"What would happen, then, if a totally healthy person took Isoprinosine?"

"Probably nothing.   The body would say, 'Oh, yeah, I recognize this,' and just get rid of it, and that's it."

"Okay.   Great.   I'm trying to learn about the industry from your experience, so let's continue.   You and your company had this product idea, and then you tried to test it out, right?"

"We developed our laboratories here, and we tested the drug. Originally, we thought it would affect learning and memory.   Our thinking then evolved.   We believed it might prevent viruses from multiplying.   We tested in animals against influenza and found -- it worked!

"Now the drug was already approved for testing as a learning enhancer.   So when the viral thing came up, we'd already proven the drug safe for humans.   We could quickly go in and test against virus.

"But -- when we got the idea, it was June of 1970.   You know June to September is not the height of the flu season, right?   Well one of the characteristics attributed to me is impatience.   I couldn't wait till October or November for people finally to get the flu.   I couldn't wait to see if our observations in animals would also prove true in humans.   So I went to Argentina at the beginning of their winter.   They said I was crazy.   They believed in vaccines, not anti-viral drugs.   They had all kinds of reasons why it wouldn't work.

"I said to one of the Argentine professors, 'okay, if you think I'm wrong, you have a moral obligation to to the Argentine people to prove it.   You'll only do that by running my test and showing how crazy I am. Otherwise, I'll certainly find someone in your country to run it for me --'"
Again, he laughs that short little laugh at himself.   He takes pleasure in his own stubborness, I think.

"So, he took the bait . . .and he found Isoprinosine worked in humans!   We rapidly got clinical data showing the drug had efficacy, treating viral disease in humans.   This was 1970."

A vaccine stimulates the body to produce antibodies, Dr. Glasky tells me. The antibodies then circulate in your blood and if a virus enters your system, the antibody's already there as an internal barrier.   An anti-viral, however, is injected after the virus is already in you; it seeks the virus out and kills it. "So vaccine is conceptually quite different from anti-viral treatment," he says, "even though they're related to the same disease." It was "news" to see Isoprinosine apparently succeeding as an anti-viral.

Now that Dr. Glasky knew the drug worked in both animals and humans, he needed to go back and fill in a gap: work in test tubes. But to everyone's surprise, Isoprinosine didn't work in the lab. This was a puzzle.

"That started to build the controversy on the drug," he says. "'Ah! It doesn't work in a test tube. How can a drug have any value if it doesn't work in a test tube?' Without test tube proof, no one believed us."

Dr. Glasky was surprised, but not daunted. "I have always been very biologically oriented. I am a great believer that the body has intrinsically in it much more than I, as a scientist, can fathom. It didn't bother me that there was something special happening in the body. To those people who know everything, it bothered them." (Again, I hear that ironic laugh.)

"Now a piece of modern history: Dr. Robert Good discovered the human T-lymphocyte in only 1972. It was revolutionary. You see, Mike, people only started to work widely in cell-mediated immunology within the last ten years! Most of the practicing physicians out there understandably never had training in that particular branch of immunology. That fact can impact on attitudes, as with anything new, I suppose."

He explains that the humoral or antibody-mediated view of immunology has been familiar for a long time; it was discovered by Louis Pasteur over 100 years ago. A great deal of research on cells and humoral immunology has been done in animals for many, many years. But Dr. Good's *human* T-cell discovery, and the cell-mediated immune functioning it involved . . . that was a major new contribution to the field. It's very newness, however, became a complicating factor in various test designs and interpretations.

So virologists were experiencing the failure of Isoprinosine in the test tube. But clinical immunologists -- who tested in humans -- were saying it worked. Why the discrepancy? The drug's reputation for controversy began to grow.

One night, purely by happenstance, Dr. Glasky read an article about a conference on immunology. "Aha!" he suddenly said to himself. "We haven't factored in the immune system!" That was the answer to the mystery. The drug was working through the body's own immune system when it was tested in humans, but the immune system wasn't being accounted for yet in the test tube environment. It was 1975.

"We had another 'problem,'" he says. "Isoprinosine worked against all sorts of diseases! How the hell can you have a drug that does everything? It worked with the flu, the common cold, herpes, hepatitis, measles, mumps. My God -- it was snake oil! It worked on everything, which diminished its credibility. It was too effective to be believed.

"But, Mike -- do you see? -- it didn't really work on ANY of those diseases. It worked on the *body* instead. It worked on the immune system itself. It helped the body fend off the diseases. If your body is intact and is functioning well, you don't usually get sick. You could walk into a room where everyone has a cold and sneezes, and you could walk out again still healthy. Because your body has defended itself against infectious agents!"

"Let me be sure I'm with you," I say. "The body's immune system is the basic tool we have to fight off disease. Isoprinosine helps that system work."

"Right. Helps it function in a normal, effective manner."

"It sounds like -- I'm jumping ahead, maybe -- but it sounds like, if you're really, absolutely right . . . ." I stare at him. IS this man a clever salesman disguised as my Dad? "It sounds like I might personally want to take Isoprinosine every day, because I don't want to get colds, I don't want to have my work and life interrupted."

"There are people who believe that and who take it themselves," he says slowly.

"Like an apple a day." (I'm hearing "Brush Your Teeth With Colgate" in my head. I have a momentary flash to Bucky Beaver, whom I watched in black and white on the Mickey Mouse Club at the age of twelve. Did a chemical used in Isoprinosine just transmit that ancient memory across the nerve endings of my brain? Does Dr. Glasky need my help in writing a jingle for Isoprinosine?)

"Conceptually," he replies, "if you can keep your immune system functioning at a normal, effective level all the time, you could reject the foreign material that enters your body. That's what your immune system does all the time. Whether it's a virus, bacteria, cancer cell, whatever. Your body was designed to repel and expell foreign materials. That's how you preserve yourself."

"Listen," I say. "I'm thinking to myself that if I knew a 'pusher' of Isoprinosine, and if I really KNEW that what you're telling me were true . . . I might want to HAVE it, just to protect myself. Even if I didn't know anything about AIDS."

"AIDS is incidental to the drug, really. AIDS is probably the most critical part in establishing the credibility of both the drug, and this field of science. People used to be unwilling to accept the importance of the cell-mediated immune system. They didn't learn anything about it in school.   Five years ago, if I'd walk up to the average doctor and say, 'What do you know about immune deficiency?' he'd say, 'There was some kind of Bubble Baby who couldn't live outside a bubble since he couldn't fight off any diseases. Is that it?' He'd be able to look up in a textbook a long string of rare but related diseases. Now if I ask a doctor, even if he got his training before cell-mediated immunology had come into the spotlight, just look at what he's quite familiar with. He knows about 'AIDS, the Acquired IMMUNE Deficiency Syndrome.'"

"What about big drug companies?" I ask him. "As the new field of immunology was developing, were they beginning to follow it?"

"No."

"Are you sure?"

"They weren't.   They were following the NIH approach to development of anti-viral agents. We hadn't come up with the 'Magic Bullet' yet to kill a virus. The research money was hunting for it. This aspect of immunology was too provocative. In a choice between Magic Bullet and 'Body Heal Thyself,' the latter sounds like quackery. The NIH wasn't favoring that."

"Summarize for me what the NIH really is, then. What its role is."

"About thirty years ago,the government decided we needed a national center of excellence where innovative work could be done. They created the National Institutes of Health.   A Federally funded group of laboratories, facilities, and hospital beds for supposedly state of the art research.   Something like the Pasteur Institute in France.   As time went by, one or another Congressman had a new favorite disease, and created an Institute for that disease too.

"The Institutes eventually became the conduit for the majority of Federal research money.   They got to approve grant requests from universities. The idea was to direct the tone of national research. In order to get the money, you've got to be doing favored work.   Unfortunately, that can become a restriction on the development of new ideas. It's hard to get consensus on something that's really different.

"So in the viral field, they determined that the Magic Bullet was the way to treat viral diseases.   That's been the official, dogmatic policy for the last twenty years."

"Is it still today?"

"Yes."

"So, let me sum up. You personally got involved with a very new field, the 'cell-mediated' branch of immunology.   But it hasn't been much in favor in Washington, because the people in charge of influencing U.S. research are more traditional. Am I understanding you?"

"Yes. They're competent, legitimate scientists, of course. They have their own personal biases and prejudices. The same way I feel this aspect of immunology is important, they're looking at it from their point of view."

"Okay. If that's the research context for a drug you've been struggling to get approval for, tell me what happened after you realized why it wasn't working in test tubes."

"Yes. We then designed studies to incorporate the immunological factors into lab work, and results began getting better. But -- a lot of people, and particularly those who felt insecure -- had fixed their position prior to '75 on the drug. How do you get an insecure person to get up and say, 'You know, there wasn't enough information then, and so I reached that conclusion . . . but now that you have more data, I was wrong, and I've changed my mind.' That's difficult, particularly when people hang on to outmoded, antiquated concepts."

I am sitting across from either a brilliant and flexible man or a lunatic, I decide.

"What did begin to happen was, the drug got approved in many countries. Sophisticated countries, not just Third World countries."

"Because you were beginning to try it in these different countries?"

"Oh, no, no! They approved it from U.S. data. We sent them the results and they said, 'oh, yeah,' and approved it. In most of the countries of the world, it got approved as a drug to treat viral disease, not worrying about how it worked. If you had the disease, you got better. Patients walked away two, three, five days later, healthy and happy. That was fine.

"At the same time, our knowledge of immunology and viral diseases was growing. We were at the forefront of learning the immunological implications of viral diseases. This was all pre-AIDS. The critique of Isoprinosine by someone during the period of our worst relationship with the FDA was, 'Isoprinosine is a drug in search of a disease.' That's an FDA quote. It was meant to be sarcastic and derogatory, but it turned out to be prophetic. Because the disease that Isoprinosine was searching for was the first disease that became publicly recognized as an immune deficiency disease. Prior to AIDS, the drug never had an 'identity' because there was never a disease recognized so clearly as an immunological disease of importance. Yes there was lupus, yes there was arthritis, but they don't have the generally widely accepted image of an immune deficiency disease."

"But tell me," I say, "now that you've got me thinking that your drug helps build up my immune system in general, if I have arthritis and if I take your drug, am I going to get better?"

"Probably. Because it controls the immune system."

"And the immune system is one of the reasons I have a problem with arthritis in the first place?"

"Yes. It's a defective immune system issue."

"Well, then, one could say, if I were doing a campaign like Colgate toothpaste, that Isoprinosine *is* a drug in search of a disease. `What disease? Whatever immuno-deficiency disease you've got, baby!'"

"That's right. It wants to help the body cure itself. Any kind of external or internal manifestations, subsequent to a defective immune system, can be helped by an immune modulator like Isoprinosine.

"The immune system has suppressor cells, or T-cells, and helper cells, or B-cells. When you hear someone talking about an ARC or AIDS patient's T-cell ratio being off, they're talking about an imbalance from the normal ratio of thos two kinds of cells. Now here's what Isoprinosine does: it stimulates the *body* to produce 'precursor' cells. Those cells are flexible in terms of what they can lead to. The *body* then decides, so to speak, if it needs more suppressor or helper cells to get back to its proper balance. That's why Isoprinosine is an immune 'modulator': the body can use it to modulate its balance of cells back to whatever balance it needs."

It's not quite as fast a story as a toothpaste jingle, but he certainly has me interested. "When did you first try to get the FDA to approve this drug in the United States?"

"The first application was in 1974 for herpes. It was rejected for insufficient data, and I'd have to say . . . probably they were right, we needed more hard data proof. Next was 1980, we applied for measles encephalitis. That's a fatal form of measles, in which the virus goes into the brain. That disease is very rare, but it's 95% fatal. Some specialists had obtained our drug and were testing it on the problem. All of a sudden we saw a published paper -- seventy percent of the cases tested in Georgia were alive! So we submitted the data to the FDA. To make a long story short, this usage was also rejected by the FDA. Why? An entrenched position vis-a-vis immunology, and the fact that by now we'd become confrontatory to them."

Newport Labs took the FDA to court on the measles case -- and lost. "It had been a 95% percent fatal disease with maybe 200 total patients in the country. They said maybe we had inadvertantly picked natural survivors -- but that would be only 5%, or ten people in the entire country. All of a sudden, many more people were surviving, after taking Isoprinosine."

"This kind of process," I say, "trying with the FDA and maybe being accepted and maybe being rejected -- this happens all the time, right? To all kinds of drug companies."

"Of course. But what most people do when something like that happens, they drop the drug. 'Why jeopardize our relationship? Let's move on to a new form of penicillin, or a new this or that.' We had no choice! We couldn't move on. This was our product, period. And it's the position of the FDA that once a drug is approved for *any* disease, a physician can choose -- on his own responsibility -- to prescribe it as he wishes, even for others. So we had to keep trying to get in the door, one way or another.

"We continued, then. In '81, we lost the measles attempt. In '82, we began work on AIDS. When AIDS first came out, we tried first to save the lives of terminally ill patients. And while we had a little bit of immunological effect, they died within two or three weeks. There also happened to be some ARC patients, and we saw a bit more positive results. But again, it was only short-term administration of the drug. They didn't take it over an extended period of time.

"Then we heard from Bekesi -- you've spoken to him. He convinced us to go into the pre-AIDS area. He was one of the independent people to do testing for us, and he convinced us to run the study. He figured out what the test would cost, but it's up to the drug company to pay for it. It typically used to cost $2,500 per patient. So a study of 100 patients would cost $250,000. It's now probably closer to $5,000 a patient. That's just for one study, Mike. So we can't do them all, you see? Or not all at once. We don't have those kinds of resources."

He tells me the Bekesi study showed immune system improvements with seventy percent of the people tested. Also, the test showed it takes time for the immune system to improve itself. A twenty-eight day dosage of Isoprinosine often began the process; additional time passed before full improvement was achieved.

"That was a novel concept for therapeutics," he says. "To start something off and then let the body finish by itself. Some AIDS clinicians still don't accept it. 'The drug's already been gone for two months,' they say. 'How can it still be doing something in the patient?' The answer, of course, is that the drug has started the immune system healing itself. The drug starts the process, the *body* then finishes the job."

Dr. Glasky tells me, further, that fifteen percent of people infected with the virus go on to develop AIDS . . . followup on Bekesi's test group showed this figure reduced to only five percent during the one year after taking isoprinosine. "It doesn't cure everyone, that's true. But if it can decrease the rate of getting AIDS at all, that's valuable too. Think of the one or two million people exposed to the virus already."

He reminds me now that the Bekesi test was only twenty-eight days of therapy. What about sixty days? What if the twenty-eight day cycle is repeated every second or third month? "The immune system may well be one of the most fundamentally important things in your body. It prevents you from dying every day. So mightn't it make sense that one

332

can't easily make changes in it? Either depression or improvement? It makes sense that it might take prolonged time to affect it, and I can't tell you the precise times required.

"I just don't know those answers yet. All I can say is, what one dose of twenty-eight days can do. I've got lots of questions, just like George did. We couldn't answer them all at once. We had to verify his study, and this time we involved the FDA in exactly how they wanted us to verify it. We didn't want to take any chances at all! We wanted to test in whatever way they wished to see the data, so we'd have the maximum chance -- if the drug continued to work -- of getting approval."

The process of FDA agreement on how to test took six months. The result was the study that Ron Grossman has been part of. It began in November of 1984. Different doctors in different test centers have entered at different times.

Now, as Dr. Glasky sits across the desk from me, he tells me the FDA has in fact approved Newport's application for filing -- that means there's at least enough positive data to make the application worth considering. The FDA has also just completed a tour of the company's manufacturing facility in Ireland. He is confident they'll have found it sufficiently hygienic.

What remains is -- the final verdict. By regulation, the verdict must be given within 180 days of the application's having been filed. It was filed on September 3, 1985. So by early March, 1986 Dr. Glasky will know whether, this time, his company's only product has finally been approved for public safety by the Food and Drug Authority.

He is optimistic, he tells me, and he's continuing to receive new data. He knows his product is controversial. He knows there are doctors who don't believe in it. But he is confident that it works . . . that time will reveal it really does. He knows right now, he says, of people with AIDS -- yes, real AIDS -- who are getting better because of these pills.

We've been talking intensely for hours. I arrived in California at noon, checked into the hotel, and came straight to his lab. I'm feeling hungry, sleepy, and I'm remembering an article I've read about the stress of different time zones . . . a strain on one's immune system. Now as I hear this man say his unapproved pills can make even people with full AIDS get better, I feel an exhausted and fragile gratitude at the prospect.

I have seen many more weakened people than I expected at the start of this journey. I've seen many more frail arms, thin legs, purple lesions, and oxygen masks on shrunken faces.

"I don't know how many people with AIDS you've seen," I say. "Have you seen a lot?"

"No."

"Have you seen any?"

"No." He has never even seen one AIDS patient? He is working his twelve-hour days, he is counting the minutes till the FDA speaks, he is following 1800 published papers on Isoprinosine . . . and he's never even seen one AIDS patient?

"I have," I say. My fatigue is now overcoming me. I am mumbling, but I'm too tired to make myself speak crisply to him. "When I started this project, I never expected to have such contact with misery. So I can't help being moved when you tell me you can make a difference. It seems very important to me. I -- wait, I've just got to ask you something. You haven't even SEEN one person with AIDS? I'm feeling very emotional right now, because I now know some of these people who might ultimately be able to get better if Isoprinosine can help them. I'm thinking right now of specific people I've encountered. But what do *you* feel? What do you FEEL?"

"I feel . . . I don't view AIDS in the same way other people do. AIDS is one of the immune deficiency diseases that are important to mankind. It is only one, Mike. I'm not obsessed with AIDS. Even though I've not seen people die of AIDS, I have seen people die of other viral diseases. I empathize. And I cry with them and for them. I can visualize the pain.

"I can feel what it means in the AIDS thing, but I view AIDS as part of a family of human diseases. When we did a study in the Ivory Coast, with children who are dying of measles . . . measles is a disease that nobody dies from in the United States. Its mortality rate in the Ivory Coast is forty percent. Forty percent of the children who have measles there die from it, and it's a disease they don't have to die from! When we gave Isoprinosine to those children, we decreased the death rate to between five and ten percent."

"I assume it's a culture that can't afford to vaccinate everybody?"

"That's right! But -- we could do that, and I can keep children from dying. That is meaningful to me."

"Right."

"There is a disease in South America. It's a tick-borne viral disease. In the Far East, it's called 'denge fever.' It causes hemorrages, 'hemorragic fever.' When we first tested the drug as an anti-viral against influenza in Argentina, I was in Buenos Aires. They had an outbreak of hemorragic fever on the Argentine-Bolivian border. My friend who was skeptical took the drug and sent it to a village, a doctor he knew there wanted it. A little child had contracted the disease, had been bitten by a flea, and was dying. They had no coffins. The child had not yet died...."

When he says "died," his voice catches. I think he's surprised to hear it himself. "Died" becomes a two syllable word, the second syllable lost in his struggling breath.

"They were building a little coffin for the baby. In this village."

We are looking at each other closely, he and I, as he tells me this story. I can feel his feeling right now. I see that his eyes are watering, just as mine are. I sense he is embarrassed. I'm *sure* he is. He stops talking. I see the tightness on his face quiver in silence. And now he starts to cry. Now I feel tears on my own cheeks, too.

He reaches stiffly under his desk and finds a box of Kleenex. This confident, somewhat abrasive man touches me now as he wipes the tears from his eyes, first with a shirt-sleeve, now with a Kleenex.

"I'm glad to see you feel," I tell him. My own voice sounds cracked, too. "Please feel. Please feel."

"This was one of the most moving experiences I've ever had in my life," he says. It is perhaps an apology.   Maybe scientific Ph.D.'s and company presidents aren't supposed to cry.

"The drug got to the child," he says breathlessly. His words are mixed with air and a sigh of gratitude. "The mother walked 200 miles." It is a trembling whisper, he is trying to speak the words so I hear them. 200 miles. "And she brought the child to show me." I can barely hear the end of the sentence. We are both, frankly, crying.

"I was sitting in my room," he begins again, now with more control. "A hotel in Buenos Aires. And this poor peasant mother had brought the child 200 miles to thank me for saving its life.   That's what makes you fight, you know.   Those are things that are simply very moving. They keep you going.   When people don't understand, it hurts. You try to prove it, and you say, 'what can I do?' For many years, I would bat my head against the wall and say, 'if I could save that child's life, why don't they let me save others?' This was an event that occurred in 1971."

"1971?"

"Yes! Since then, we have known what the drug can do. We didn't know about the immunological aspects then. But we knew what we could do."

"Since 1971, you've had a product you've been developing that you knew could save human life? When you said in the car, when I asked you about your motivation and what would success mean to you . . . when you said, 'the end of years of struggle,' is this what you meant?"

"Yes. You almost go crazy for a while.   Then you have to hold back and get yourself on a logical pathway. You have to accept that there are people dying today and you will not be able to help them. But if you don't have discipline, you're not ever going to help anyone."

"Yes."

"So when I got the Bekesi study, and he wanted to know what would happen with doses over longer time, no matter how much I wanted to know, too, I had to hold myself back. We have to start somewhere, but it has to be with discipline. It has to be that way for the drug to get approved and begin saving anyone."

"I have to admit to you," I say, "I realize now you don't have to see someone dying of AIDS itself to care about it. You're seeing AIDS in the broader context of the immune system. I understand that now. I know you're trying to help solve the AIDS problem, but I realize you're actually trying to solve a number of related problems, too."

"AIDS is one of many illnesses I think can be helped," he says.

"I care about AIDS especially right now."

"Of course you do. And you should care. But the context is broad, you see, and that's important too. What can come out of AIDS . . . if we can get this concept of restoring the immune system, getting it to function normally all the time, if we can get that from AIDS . . . then the 7,500 or 8,000 people who've died of AIDS, they have really made a major contribution to mankind. Because their deaths will have triggered public awareness and appreciation of the immune system. That is the pathway for research and treatment for many other things as well.

"Not only for gay people and drug addicts, but for all of us. For human beings."

~ ~ ~ ~ ~

DECEMBER 19, 1985, NEW ZEALAND: Douglas Pharmaceuticals, Ltd., a licensee of Isoprinosine from Newport Pharmaceuticals, receives approval from government health authorities to market Isoprinosine for the treatment of AIDS and ARC in that country. New Zealand is the first government to approve Isoprinosine specifically for AIDS-related diseases. The drug will be marketed in that country under the tradename Imunovir.

Isoprinosine therefore becomes the first drug approved by *any* government to be marketed specifically for the treatment of AIDS and AIDS-related complex.

Chapter 30:
Los Angeles

Los Angeles was very much in the national AIDS news, not just because of its substantial number of people with AIDS. It is also the home of Hollywood and all the issues associated with the entertainment industry and Rock Hudson. And it was the first city in the world to pass an anti-discrimination law for AIDS.

Here are interviews reflecting four sides of the Los Angeles perspective -- political, entertainment, public health, and fund raising for AIDS.

Mark Siegel -
Deputy to Los Angeles Councilman, Joel Wachs
My Indian taxi driver takes me through a section of Los Angeles he calls "Korean Town." The smog is so thick that the palm trees and buildings ahead are drained of color, lost in grayness like an old black-and-white TV screen. After a twenty dollar cab ride, he lets me out at City Hall. Several fat buildings are connected by a pedestrian tunnel; it crosses in the air high over the street.

"I'm Legislative Deputy for Councilman Wachs," Mark Siegel tells me, when I've located his office from the puzzlement of choices. The councilman's name is pronounced "wax."

Mark grew up in Los Angeles, and has worked with Councilman Wachs for five years. "Part of my job is simply to deal with any issue that comes up, from last week's motion to declare Los Angeles a sanctuary for immigrants, to AIDS discrimination, to providing a park where people can run their dogs without leashes. It's a whole wide range of issues, which makes this job so much fun." He is thirty-three, married, has one child and another on the way. He's a slender man with thinning brown hair.

I notice he wears dull gray leather loafers and short socks that show his leg. I had learned early in my career that it's mandatory in business to wear knee-high socks so your legs never show . . . you maintain more illusion of power that way, less humanity. Mark's job is to represent people and their personal needs, so a show of common humanity probably helps.

"How many Councilpeople are their for Los Angeles?" I ask him.

"Fifteen. There are three and a half million people in Los Angeles, and each Council District is roughly 191,000 people.

"Our District is a wide and diverse cross section. In the Hollywood Hills, we have the entertainment industry -- very wealthy. In the San Fernando part, we have the second highest number of senior citizens of all Council Districts. In North Hollywood and other areas, we have Hispanic sections with gang and crime problems. And in the Mount Washington, Highland Park, and Studio City areas we have an increasing number of gay residents, and also Chinese and Asian residents. It's very diverse."

"How much of a Councilman's stance on issues represent what he feels personally, versus his constituency?"

"That's a fluid equation," he replies. "It changes on every issue. But if push comes to shove, and there's really a total divergence, Joel will do what he feels is the right thing to do. It will come from himself. That is becoming more and more true as he's in office longer. He's been in office fifteen years now.

"On a strictly neighborhood issue, he'll follow their lead. If they don't want a tall skyscraper or discotheque, he'll be on the front lines fighting it. Even though he's not puritanical or opposed to discotheques.

"But on an issue like AIDS, it was something from inside himself. He did what he felt was right, regardless of what his constituents would think." I know Mark is talking about the anti-discrimination law.

"Can you remember when AIDS first began to be a relevant issue for your assignment?"

"Yeah. Take a look behind you." I turn and see a cardboard box filled with newspapers.

"I go through those every day and look for re-occurring stories, items of interest. Three or four years ago, Joel and I started trading clips on AIDS.. He'd write me notes about the topic, it began to be something he'd pick up on.

"Three years ago, he gave me a note that said, `AIDS is going to be *the* issue of the 1980's and perhaps of the second half of this century.' He predicted that. I believe when they go back and do retrospectives of the decade, he will be right. AIDS is a pre-eminent topic."

"Why? What's so important about AIDS?

"It touches people so deeply. Sure, it's true most of the country has never met anybody with AIDS. Most of them probably don't know

338

anyone they realize is homosexual. Yet, there's something about this issue that affects people enormously. It evokes very strong emotions.

"It's probably because of the combination of three major human issues AIDS touches -- Sex, Death, and Religion. They all come together. Everyone has deep, internalized feelings about each of those issues. `Is it a curse? Is it a virus? Should I have compassion? Should I have anger?' People are forced to sort that through. They say the sexual revolution of the sixties seems to have ended. You hear more and more talk of religious fundamentalism, of restraint on sexuality, of neo-Victorianism.

"AIDS flies right in the face of all that. Not that it encourages people to have sex, but it's an acknowledgement of sexuality. It's the opposite of, `Let's ignore sexuality. Let's drive it back into the closet.' AIDS is an acknowledgement, particularly given the way the disease first occurred in this country, of homosexuality itself, which people have a very rough time with.

"When somebody like Rock Hudson gets diagnosed, a man who was a sex symbol, suddenly everything's turned inside out as all the revelations come forth. `He must have been a homosexual. Here is somebody I've liked, had fantasies about, etc. Someone I idolized, and suddenly he is not what I thought he was.'

"The revelation is one of his sexuality. That causes contradictions and emotional turmoil across the country on an individual basis. That's significant."

"So," I say. "That's why you think Joel was right about AIDS' importance. I'm going to start calling him 'Joel' now instead of 'Councilman Wachs.' While you were noticing the disease three years ago, was the community?"

"Not so very much. But the gay community was. It was once called 'Gay Plague' after all. It was the mysterious 'gay disease.' While watching it closely, we were wondering what the city could do about it.

"You see, the city doesn't deal with health issues, primarily. In Los Angeles, the Health Department is run by the County of Los Angeles, a separate jurisdiction. The County Hospital, the public health officers, the issue of closing baths or not . . . those are mostly concerns for the county."

"What kinds of pressures were you feeling, if any, in your city position?"

"Well, the people within the AIDS community increasingly began to come to us. `AIDS community' means social service agencies, medical officals, public health officials, all in addition to gay community organizations. They were coming to the city to ask for money to provide emergency services -- food, housing, clothing, and public education.

"We were watching a new issue, and beginning to hear new concerns. Several people that Joel and I worked with politically died of AIDS. That makes it very real to you, when somebody you've walked precincts with and gone to fund-raisers with is dead at age thirty-three.

"That's a difference with AIDS. When someone's in their seventies, their eighties, somehow you say, `It's terrible that they died. I feel great loss. But they lived a full life.' But when somebody dies at age thirty, or twenty-five, or a child of two, you feel a greater sense of injustice. This is a person who had so much more to contribute, so much more to live. It's just not fair. Those are your feelings, anyway.

"I can really point to the beginning of AIDS discrimination work for me at a meeting we had with Gary McDonald, on the AIDS Action Committee from Washington. That's a group of AIDS organizations lobbying government. We all thought the best thing the city could do was education -- trying to make people be rational.

"It was at that point we thought the City should have hearings, a way to say one more time that you can't get it from casual contact." He laughs at how many times he's heard himself repeating that. "It just needs to be said, over and over and over again.

"At those hearings, various organizations testified. `We need more shelter, because people get evicted.' `We need emergency monies, because people lose their jobs when diagnosed, whether they can still work or not.' `We need emergency food, because --.'"

"It became this litany. `We need support for people who have the virus, but are not in bed. We need support because of discrimination against them. For people who, if it were not for discrimination, could still be productively mainstream in society.'

"This was in June of this year, 1985. And it just 'clicked' for Joel. As he was listening to all this, he thought to himself, Hey, what we should do first is *prevent* them from being evicted!"

"Then you wouldn't have to spend the money," I say.

"Then we wouldn't have to spend the money," he repeats.

"What does the law accomplish?"

"The law prohibits discrimination in housing, employment, public services, businesses, and places of accomodation."

"This is the first such law for a major city in this country?"

"Yes. It was the first such law of *any* city, as we know it, in the world."

"And, was Joel the sponsor of it?"

"It was Joel's idea. Joel sponsored it all the way through."

"Was it a hard thing to get people to agree to?" He tells me they didn't get a lot of media attention for their first press conference about the proposed law. He remembers they got "page three of part two."

After the first announcement came a second hearing of experts, this one for the committee considering the law. For example, Dr. Shirley Fannin, head of the Communicable Disease section for the County Health Department, testified that tenants in a building couldn't get AIDS from casual contact with another tenant who's contracted the disease. The Apartment Association said that landlords themselves get pressured by other tenants and might actually welcome a law to prohibit discriminatory evictions.

Subsequently, the proposal left the committee and was brought, again with expert testimony, before the City Council. Now it was receiving more prominent coverage. When Rock Hudson was diagnosed with AIDS, "suddenly the issue was a cover story." Ultimately, the Council voted fourteen to nothing in favor of the law.

"The Mayor signed it two days later, in mid-July. "Then the shit hit the fan," he says. Despite three public hearings and four different press events, "we had some of the most vile and ugly hate letters." I ask him for a sample, and he opens a very thick file.

"We also got a lot of support. Papers as remote as the *New York Times* editorialized in favor of the ordinance," as did most L.A. papers, medical experts, dental associations, restaurant associations, etc. Joel was interviewed by TV reporters from Australia, Japan, France, and other countries about his reasons for conceiving the law. A similar ordinance has since been passed by San Francisco and other California cities. It is now being considered in many other locations.

He finds a letter for me:

> "'They' have molested our young boys
>   ruined the health of our youth,
>   even killed each other.
> Now 'they' expect sympathy, coddling,
>   and respect from us. No way!!!
>   Let the sick, sick, sick DIE!
> The rest start living like normal humans.
>   Neighbor of Gays"

And another:

> "Homosexuality is bestiality, even worse.
> How many animals drink urine and eat shit? Ha? Ha?
>   Homosexuals are deviates.
>   Sinful, dirty, and they spread diseases
>   because of their uncleanliness.
> The Bible states clearly that homosexuality is verbotten.
> You cannot change what God has wrought." (no signature)

And another:

> "If you think I'm going to rent
> to the shit-eating goddamned queers
> I promise you will be sorry.
> Quarantine them or shoot them.
>   Central Hollywood Apt. Owner
> This is your first and last warning!
> I intend to start a landlord-tenant program
> that will blow you into oblivion."

"So," Mark says, "now we're primarily working on promoting enforcement, compliance with the ordinance. And also greater public AIDS education. We went to the Board of Education, urging that there be greater and more focused AIDS discussion in high school as part of the health programs. The Board has agreed, and they're now preparing materials which should be ready in January."

"So high school students of Los Angeles, starting in January, will begin being educated about AIDS?"

"Yes."

"Does that mean, what safe sex is?"

"Potentially, yes. I think it will. I hope they do address it in a straightforward, plain English way."

"Does the public know this yet?"

"It was in the newspaper."

"Would you anticipate that when the time really comes, and when a student comes home with a leaflet on the topic, that there'll again be negative mail? From parents who do not want their children to hear about sex in school?"

"Yes. I expect there will be. But I think this a leadership stance and reflects a real commitment to education about AIDS. While the scientists are working to develop cures and vaccines, what the public can do is educate itself. We do get calls -- 'you homo-lover' -- that sort of stuff. But we have to do what we have to do."

Mark would like to say this to readers:

"We need, as a society, to conduct a war against AIDS. But it's a war against the virus, not against the victims. It's everybody's personal responsibility to educate themselves about that, so they'll be able to forego hysteria and offer compassion and caring instead."

Lunch with the Movie Marketing Man

"What a nice life," I think dreamily. For the first time this trip, I am idly scanning a magazine. I'm in a picturesque restaurant under skylights and hanging greenery. Le Serre, with its exquisite cuisine, is in Coldwater Canyon, between Beverly Hills and Sherman Oaks. A friend of a friend, quite well known and successful in motion picture marketing, has invited me to lunch to talk about Hollywood and AIDS.

"I hope you're telling the human side of Hollywood," he says. "With very few exceptions, this community has rallied remarkably in the face of the AIDS disaster. Hollywood is a kind of 'company town' for the movie business. Some small towns hold bake sales after floods and fires. AIDS is our 'flood.' Instead of baking cakes, people buy benefit tickets at $1,000 a plate. The spirit is exactly the same, though. Caring, generous, concerned."

I ask him, of course, about what I've read since Rock Hudson's diagnosis and death. Are gay actors being discriminated against? Is there panic by actresses about deep kissing?

"The truth is," he replies, "and I'm telling you this as a gay man, myself, the alleged discrimination issue is based more on media reports than reality. I don't question the motives of the people who held press conferences about the right NOT to deep kiss. I believe they were sincerely concerned. However, as we know -- it was in a December *Variety* and in *Hollywood Reporter*, for example -- medical experts say that kissing in any fashion was NEVER connected with the spread of AIDS.

"Often in Hollywood, people tend to talk with the press first and get the facts later. After all, considering all the drama at the time of Rock Hudson's announcement, there wouldn't have been much of a story in announcing that kissing *doesn't* cause AIDS, would there? Among true Hollywood professionals, and that's most of the people in the business, there was never any great panic. Concern? Yes. But not panic, I don't care what the *National Enquirer* said.

"By the way, the people in front of the camera have always had the option of either faking a punch or doing the real thing. They could use a stunt person or perform it themselves. They could make love for real, maybe with just a single cameraman on the set, or they could pretend and have the result end up exactly the same on your movie screen. Same with deep kissing -- it's an option they've always had. Do it for real, or do it as 'make believe.'

I ask the executive about the articles I've read in which people have expressed worry about discrimination against gay actors.

"Mike, I know it'd be more exciting copy for you if I could confirm that. And obviously I know plenty of gay actors. But the discrimination thing just isn't so. Is an actor the best person for the part? If the answer is yes and if all other things are equal -- the salary, the contract, and so on -- then the person gets the part. Sexual orientation has nothing to do with it.

"You've got to understand that first and foremost -- no matter what we try to make you think in your living room armchair -- Hollywood is a business. What people don't realize is how much money depends on getting the best results for every production. That's why there's not a 'casting couch' except, maybe, in the very lowest levels of the business. With millions of dollars riding on each scene, you can't afford to calculate your choices on anything but producing the best results. It's a *business* , Mike, like I said.

"As for tolerating each other's lifestyles, Hollywood doesn't care about personal preferences. 'She likes to do it with goats? Fine, babe. Just make sure she shows up at the studio on time. You want me to attend a cocktail party with her goats? Sure, I can make it. You want me to pose for pictures with 'em? Hey, no problem.'" (He imitates across the lunch table smiling for a camera and being surrounded on either side by snorting, sex-crazed goats.) "`Just make sure she's fabulous in front of the camera and makes plenty of money for us, okay? Don't sweat the rumors, babe. We'll say she's kind . . . she truly loves animals.'

"Seriously, Mike, everyone here is and has been very tolerant of each other, except in the dark ages of the '50's Black List, or in response to the occasional group concerned about sex and violence. What it all comes back to is the results on the screen -- that's what makes dollars at the boxoffice. You'll always have rumors here, that's part of our way of life. It spices things up. But even a good one hardly lasts long enough to make it from breakfast at the Polo lounge till dinner at Morton's. The main thing is making movie magic . . . and money."

It is absolutely true, he tells me, that AIDS has had a chilling impact on sexual ease. Once people within an entertainment corporation might have noted, "he's got an affair-ette going with him, but he's also sleeping with her." Now the talk is more likely to be who's NOT having sex with someone, even though he'd like to.

"People are scared, that's for sure," he says. "The thing I most care for the public to realize is that Hollywood people are NOT shallow and heartless to people with AIDS. There is enormous concern and kindness, you see it every day. People show great sensitivity to each other, and many are devoting considerable resources to help fund research and treatment.

"Of course we want you to think of us as magic. And we are, in a way -- just bits of light and sound that can make 700 strangers cry at once, or laugh as a family. But behind the magic and behind the publicity glamor there are good people here, real people. Most of all, they care about their fellow human beings."

We stroll outside into dazzling afternoon sunshine. A limousine smoothes to the front of the restaurant for my host.

My own taxi driver has said that business is so bad this week, he'd be still right there at the restaurant, waiting for me at the end of our lunch. Sure enough, there he is: "my driver." My fantasy of being a star requires ignoring the shabby condition of his cab. I say goodbye to the movie man and thank him for lunch and his comments. He glides away, back'to his headquarters.

"Please take me to the Los Angeles County Public Health Service," I say. As I name the destination, the fantasy begins to evaporate.

Dr. Martin Finn - L.A. County Public Health Dept.

A secretary on the elevator says she doesn't herself work closely with Dr. Finn, "but everybody who does says he's an unusually lovely human being, one of the beautiful ones."

At first impression, he is a mild, low key man, large-framed, sandy hair, cautiously friendly. He is fifty-one. As we talk, a single feeling begins to summarize my sense of him: if I were sick, I would feel safer with him by my bedside. One feels his concientiousness and a kind of benevolence very readily.

For about ten years, he's been Medical Director of Public Health for the County of Los Angeles. Census figures say he's responsible for eight million residents. With undocumented aliens, he believes ten million is probably more accurate. These people are spread over 423 square miles. A major public health focus is education to help prevent disease, spreading wor of even with simple truths like the importance of washing hands before food preparation. His annual budget is $100 million -- about ten dollars a person.

This week, he starts a new job, one that he requested. He'll work full time on the public health issues of AIDS. He'll coordinate County hospitals, forty-four AIDS clinics, and private agencies.

Dr. Finn was influenced to be a doctor by his family physician in Pasadena. He was planning on pediatrics, but serving in East Los Angeles changed his mind. He became fascinated by the social consequences of disease, by how illness affects the various segments of society.

In medical school, he says, a doctor's training focuses on organisms, on the body's responses, and on chemical intervention. But his experience with Hispanics taught him that education can be far more important to far more people, to stop disease from further spreading. He learned that cultural attitudes really matter -- how is the illness perceived? What are the human targets of a disease willing to do to avoid it?

He tells me how he first got involved with AIDS. The Atlanta CDC leads our Federal public health system. The local delegate in the fall of 1981 was David Auerbach, an "Epidemiology Intelligence Surveillance Officer." Auerbach worked closely with Michael Gottleib at U.C.L.A. Dr. Gottleib is considered "the man who blew the whistle" by formally identifying and describing a patient with the strange new disease. Dr. Auerbach quickly involved Dr. Finn. Everyone wanted to see, first hand, what these cancerous lesions actually looked like.

Soon, however, it became clear that AIDS patients had unusually draining needs. To help develop the best ways to support them, Dr. Finn became involved with AIDS Project L.A. Eventually he served as Chairman of the Board in addition to his Public health position.

By the fall of 1983, he was beginning to have concerns that this disease was not really "gay related." He began to perceive AIDS as a disease that, if continued unchecked, "could genuinely be a threat to civilization as we know it. An extremely serious illness, fatal, extremely expensive to care for, with a continuing, exponential increase in cases."

AIDS, he believes, is "the public health issue of this century." He freely admits there are times when his responsibility in the face of potential catastrophe can be frightening, especially when people are so uninformed. He's had to overcome, as a frequent reaction, "it's just a gay disease" or "can't you simply handle it medically?"

His interest in the social ramifications of disease made him alert early on to the poignant results of AIDS on various groups. Like, hemophiliacs. They had just, within the past decade, received new hope from "cryoprecipitate." That's an injection that helps blood clot more effectively. But the transfusions that were meant to save their lives contained the virus that has infected 95% of them. As we talk about the spread of AIDS to heterosexuals, I ask Dr. Finn about his experience with bisexuals as transmittors.

"I've had considerable experience working with bisexuals in venereal disease clinics and in my AIDS volunteer work." Many married heterosexuals with families, he says, are privately worried about covert homosexual experiences. "There's no doubt about that."

The general public, however, exhibits "denial" of how widespread bisexual experiences really are. "I'm not making a value judgement one way or the other," he says. "I just think we have to realize the human predicament of such individuals. I don't believe any such people we deal with have chosen to feel the personal impulses they may feel."

I ask him what the future thrust of his AIDS education efforts will be. He mentions 23,000 health services employees who need to be better informed. He cites the medical community which is still under-informed about AIDS.

Los Angeles doesn't today have the extreme IV drug problems of New York and New Jersey. 95% of local AIDS cases have been gay or

346

bisexual. $135,000 has been targeted for education to these high risk groups. The broader public will receive more reassurance, e.g. you needn't worry about catching AIDS from sitting in a bus.

"What about school children?" I ask him. His office supported the recent decision by the L.A. school district to specifically educate children in the classroom. "The teen-age years are when so much experimentation takes place. We can't allow the virus to become prevalent within that population."

"When school kids begin being educated," I ask him, "about what 'safe sex' is and what it's not, do you expect some parents to become uptight and angry?"

"I'm sure that will be so," he replies. "There are already parents who have difficulty accepting discussion of general sexually transmitted diseases. I want parents to know what the education of their children is, of course. Some parents probably need the information as much as the young people. In any event, we simply cannot allow adolescents to be kept in ignorance. To do so is to set them up for a fatal disease."

"We see no medical reason to prohibit children with AIDS from going to school," unless they are neurologically handicapped or under the age of three (therefore having difficulty with the handling of body fluids.) "We would not support the exclusion, across the board, of AIDS children from school."

"Let me ask you some highly specific questions about sexual transmission," I say. "Some of these come from readers who've been following *CHRONICLE* via computer."

"Go right ahead. Education is really the best weapon we have to prevent AIDS from spreading."

Here is a transcript of our discussion:

MIKE: "If I'm a single, sexually active heterosexual male or female, what advice should I get?"

DR. FINN: "This is the era of sexual responsibility. Male or female, gay or straight: anonymous sexual activity, having relations with someone you don't know . . . or multiple sexual activity with multiple partners . . . either is dangerous right now. People might as well adopt an attitude that will limit their number of sexual partners. They should know who they're having sex with and the health status of that individual."

MIKE: "I'm going to be Devil's Advocate now."

DR. FINN: "Sure. I expect you to."

MIKE: "First. Suppose I'm a heterosexual woman, and I'm having sex with a man I don't know. What if I use a condom? Doesn't that stop me from being at risk?"

DR. FINN: "I would certainly advise that woman to use a condom, but I will never give 100% assurance of prevention. We know in family planning that it's just not 100%. If you're going to have sexual intercourse, use it, fine. But I'd prefer that she not have sexual activity with someone she doesn't know."

MIKE: "Well, speaking on her behalf, `If I'm making the decision to move from no sexual activity with someone to thinking, now I know him sufficiently, what should I have learned about him? What do I want to know?'"

DR. FINN: "You have to become, I guess this is outside of marriage, you have to become almost sexual negotiators. Get to know him. Any health problems? There are certain activities I would not participate in. For a woman, anal intercourse makes no more sense than it does for gay males. It's just as dangerous. I don't think people realize how much anal intercourse there is in the heterosexual population. We know because of the rectal gonnoreah we've found in females. The CDC began to advise us not just to culture for vaginal gonnoreah, but also rectal."

MIKE: "Do you have any guess or research on the frequency of rectal intercourse with heterosexuals?"

DR. FINN: "I really don't. I just know it's there. Quite honestly, some individuals tell me they use it as a method of birth control. But AIDS is just too serious a risk. It's education, not medicine, that has to protect people right now."

MIKE: "You said condoms have sometimes not worked as preventive measures for birth control. What if I reply, `Well, it's because the condom broke. Or because the man withdrew carelessly, allowing sperm to leak. If we solve those two problems, then we're okay.' What about that?"

DR. FINN: "I suppose . . . you'll be talking with Dr. Voeller you said?"

MIKE: "Yes, but I'll be seeing him in New York."

DR. FINN: "That's been an area of specific interest for him, so ask him about it. One tip I heard recently is, you can't expect to leave a condom in the glove compartment of your car for two years and think it's offering the protection it once did. Heat over time can make a difference. There are even differing condoms with respect to quality, thickness. Certain lubricants are destructive to the materials. So you see, there are quite a few reasons they can fail."

MIKE: "Let me press you for more specifics. Suppose I tell you, `Okay, Dr. Finn. I don't like to use a condom, mind you, but you've talked me into it. And I'll even use a fresh one as a concession to taking care of myself. But what I do not want to give up at all is deep kissing. I've read that the chances of viral transmission from deep kissing are *much* less than, for example, anal intercourse.' Can you validate that?"

DR. FINN: "Well, certainly epidemiological investigations with those who have AIDS have shown far more evidence that anal intercourse is implicated rather than deep kissing. That's all we can say at this time. Yes, the virus has been demonstrated in saliva. But that doesn't say the virus is present in enough dose to transmit the disease. Something like deep kissing right now has to be left almost to conjecture. If one wants to be absolutely sure of safety, I wouldn't allow myself to become involved with deep kissing, certainly not with strangers."

MIKE: "And the point of acquaintance, again, at which I might decide to experience deep kissing with someone is after first assuring myself, to the best degree I can, that the person is healthy and hasn't been overly promiscuous?"

DR. FINN: "Yes . . . these are variable decisions for each individual."

MIKE: "Okay."

DR. FINN: "I think part of the new education -- I'm not, of course, promoting sexual experiences between people -- but people have to know these things. With some lifestyles, they need to accept the idea of, `we'll talk before we go to bed.'"

MIKE: "Right. Now, let me go to what some would perceive as a middle ground I've gotten questions about. So — we've talked about deep kissing on the one hand, and about the established dangers of unprotected anal intercourse on the other."

DR. FINN: "Right."

MIKE: "Suppose I ask you now, whether as a heterosexual female *or* as a gay male, `Dr. Finn, I happen to practice oral sex. I feel sadness for people who get AIDS. But, given that my particular interest hasn't involved anal intercourse so much, I feel personally fortunate. I'm glad the stomach has enzymes to attack foreign matter. I'm glad the walls of the colon are different than the lining of the stomach. Therefore it's at least MORE okay for me to swallow sperm than to receive it rectally, right? After all, there's not the same skin rupturing orally that can come with anal intercourse. Can you validate my perception, Dr. Finn?'"

DR. FINN: "Oh, I suppose I would agree with the relative risk being less. I'm not so sure my concern is only for the stomach, however. There can be minute abrasions in the mouth for many reasons. You could be mixing, at that point, sperm with blood. We know the possibility of Hepatitis-B, for example, being transferred during dental procedures. That's from the hand of the dentist to a patient. There's some similar potential there for AIDS in oral sex, although because of the trauma to the rectum, that risk may be greater. People have to make personal decisions about risk."

MIKE: "All right, then. Still one more degree of decision-making to pose at you. `Okay, Dr. Finn. Maybe, just to be safe, I'll decide not to swallow sperm. But would you agree, at least, that it's a lot less risky if I indulge in fellatio with someone and then I withdraw before they ejaculate?'"

DR. FINN: "Well . . . again, I don't know how I could measure precise degrees of risk. There's a certain loss of seminal fluid even before one ejaculates, during the process. The virus may be present in those preliminary fluids too, just like in the ejaculate. What is the actual amount of virus present? How low a level is it? And what about the risk, particularly during sexual excitement, of loss of control by your partner? I certainly wouldn't want to be giving any 'full assurance' of safety to anyone.

"People ask for concrete assurances, of course, I understand. But I don't believe we should give assurances without qualification. The questions you've been asking me are questions people genuinely want to know. They ask them on the telephone. They ask them everywhere else."

MIKE: "We are talking, aren't we, about people giving up particular pleasures, habits they may have learned to enjoy and make part of their lives."

DR. FINN: "It's difficult. Extremely difficult. That's probably our major impediment in terms of behavior change. `This is a big part of my life, and I don't want to give it up unless there's a darn good reason.' Quite honestly, our best chance is to sell other sexual activities as being satisfying."

MIKE: "That's really marketing you're talking about."

DR. FINN: "Yes, and we've gotten into trouble over that. Negative reactions to brochures that some people considered too explicit. Like 'Mother's Handy Sex Guide' produced by AIDS Project L.A. It attempted to eroticize safe sexual activity. The Board of Supervisors found it offensive to the general population. There were three photographs of males together; one dealt with masturbation, one with massage, and . . . I can't think of the third situation, but they all were 'safe' situations. The language was considered offensive, although it was common to the gay population whose behavior the brochure wanted to influence.

"In general, I think you cannot talk about AIDS and its transmission without employing some degree of explicit conversation. I hope people are becoming more comfortable talking frankly because, without yet having a vaccine, I don't know how else we can prevent AIDS from spreading."

MIKE: "Even if the pamphlet were allowed to speak directly to its audience, to talk its language, is it realistic to think a brochure can make such a difference? Can a pamphlet make behavior that feels 'tame' seem exciting? Versus the practices one learned over decades to consider erotic?"

DR. FINN: "It's a tough job, I admit. I don't know how successful we can be. But I know we must try. Every percentage of the population that converts from a negative to a positive antibody creates greater communicability within the population as a whole."

MIKE: "Let me ask you something else. You said you have a particular interest in the social impact of disease. Here we have one that, in the United States culture, began with homosexuals. What do you think will be the societal impact of the loss of life among that segment?"

DR. FINN: "My great concern is that -- I've learned over time that you can expect an ongoing percentage of human beings to be gay."

MIKE: "So there will be new ones coming along?"

DR. FINN: "Oh, yes. They will be coming along. My great concern, putting aside the death and illness of today, is what AIDS will mean to the perceptional life of younger gay people? Will it force them back into extremely difficult situations? If we're going to make this a better world, we have to make it better for everyone. There will absolutely be many gay youths in the future, as there have been all through time.

"People who say, 'let the gays kill themselves off' -- well, I know these kids are their own sons, daughters, and cousins. I've dealt with them. I've observed the problems of closeted lifestyles, the separation of children from families. Those stresses cause a less healthy society. We ought to progress in our understanding what our various life experiences really are.

"Meanwhile, as to the loss of today's homosexuals, we are losing some extremely talented human beings at the height of their most productive years. I can give you full assurance that here in Los Angeles there are many vital areas of society in which gays play large, large roles, unbeknownst to the rest of society. 10% of any productive element of society may well in fact be gay. I don't think we can afford to lose that."

MIKE: "What would you most want readers to know?"

DR. FINN: "I've never before faced a problem like AIDS. It's the number one public health problem of the century. At least it will also help us learn about cancer and viral diseases. People owe it to themselves and their government to educate themselves about this disease. Unless the public becomes more knowledge, AIDS may not only be medically devastating, but financially, economically devastating too."

Bill Misenhimer

Only the cigarettes pushing from the vest pocket of his three piece suit interrupt the trim, tailored lines of banker's pinstripe. "Yes, I'm a 'Type A' personality," he says about his intensity. "I need to accomplish things that matter."

He's from Oklahoma originally, and moved to California at age eleven. He's thirty-six now, despite his mostly gray hair. He's worked for Pacific Telephone, BMW, and Xerox in financial administrative management.

He remembers a business trip to Washington, D.C. in November, 1982. By that time, "I hated what I was doing, and I was a major hypochondriac. I was not real satisfied with my life. I got sick -- and I never get sick. Being a hypochondriac, and with AIDS so new, I was convinced I had it."

352

His doctor back home told him he had CMV, a virus believed at the time to cause AIDS. Now he was further convinced he had it. "I laid in bed for a couple of months and was ready to die. And I didn't die. I didn't even get any sicker. But I was scared to death."

He decided to turn his fear into positive action. He organized letter-writing parties. "I'd have people over and we'd all write letters to the Administration, telling them they had to do something." He did volunteer work for AIDS Project L.A., "to support people with AIDS and to educate everyone." He organized a petition for government action and gathered 13,000 signatures for the White House and 8,000 signatures for local cities.

"Before this time, I had never gotten involved with anything gay or political. I was totally middle of the road and not particularly concerned about causes or issues."

"Were you a 'closeted' gay man?"

"Not to the people who knew me. I am who I am, and one part of that is being a gay man. But in some ways that's incidental to who I am, especially nowadays when I'm really just *living* my work for this organization."

Bill knew Xerox had a paid employee-leave program by which the corporation assists employees to volunteer for worthy tasks. He applied for a grant in mid-October, 1983 and learned in early November that Xerox had approved it. Now he could work for AIDS Project LA full time and soon he was Executive Director.

"It became my life. Friends, personal life, those kinds of things became non-issues. It was the first job I ever had where I knew I had real purpose. I got a strong sense of fulfillment, even though it consumed me. I worked seven days a week, an average of twelve to thirteen hours a day for nine months. Once I calculated the number of hours I'd worked in a year and four months -- a thousand hours additional to a normal forty hour week."

It was agreed that he'd return to Xerox at the end of nine months' volunteer work. But in November '84, he applied seven weeks of back due vacation to continue the AIDS Project work. In the New Year, he applied his 1985 vacation time.

"Then I resigned from Xerox. I had to keep going on this." He'd led the AIDS Project from a budget of $122,000 to almost three million dollars a year -- "from events, contributions, and government money. You have to find out where money is; then you have to find out how to get it."

Since only two months ago, he's Executive Director of the American Foundation for AIDS Research. AmFAR has merged with the AIDS Medical Foundation, founded in New York by Dr. Mathilde Krim. So it is now a truly national organization.

"Our focus is to raise money from the private sector to fund peer-reviewed research on AIDS. We've assembled the top researchers in the country, all names you'd know in the field. They'll meet and speedily review applications for funding. Based on merit and relevance, they can evaluate, free from government pressure or administration preference, which programs get funded. That's solely on scientific merit as judged by fellow researchers.

"Another advantage is, we can do it all so much quicker: two months turnaround from receipt of an application versus six to twelve to eighteen months one experiences with the government. We can actually complement what the government does by granting money for something worthy while government approval is pending. The point is, obviously, time matters!" We talk briefly about how computer conferencing could shorten still further the communications among scientists reviewing projects.

"How long do you expect to be doing this job?" I ask him.

"As long as it's a problem. That may be a long time, I'm afraid. I mean, I may die of AIDS, who knows? My best friend is sick right now. That's real hard."

"How sick is he?"

"He's sick. He has pneumocystis and Kaposi's."

After a pause, I ask, "have you had yourself tested?"

"No."

"That's a conscious decision, obviously. Can you talk about that?"

"Yeah. I personally don't need to know. I would do nothing differently. I've already modified my personal activities to take safe guidelines into account. And frankly, I care so much about what I'm doing here and what it can mean, and the time pressure is so urgent . . . sex itself is the least of my concerns right now. What I care most about is AmFAR, period, getting things to happen as quickly as possible."

"What kind of personal, emotional price do you imagine you're paying for the life you lead?"

"It's hard to say, Mike. I don't know what's going on subconsciously. I'm in the middle of the forest and I'm trying to make a difference. AIDS is all I talk about or care about right now. I have to balance both personal denial and acceptance of all that's going on around me in order to maintain my own effectiveness, in order to stay on my purpose.

"Many people who've been in this thing burn out really quick. That's one of the reasons I left the AIDS Project. I couldn't take that any more. Many Executive Directors, in work like that, burn out after a year and a half.

"You go in excited at first, with an extreme sense of urgency. Then you realize the odds against you are more than overwhelming, they're absurd. You do your best anyway, and you succeed in little chunks. But given the realities of what people with AIDS really need, you never give the level of consistent support and excellence to *every* caller or *all* the time like you'd really like to. That's a frustration. So you push your volunteer staff just as hard as you can, but there are limits to what they can take. Eventually you feel overwhelmed and it's time to back off, to let someone else in.

"Remember the context, too: a society that doesn't approve of the disease, and many politicians who don't really give a damn. Their homophobia gets in the way of human caring. They're afraid of educating the public -- of talking openly about sexual practices and how to avoid a sexually transmitted disease -- for fear of being considered politically offensive."

He opens his brief case to get the current issue of a journal, the *CALIFORNIA HISTORICAL COURIER*. "This epidemic is following the path of all epidemics," he says. He quotes an article by Eric Abrahamson which describes the bubonic plague in San Francisco in 1900. The Chinese section of town was roped off, and the Oriental population of 14,000 was quarantined. It took nine years, the article says, for the disease to be recognized as human rather than just "Asiatic." Despite white men's funerals, and despite the eventual findings of plague transmission by rats, people considered the disease "peculiar to rice-eaters."

The article quotes historian Henry Harris writing in 1932 that the major lesson from plague epidemics is "moral and political, rather than medical." It's in the nature of democracy to reject the advice of experts, Harris concluded. Moral and political issues affected policy more than the medical factors that should have. Society is behaving the same way with AIDS, Bill says, in the same historic pattern.

"At last now, the government's begun to do something. My personal fear, though, is that AIDS will become lost in institutions, committees, paperwork, procedures. There's no time for that, you see. We are not going to let that happen at AmFAR. Our turnaround time, our responsiveness . . . those things matter extremely.

"My current job is one step removed from the direct pressures I had enough of at the AIDS Project. So I expect I can keep going, and I'm determined to do my best. We are going to help get funding for the best AIDS research just as fast as we possibly can."

"Tell me," I say. "About you, personally. You've painted a picture of someone who's driven. That is a fair description, isn't it? `Driven?'"

"Yes."

"What is it that drives you so? WHY are you so driven?"

"Don't ask," he says. His voice is distorted as he controls it. "I can't talk about it."

"Please," I say softly.

"How can I?" he says. "One reason, for example, is in the hospital right now . . . ."

I honor what I can see clearly is the wish of this man who lives his life to raise money for AIDS research. I turn off my tape recorder.

Chapter 31:
San Francisco — Part 1

I'd heard people say, "well, of course you have to go to San Francisco if you're writing about AIDS." I assumed, at first, they were referring to the fact that a significant percentage of the city's population is homosexual, and that San Francisco has experienced the largest per capita incidence of AIDS outside New York.

It wasn't long before I realized that one reason for a visit was that San Francisco's creative medical response to AIDS might ultimately lead to health care benefits for all of us. Example: this chapter presents three health care professionals discussing a new approach to organizational teamwork among hospital staff. Might the positive results influence, even slightly, the future training of doctors and nurses?

Dr. Mervyn Silverman

I'm having breakfast in the hotel restaurant with the city's former Director of Public Health. With his loose sweater and parka, his slight slouch and his gray beard, he's a laid-back veteran of the socio-medical wars. I quickly perceive his caring and intelligence.

He's from Washington, D.C. originally, and he got his medical degree from Tulane. Before long, however, he began to dislike seeing idealistic young medical students "transformed," learning to think of themselves as lofty and infallible, sometimes at the patient's expense. So he left for Thailand and the Peace Corps "for a chance to think."

Eventually he returned to the U.S. for a Harvard Master's degree in Public Health. He served as Director of Consumer Affairs for the FDA. He was County Director of Health in Wichita, Kansas, where he and his wife actively supported local gay rights. He was the Medical Director of Planned Parenthood.

He was San Francisco's Director of Public Health from 1977 until he resigned in January, 1985 in the midst of the city's gay bathhouse controversies. He actively consults on health care for the City of San

Francisco and various other clients. He still spends "110 percent" of his time on AIDS. He is forty-seven and has three daughters.

"I think we developed pretty much a model AIDS program for the nation here," he says. He acknowledges a certain irony in being able to make that claim because at first, as the city's Health Director, he resisted the proposal for a distinct and separate hospital ward for AIDS patients. His concern was to avoid any further isolation of people who were already set apart by much of society.

"I'm glad I was convinced otherwise," he says. "It's an outstanding unit." He worked with local organizations, like Shanti, to create a "continuum of care" with many separate functions operating in harmony.

The overall thrust of the San Francisco approach was NOT to maintain the traditional medical hierarchy -- the Power Ladder of doctor, then nurse,then orderly or volunteer -- and instead to create a cohesive team of involved health care workers, each with important skills to offer to the patient and to each other. One function is not "superior" to another; the structure is more a network than a ladder.

"I believe we actually have set up, both inpatient and outside, what probably should be done throughout medicine in general . . . a compassionate, sensitive, comprehensive health care system. You'll hear statements from patients in the AIDS unit that you don't get from most patients in most hospitals. They feel safe. They feel content. They feel cared for. And the staff really enjoys working there.

"There's been no attrition on that ward, which is incredible given the frequent deaths of formerly healthy young people. Burn wards in a typical hospital organization, for example, often experience high attrition because the work is so emotionally demanding. Yet, despite the awful intensity of AIDS, the morale of staff and patients on 5-B is extraordinary.

"On the AIDS ward, there's an *esprit de corps* that comes from not having each service categorized in a hierarchy. Quite often, in a typical hospital structure, conflict can arise because the doctor assumes he is superior. Obviously he's the ultimate decision maker, but sometimes his perspective ignores the fact that the person with the patient twenty-four hours a day is the nurse.

"The doctor bops in, `Hi, how ya doing?' He thumps your chest, and is gone. The nurse is still there, taking care of your needs, seeing you get your medication, proper fluid intake, proper food, being there for an emergency. Nurses for a long time have been put down by some doctors. Nurses, of course, aren't immune from giving doctors problems either. No one likes to be treated as a subordinate. The point is, the basic structure leads to conflict.

You don't see that kind of struggle going on in Intensive Care

Units of hospitals. Why? Because there's more of a team approach."

Our waiter finally brings Dr. Silverman's toast.

"Could I have some extra butter, please?" he asks the waiter.

"There's a lot of butter on there already," the waiter says sternly.

"Well . . . ." The doctor shrugs. We are marooned at the table, I think, at the mercy of the Butter Keeper. Like a patient confined to his bed. The waiter disappears. How long before the treatment arrives?

"I hear you saying, in effect, that the particular demands of AIDS led San Francisco to establish a style of medical care that could actually revolutionize how *all* kinds of patients are cared for. Is that accurate?"

"I'd like to believe that could happen," he replies. "It should. But it probably won't. You'd have to start back at medical schools, in nursing schools, with the basic mindsets and attitudes formed there."

"What about people who would favor the current structure? If someone thought, `that's fine for AIDS. It's a dramatic and mysterious illness, so it's okay to make an exception. But it's not a good way for doctors and nurses to work together in general' -- what's the best argument *against* the hospital teamwork you now favor?"

"Honestly, I can't think of a really good argument against it. But someone could tell me, `Listen, the doctor has to be in control. He has to.' No. I don't know anything that could be said against it, even though that sounds strange. I mean, in going to this system, is our patient care suffering? Is our nursing suffering? Is the doctor-patient relation suffering? NO!"

"Then let me ask you. If you think this way of working is a health care benefit that will result from AIDS, are you going around the country trying to interest others in trying it?"

"When I give talks about AIDS, which I do frequently, I bring this up all the time. I always see the nurses in the audience shaking their heads, 'yes!' If you think about it, the approach is not so unique. It's what made Japanese management so successful, the worker and the employer working *together* and not in a hierarchy."

"It calls for people at the top to give up a certain amount of power trappings, yes?"

"Absolutely. It can feel quite comfortable to think of yourself as the doctor *'in charge'* rather than as one respected member of a coordinated team of health care. Especially, I need to say again, if that's the way you were taught at the beginning, in the institution that molded your attitudes."

"Tomorrow I'm going to see Linda Maxey who coordinates the Shanti Volunteers for the ward," I say. "I don't know much about them. That's an external organization, right? Should whatever Shanti is doing with AIDS be done for burn victims, too, for example?"

"Yes. Shanti is an external organization that is now part of our ongoing patient treatment. Certainly for burn victims, that would be useful, where there are a lot of psychological problems and trauma. What Shanti does -- and again it's not seen as a foreign invader -- they assign a volunteer to every inpatient. As an advocate and as a support. They receive special training, of course. They're a great adjunct to the physician and the nurse. The nurse can't literally be there all the time, for example."

Our waiter is still nowhere in sight. I wave my arms flagrantly to attract the attention of another one. He comes over from his section and I ask for extra butter for the doctor. "Sure." A saucer with large slabs of butter is set down within 120 seconds.

"The other guy is probably down on cholesterol," Dr. Silverman says. "So -- the presence of the Shanti volunteer helps relieve some burden on the nurse. When you come right down to it, I don't think these various disciplines are seen as 'threats.' The support from members of a team can relieve burdens for each individual on it. I can tell you that patients from elsewhere in the hospital system are trying to get into this special unit. It *feels* different being treated by people who work together this way.

"I think medicine in general has told its care-givers, 'Look. Relate to your patient, but keep a certain distance. Distance is good. Don't get too involved.' Here, people do get involved. And because of the support system, it turns out not to be debilitating. You see nurses hugging patients."

"What about when you lose a patient?"

"Very difficult."

"And wouldn't it be less difficult if they hadn't gotten so involved?"

"Probably."

Our original waiter arrives. He has a small ceramic ramekin of butter. He sets it -- clack! -- on the table. He's annoyed to see we've gotten some from another waiter.

"I'm *glad* you like butter!" I say to Dr. Silverman who now has two mounds resting before him. "Enjoy!"

"You know, your question about handling loss after you've gotten involved is a good one. Ask some of the people doing the care-giving when you see them tomorrow.

"I have to say that many hospitals probably would not be smart to have a dedicated AIDS unit. Maybe it would be too small. Maybe the community itself isn't ready to give volunteer support. And since this way of working is entwined with AIDS, maybe it could all be dismissed in some other city as 'not right for us.' But I think the lack of hierarchy, a real team of care-givers, could exist on *any* ward, and with any illness."

We talk about the tempestuous bathhouse issues of almost a year ago. Mayor Feinstein wanted the bathhouses closed. Dr. Silverman didn't agree for a variety of reasons. Ultimately, after a court case, the baths are now open, but must not permit sex on the premises. It's a far-away issue as he discusses it, settled and done with. But the issue was the catalyst for his new role as an independent consultant, which Dr. Silverman is now savoring.

"I loved my job. Seven and a half years, it was crazy, it was challenging, it was exciting. But enough is enough. I'm happy now, too. You've done the same thing, leaving your corporate life. You know what I mean."

"What would you most like to say to the public about AIDS?"

"AIDS pretty much tells us about ourselves, about how we look at things. We keep telling people it isn't casually transmitted, but our advice isn't being bought by most of the population. They react in more emotional ways. `Make everyone take tests, isolate them.'

"It's a terribly tragic disease -- a disease of consenting adults. If you don't place yourself at risk, you won't be at risk. We shouldn't be mistreating people because of irrational fears. We should be showing compassion and sensitivity and support, rather than anger, isolation, and denial."

We leave the restaurant together and shake hands warmly. I'd resisted the temptation to order a doggie bag for his butter.

Dr. Paul Volberding
He has an illustrated poster on his office door:

> You Cannot Get AIDS From
> Working with Someone
> Restrooms
> Swimming Pools
> Touching A Door Knob

He hears me reading these examples into my microphone and teasingly announces, "it is truly okay to have sex with a door knob!" He asks me please not to set my coffee cup down on his grant application.

His father was a dairy farmer in Minnesota, but Paul Volberding decided in high school to become a doctor, partly because of "the excitement of medicine." He is thirty-six and has practiced medicine for ten years.

"What is 'the excitement of medicine,' anyway?" I ask him.

"In part, the communication between patient and physician. That was a major factor in deciding to go into cancer medicine, and working with AIDS . . . there's a joy in talking to people and being honest, of sharing difficult moments in their lives and in helping as best we can in a difficult situation." He'd intended to be a researcher and realized in San Francisco that he preferred working with people more directly. "Especially taking care of cancer patients."

"Why 'especially'?"

"The communication and honesty between doctor and patient with a serious disease is striking. Being able to see people facing death is an inspiring way to spend your time. You get to see, really, the absolute best in people. The courage. The amazing desire to live. Most cancer specialists get tremendous personal reward from being allowed to participate in that process."

He has dark brown eyes. I notice that his stare is unwavering and direct and I can picture him keeping eye contact with a patient even as he delivers terrible news. I am interested by the craving he has for dealing with people's intimate feelings. It's the reason I, myself, almost left business to become a psychotherapist. I'd never thought before about that interest in human *emotion* being central to a *medical* specialist.

"You mention `honesty.' I've wondered at times," I tell him, "if I had a terminal disease like AIDS or cancer, could I count on my doctor being absolutely honest with me? I wouldn't want to have false hopes."

"It's a complex thing, Mike. Medicine isn't monolithic. There are good doctors and bad doctors, good oncologists and bad oncologists. I think as a rule, oncologists tend to be very sensitive physicians and very honest. They're motivated that way. I think a lot of oncologists, myself included, debated in medical school whether to get into medicine or psychiatry."

Dr. Volberding is head of the Cancer Institute at General Hospital, which is essentially a branch of the University of California. Part of his assignment was to organize the hospital's first oncology unit, finding effective ways to deliver cancer care and to teach other physicians in training. Dr. Volberding joined the hospital on July 1, 1981; the first AIDS patient had been admitted one week before, a twenty-two year old man with KS.

"When I came here, nothing existed to take care of AIDS patients," he says. "There wasn't an epidemic yet, and the hospital was absolutely traditional in its hierarchy. But AIDS forces you to challenge all your pre-conceived notions of patient care. It crosses traditional sub-specialty boundaries. It also brings psycho-emotional problems that are just as important as medical ones. Something I'm personally proud of having realized is that efficient patient care requires both oncology and infectious disease people involved together. As our AIDS program has grown, we've added general internal medicine and family practice. We created a team."

362

He explains that normally, if someone is being seen for an infectious disease and a cancerous malignancy is suspected, the patient must be referred to a separate clinic for later examination. In San Francisco General's AIDS program, however, specialists work together for faster diagnosis and treatment. "I can literally turn around and there's an expert in the field I need, standing right there. I'm convinced that's the only way to take care of AIDS patients."

"Do you think this system has application to other diseases?"

"Sure. The attention we're getting now is focused on AIDS. But comparing the care of this disease to the care of typical cancer patients or other complex needs, there are a lot of lessons that can be learned. The integration of staff, for example. The interaction between nursing and physicians, the integration of clinical researchers into the team, the involvement of community volunteers.

"This system is not only better for patients, it also helps the staff. AIDS is a stressful disease to take care of. These are thirty-five year old human beings, dying. Most of my staff is about the same age. Knowing that we are directly involving experimental drug researchers with us as part of our daily care, for example, helps us keep going -- we're all part of a total effort that can help things get better."

"Do you think what's been created here for AIDS will ultimately influence the way American health care is handled?"

"At the times when I'm optimistic, I'd say yes. When people visit from other hospitals, it's hard for them to miss the effects -- the sense of commitment from the staff, the fact that attrition is almost zero. In most high-stress care situations people burn out.

"We also share here, I guess, an almost religious commitment to the care we are giving. It's more important that the person working alongside of you has the same commitment than what their job title is. What I feel about this place is that, without intentionally doing it, it has the flavor of Japanese business, where people are serious about accomplishing a mission. The task is the overriding concern, not who's where on the ladder.

"I think American medicine, though, is going through a tough period of self-assessment. Nursing has increased in its professionalism in the last decade, and I think some physicians are threatened. So I think there's a tension that needs to be worked through before I'd expect this clinic's system and this devotion to what we're doing to happen on other, lesser diseases."

He talks about his adjustment, as a heterosexual from a Minnesota farm, to working so directly with urban homosexuals and their lovers. "Things that were shocking to me at first just aren't now," he says. "As you learn about people, the differences become less apparent and the similarities become more apparent. I think most of the public can't really, on some level, let themselves imagine two people of the same sex having a genuine physical attraction and relationship with each other. I think that's the crux of an understanding block with the public. For myself, I'm not shocked anymore. I appreciate the relationships for what they are, relationships between two people that can be good or bad just like any two people's relationships. I think the public has a lot to learn still."

He contrasts the social climate for gay people in the City of San Francisco versus the suburbs surrounding the city, or the east coast. There are probably fewer married and closeted "bisexuals" here, he speculates. A number of people who consider themselves "gay" have also had heterosexual contacts, but it's easier to acknowledge one's own homosexual preferences in the San Francisco environment. Therefore, it seems likely that fewer married people lead "double lives" here, with the attendant stresses that can arise. The vast majority of San Francisco AIDS cases are "gay."

He tells me his own speculation is that AIDS will not be largely transferred into the heterosexual community. "It will be like hepatitis B, just as it has from the start . . . a disease that is terribly endemic in gay men and IV drug users and only peripherally affects other people. In Africa, hepatitis is a disease that affects everyone, huge areas of the population, growing out of social and cultural factors that are different from in this country. I think the same scenario is happening with AIDS.

"However, I don't think there's any such thing as 'the general population' versus the 'gay segment.' When it comes to a fatal epidemic, we're all 'the general population.' The problem of gay men in San Francisco is everyone's problem."

"What would you advise the reader who is a heterosexual, single woman who wants to lead an active social and sexual life?"

"I think we should encourage people to lead active social and sexual lives. I'd hate to see people paranoid if their lifestyle doesn't put them at risk for AIDS. My opinion is that heterosexual contacts, by and large, are very safe. I don't think you can relax with such a terrible disease, however. The ways to stop from getting AIDS are the same ways to stop from getting gonorrhea. For single people, reducing the number of different partners will statistically reduce risk. Use of condoms will probably eliminate the risk. You need to get to know the partner you're about to have sex with, even though many people don't feel comfortable asking someone in a bar, `Do you shoot drugs?' or `When was your last homosexual encounter?'

"I would also say, based on the United States experience, that anal sex without a condom is the most risky circumstance for the passive

364

partner; it's the most likely to transmit the disease. At the same time, we have to look at Africa and say we don't fully understand the disease there yet. IV drug use and anal intercourse don't happen so much there, it seems."

"What would be your perspective on ingesting semen during oral sex?"

"I think it's much less risky than anal or vaginal intercourse in transmitting the virus. That's my guess. Penile-vaginal intercourse *seems* to be the way it occurs within the African context.

"You know, there was a very difficult period for me, personally, when we suspected a fatal virus caused AIDS, but didn't know which virus it was. I was absolutely convinced I was affected. Most of us working with AIDS felt the same. My wife works here, too. Both of us awoke with recurring nightmares. I feared, daily, picking up my infant son, feeling guilty -- was I giving him the disease? So I can really understand the public's fears.

"But now the antibody testing is incredibly accurate. Taking the test itself is frightening, because of your worries. You know what's at stake. But when the negative result is back, there's nothing more reassuring."

"What would you most want people to know about AIDS?"

"I'd like them to see that even in the middle of an epidemic, even when we are sometimes afraid for our health, we can go on doing our job in a very professional way. Also AIDS, from our own experience, is obviously not spread in any way other than direct sexual contact or blood exchange. My staff, myself, we've been tested for the virus. We're not infected even after four a half years of daily contact.

"Five years from now, I hope people will look back on a disease that's no longer an increasing epidemic. I think within five years it will plateau in the country as a whole. At that point, I hope they will still realize that a profession, a city, and a hospital were able to start from scratch with a new disease and deliver patient care even when we didn't have all the facts. And that the results were improvements in overall patient care. I hope they'll be able to see that."

Cliff Morrison

He grew up in Florida, in "a large, rather poor family." He was the first to graduate from high school. While a student, he worked in a hospital saving money for nursing school. He's a meticulous dresser with closely cropped hair and a neatly trimmed beard that is just going gray. Despite the soft curves in his lingering Southern accent, the effect when he speaks is of edges and corners, from a mind that is precise.

He identifies himself as a gay man, "but I don't wear a banner about it. I believe in excellent health care for all patients, not for just one group. AIDS is not the last special cause I'll be involved with, but I saw sub-standard care being given to AIDS patients. I was in a position to change things, so I did.

"Some people think I'm a 'Gay Uncle Tom.' I work effectively within the straight world, I dress to suit them, I do everything I can to fit into that social scheme. All that is accurate, because I realize how important it is to be part of the mainstream. I represent and stand up for the public -- ALL the public."

He has a Bachelor's Degree in nursing, and a Master's in psychology and education. After moving to San Francisco, he pursued a fulltime nursing career while working nights and weekends as a Shanti volunteer. It became clear that San Francisco General needed a coordinated approach to AIDS patients -- how should they be treated? Cliff volunteered. His experience with Shanti and his interest in the subject won him the assignment of developing the hospital's approach.

"I have never thought of AIDS as 'a gay disease.' With my fifteen years of nursing, I realized that viruses don't have sexual preference. One thing AIDS is, however: a catalyst that is forcing us to deal with issues we've been avoiding. Patient rights, involvement of patients with their own care, being cost effective. The definition of 'family' and the involvement of 'significant others' in a patient's life, even if they're not traditional family members. Care outside the hospital, community involvement. Look at all those issues AIDS is making us deal with!

"When we started Ward 5-B in early 1983, the average daily census was ten or twelve AIDS patients. They were scattered all over the institution. Their care was inconsistent, and some were treated terribly. At first I thought I'd just reach out to them all separately. And to each nursing staff on each separate ward. But that was impossible. Too many issues, too many people, scattered too far away.

"Some people thought we needed a special unit . . . as a quarantine, to keep AIDS people away. Decontamination chambers you'd enter and leave in 'space suits,' a modern leper colony. Of course, I was opposed to unnecessary isolation. But finally I saw we did need a separate unit, although not to push people out. We had to centralize resources, create a more human model of health care. My goal was to demystify AIDS, to show it really is possible to give effective, consistent care in which the patient doesn't feel guilty for his own disease.

"In addition to planning the criteria for staff, I knew I'd want to have Shanti involved. I approached Shanti's director and we agreed that counselors would work directly on the ward with us.

"A lot of people said, back then, that the plan would never work. Letting patients have more of a say in their own treatment would put patients and doctors in direct conflict."

"Why?"

"They thought it would be difficult for particular physicians and nurses who don't like having patients challenge them. But the truth is, precisely because they really are involved, the AIDS group is actually one of the more compliant patient groups in the hospital! The house staff, students and residents passing through for training, tell us all the time how remarkably professional 5-B is, but also how much real *esprit de corps* they notice between staff and patients, a feeling of caring."

The ward opened in July, 1983. "I might as well tell you," he says, "because people always ask me about it. The truth is, we got enormous support from the Mayor. People want to know who I'd give credit to. If it were only one person, it's Dianne Feinstein. Of course, I disagree with her sometimes. But I'd vote for her for anything. For the one reason, that she's a savvy politician and businessperson. Regardless of how she felt about lifestyle issues or whatever, she was able to cut through all that and say, here's an issue and it has to be dealt with.'"

"Let's define a little more the kind of credit you're wanting to give her."

"As Mayor of the City, looking at the resources and seeing what needed to be done, she pulled together a group of people, along with her staff, and she said, `We're going to make funds available. It's up to you in the Department of Public Health to tell us what you need.' She took a leadership stance and she was serious about finding solutions. I normally try to stay away from politics, but I'd support any politician who really goes after problems like that."

Soon, he'll have to leave my hotel, where we're having a drink in the lobby, returning to the hospital for a 6:00 meeting. I ask him to summarize his personal philosophy of nursing.

"My philosophy of care is patient-centered, with a high level of professionalism to meet the patient's needs. Our needs should be secondary. There are lots of examples of that, but I'll give you just one to illustrate my point.

"You'd think doctors and nurses could deal effectively with death and dying. In fact, there's an enormous amount of denial. It's a reflection of the culture we live in. Our society denies death. As health care workers, the worst thing that can happen is having a patient die. It's hard for us as people. But that can lead to denial, which is hard for the patient who truly deserves better. The patient needs caring; we need to run away, unless we find another way to handle our needs.

"Our patients on 5-B were able to articulate it right from the start. Although they feared death, they were even more afraid of dying. They dreaded the process of being pushed away, of feeling guilty for being so sick. You can go to any hospital. Look at how terminally ill patients are dealt with. Look at how cancer patients are dealt with. You'll find physicians stop seeing them. They review their charts, talk to the nurses, talk to the family . . . but in their nervousness, they can ignore the patient. The patient is usually put further away from the nursing station. If you listened in to the nursing report you'd hear, `Oh, Mrs. Jones doesn't need much care. She's terminally ill.' You'd see staff going less often into her room, talking with her less, touching her less . . . beginning to separate from her. They are giving her messages that make her feel guilty for dying.

"So we need to be able to talk about issues like this. That's one of the things we've done on 5-B. It can be very uncomfortable, and we haven't found all the solutions. But we deal with things as they come up."

I imagine, some day, being in a hospital. In my fantasy, I'm old and frail, and I've got pains that hardly stop. I imagine, "Mr. Greenly doesn't need much attention, he's terminally ill." I shove the image aside. Maybe there will be a more caring approach to terminally ill patients by then, partly as a result of the approaches being developed with AIDS.

"Hypothetically," I ask him, "if medicine were pure mathematics — only mathematics — I could imagine somebody saying, `well, mathematically, Mrs. Jones is going to be dying anyway. There's nothing more we can do for her. So why should we waste our resources?"

"That's not the issue," he replies sharply. "That whole way of thinking of health care is wrong. Particularly in a civilized country."

"Because . . . she's still a person?"

"Yes. And because we're still health care PROVIDERS. Does that mean we only provide health care to those who can get well? What is `wellness'? Particularly when you're talking about the quality of life. With AIDS patients, on top of it all, we're dealing with people who are young and may have two or three years of quality life ahead of them. As professionals, we have a commitment to them, regardless of why they're ill, regardless of their lifestyle.

"And really, patients who are terminally ill need more care in some respects than patients who aren't. We cannot turn our back on the patients we can't 'cure.' Health care isn't geared to only curing, particularly nursing. Nursing is CARE. And anybody who's sick requires care. When I hear about nurses who refuse to care for some patients . . . AIDS is more of a nursing illness than anything I've ever seen in fifteen years. We're one of the few disciplines that have anything real right now to offer. The success of 5-B is that it is a nursing unit.

"As a nurse, I have the same goal as a physician: quality care for the patient. I do not feel subservient. We have different roles, both important. What matters is that we both care, and we both do our best. I've always felt that doctors and nurses are equal partners and should be in a collaborative relationship. On 5-B, we've actually made it happen. And it works!"

"Since 5-B has been such a visible success, you've been interviewed by how many journalists would you say?"

"Oh, God! Fifty? Sixty? A lot."

"What do you most wish had been better covered by the news people you've spoken with? What's not been told that you care about?"

"The human aspect, the human side. That what we're dealing with is people. Each story is different. Each statistic is an individual. The media has gotten better recently, but for so long they were giving us crazy headlines, exploiting the stories with inaccuracy and sensationalism. Or dry science, but not the real social and patient care issues. Like the social cost of this disease, not just the economics. We'll be paying a price for the loss of these young people even twenty, thirty years from now. AIDS is taking away such talent! Some of our brightest, most artistic people. Professionals. Writers. Artists. People only beginning to make their contributions.

"From the beginning the media wanted to interview patients. But the news would forget about the person and show only the disfigurement. They never gave the patient a chance to tell his story. We had one TV crew ask us to rearrange the room, 'make it look more like a hospital.' How much more like a hospital can you make San Francisco look?! Recently, I have to say, more of the people's human stories are being told. That's something I'm glad about. I want readers to know these are human beings, real ones.

"I hate it when I hear people say, 'they brought it on themselves.' Does that mean we shouldn't treat the businessman who brought his ulcer on? The lung cancer patient who smoke too much? The person who drank too much? Seventy percent of the patients in a hospital are there because of some aspects of their lifestyles.

"I think AIDS is a test of us, of society. Being a religious person, I think it's a test of our ability to be humane to each other. A test of what brotherly love is all about. Compassion. Caring. I can't allow myself to think we won't live up to it. I believe we can pass the test."

369

Chapter 32:
San Francisco — Part 2

One of the most significant concepts I learned about from San Francisco's experience with AIDS is the "team" approach to health care, described in the previous chapter. The other is an actively personal stance toward death and dying — a quality of absolute caring and nurturance — which seems facilitated by Ward 5-B's organization and interpersonal relationships.

The mix of people and philosophy I encountered produces a humane and sensitive approach to life-threatening diseases . An integral part of that mix was Shanti, a volunteer counseling organization. With great pleasure and admiration, a portion of the author's royalties is being donated to Shanti. Reader contributions may be sent to the SHANTI Project, 890 Hayes St., San Francisco, CA 94117.

Alison Moed - Head Nurse 5-B

She's a short woman, not petite but with a sense of hesitancy that makes her seem tentative and vulnerable. I can see that being interviewed makes her nervous. A media contact told me, however, that she's a "must." Anyone who's ever talked with her considers her special, he said. I do my best to make her feel at ease.

"Tell me how you got to be a nurse."

"I started to think about becoming a nurse during 1967, during the Summer of Love. I'd come to California for the first time from New York City, to seek a better way of living."

"Can I ask how old you are?"

(Pause.) "Thirty-nine."

"Is that okay to say in the book?"

"Yeah . . . . " She is wistful. I see a photo of a handsome man with a beard just above her desk. Later, she tells me he's her boyfriend.

"You know what was in the air then. It was an era of great upheaval and idealism. My goodness!" There is something delicate about the way she touches her fingers to her lips, so softly, as we remember young people who were going to remake the world. And flowers handed cheerfully to the pinstriped men on Wall Street sidewalks. Freedom. Love. Peace.

"I was working as a secretary then, and I was twenty. I wasn't sure what I wanted to do with my life except to learn how people could live meaningfully. There was a desire to break up old forms, the complicated superstructures, and replace them with something back to the earth and much more natural. So . . . I was out in California. I got in touch with my own desire to be of service to people. And with how much that meant to me for my ultimate life's work or career. I'm a worker. I've always worked. Finally, I went back to school and became a nurse in California."

"Are you an idealist?"

"I suppose I am. An idealist of the heart."

"What do you mean?"

"I have a sense, deep in me, of how things should be. Of how we should feel and act with one another and lead our lives. That's part of what propels me. One thing that drew me here, to this unit, was my disillusionment with what I saw and heard of some health care workers with AIDS patients. So maybe I'm less idealistic than I used to be. Not every nurse is the same. But I still think, for the most part, nurses are in this profession because they really want to do good for their fellows."

"Can you remember when AIDS first entered your life?"

"Yes. I was working as a 'per diem' at San Francisco General. I had just moved into the city. Per diem nurses were usually the ones given AIDS patients. Per diem people don't regularly work on the unit, so they're often given undesirable assignments — or the heavier load, since they have no seniority. They're not going to be here tomorrow, and they don't get to have much say.

"I was given an AIDS patient. I didn't really have much idea of what AIDS was. I didn't understand, at first, why these patients were so isolated. And I did get a sense of isolation. This first patient was all the way back at the end of the hall, the laaaast room away from the nurse's station. His room looked as though no one had been there for days. Clutter. Neglect. There was a sense of intensity and urgency about it, I could feel it.

"There I was, not knowing much about him. This was 1981. I was per diem, the lowest of the low." The way she describes herself is so soft and accepting of the humble station that I burst out laughing. She acknowledges my laughter with a smile and continues steadily.

"Slowly, somehow, I got a sense of him. Part of my understanding came from Paul Volberding, who happened to be his doctor.

I didn't know Paul either. He came in to see the patient and I started to leave. He didn't know me, but he said to me, 'Oh, no. I want you to stay. This is something we all need to talk about together and the patient needs to be able to discuss it with staff, not only me.' What he was talking about was Code Status."

"What is that?"

"That's a big issue for people with AIDS. It could be an important issue for any patient. It means whether a patient will be resuscitated or not if they have a cardiac arrest. When you're talking with patients who might very well have a terminal diagnosis, the issue of Code Status becomes very important."

"They're allowed to say what THEY want to have happen?"

"We want to know that, yes."

"Legally, are you allowed to honor their wishes?"

"Legally, we follow the wishes they convey to their attending physician. The attending physician must document them very clearly in a chart. It's not like, I just sit down with you one day and you say, 'you know, I don't want to be coded,' and I say 'all right, I'll pass the word along to everyone.'"

Again, she makes me laugh as she imitates a casual, gruff acceptance of the patient's wishes about his life. I'm beginning to notice steadiness and strength beneath her vulnerability. "Because, unless it's specifically written that a patient doesn't wish to be coded, all of them are and we will always attempt to resuscitate."

"Okay. So Paul Volberding wanted to discuss that and he wanted you to be part of it?"

"Yes, and I was surprised. Because, at that time and in my experience, it was a very un-physician-like approach. Usually if those things are discussed, you know, the nurse leaves the room, and the word is handed down after a closeted session with the patient. Also code status usually isn't discussed except with very old people, like an old cancer patient. Anyway, that was my first encounter with AIDS.

"As I continued to do per diem work, I saw more AIDS patients. It was kind of fun to take care of them. They were bright, and talking about things interesting and relevant to life. But there was always this business of the cluttered room at the end of the hall, someone abandoned.

"Some of the staff reactions I heard were appalling to me. For example, one nurse made a homophobic remark, like, `oh, they deserve it!' I was stopped in my tracks. The sort of situation where the smile just freezes on your face?"

She began to understand more how unpopular AIDS patients were for much of the staff. As she learned more about "the import of the diagnosis," she began to be alarmed alarm for a close friend, a gay man.

372

"A very, very good friend," she says. "A very good friend. A very close friend. Like a brother to me." I notice her repetition and I wonder about it. I have the fantasy she is stalling for time.

"So . . . ." She stops talking and swallows. "Excuse me," she says. Carefully she reaches for a Kleenex. Slowly, as though stately movements will be harder for me to perceive, she brushes her eyes with the Kleenex. I believe I sense her embarrassment.

"People often feel a lot of things in these interviews," I say gently. "It happens often."

After a silence, she tells me -- evenly as before -- "he was diagnosed recently. About four to six weeks ago, I don't know exactly. So I'm . . . I'm really . . . you know, just learning to cope with this."

"Yes." She directs her mind back to her early days on the ward. "So I started attaching this disease to, like, `what if this happened to Kent?' Or, `what if this happened to Steve,' his lover."

Being able to personalize the disease helped her get more in touch with its dangerousness. Eventually, she heard about the special AIDS unit. Friends urged her to apply and she realized she wanted to. Cliff Morrison interviewed and hired her. When he realized he needed a head nurse, he appointed Alison.

"Listen," I say. "I've just got to ask you something. I find myself really liking you, just as a person. There's something about your vulnerability that touches me. But you're very different than my picture of the words, 'HEAD NURSE.' You're not like the strong, firm movie stereotype. Can you comment on that?"

"I am a *person* who is a head nurse. My staff are people who are nurses. I want, and I think we all want, for this to be a very human place. That's what 5-B is about. If I focus on an image of starch, a hard veneer, what will I project to my staff? And they to their patients? The success of this unit has most to do with my nurses and with the community. I include Shanti and all the other personnel who are part of it. This is a place where people work together, that's why it succeeds.

"Sometimes I feel pressure within myself to be harder. Power issues crop up. But when I do use that kind of image is more often on about Step Nine, when I argue with someone not on my staff. Let's say someone from elsewhere in the hospital wanting to wear a mask here. Or when I want to get things done on the telephone. But a severe nurse, some hard image -- that doesn't say 'professionalism' to me.

"Professionalism has to do with knowing what you're doing, coming from a very sound knowledge base. It means working together with the patient, too, you know. It doesn't mean denying that either one of us is a person. It doesn't help a patient dealing with issues of life and death to be cared for by someone with a face that cannot crack. That's not professional, it's an individual who's frightened."

"Your staff is encouraged to get involved," I say, "and not to keep a distance. But if you allow yourself to care that way, isn't it tough dealing with a disease from which people are regularly dying? Don't you pay a price for letting your feelings out there?"

"Oh, no," she says firmly. "You don't pay a price. You pay a price for *not* letting feelings out. It takes a terrible toll on you. Working here, you ARE going to feel, you know. There's no way -- unless you're made of steel, and we don't have people on this unit like that -- you're going to be moved and touched. You can't not be moved by these guys. The disease itself . . . the love you see. There's often sadness, but there's a terrific intensity of living here. It's a super-real quality. Everything matters.

"I haven't before worked with many young people who had a terminal diagnosis, whose lives were so inwardly accompanied by death. There's something special about that. Whether it's our own emotion, or our emotion combined with theirs, everything seems here to . . . spring into deeper color. There's an intensity here that you have to feel. My own life is more like that now. There's more appreciation of life for working here. But you don't get that by holding yourself back, or by running away."

"Do you think the principles of 5-B could work elsewhere? For diseases other than AIDS?"

"Yes, anywhere. But if you encourage people to be vulnerable, you know, you have to support them also."

"You know," I say. "I'm still thinking about workers from elsewhere in the hospital, wanting to wear a mask here."

"Sometimes they try. But we don't let them."

"If hospital workers can still think that way, imagine the general population."

"Yes," she says. "I know. They're worried they'll get it from the air. I don't know what to say."

"What would you like to say about AIDS to people reading this?"

"I'd like people to explore their fears. Are they afraid of this disease? There's no reason any more, we know too much about it. Are they afraid of the patients, because so many of them are gay? It's time for us to drop all that. To hate someone because of what they do with their lover when they go to bed at night, it's so absurd.

"I wish people would separate themselves from their fears. The fear itself is not what's terrible. Being ruled by it is."

374

Kevin on Ward 5-B

It's true that I think I've noticed a subtle lightness among the 5-B staff, a camaraderie that may be different from what I've experienced elsewhere. But how, precisely? I struggle to label the tone. Friendly but not sloppy. Good-humored yet in control. Am I imagining this?

I am introduced to Kevin, a thin young man with pale skin and a scruffy blond beard. A Shanti volunteer sits near his bed. I expect something more formal, and I'm surprised at their easy laughter. Just like friends.

Kevin's wall is filled floor to ceiling with a home-made gallery of watercolors and photos. The bright and spacious room feels unusually cheerful to me. I decide my perception probably reflects merely a comparison to New York City and a different urban environment — different price of real estate per square foot of hospital, different percent of sky versus skyscraper outside the patient's window.

Kevin is a native Californian, age twenty-seven. He tells me of an automobile accident in his home town a year and a half ago. In the resulting hospital tests, with a look at those funny purple bruises, he became the first official AIDS case of Yuba City, population, 50,000. Before Kevin was told the news, the other patient sharing his room was hastily wheeled away. Kevin noticed that the hospital staff seemed suddenly "nervous" but he wasn't sure why.

His doctor advised him to move to San Francisco. In his increasingly weakened condition, and with increasingly visible KS lesions, he's now unable to get work. Shanti provides him with a low-cost residence shared with other PWA's.

"If it weren't for Shanti and Ward 5-B, I doubt that I'd still be alive. You have to have some will to live. Their emotional support helps me to have that. I admit I can feel myself following the trail of people I knew who are dead. I've just had my first case of pneumonia."

We talk about his lifestyle as a gay man. "I can remember in early childhood being attracted to men. I didn't understand what that meant. I tried to deny it, to run from it, but finally at twenty-one, I gave up and accepted myself.

"When I did become sexually active, I was primarily a 'bottom.' Probably that has to do with my illness now. I can see what an easy way that was for a virus to get into my bloodstream. Being a bottom just felt natural, that's all I can say. It was instinctive, like being gay in the first place. If I'd have known about a virus, I'd have probably made different decisions. Obviously I didn't use condoms, for example. But I didn't know about the virus. No one did, and that's that.

"My family has never taken it well, about my lifestyle, although at least they haven't cut me off." When Kevin told them about AIDS, his family was "upset" and said his homosexuality caused the disease. "They were worried that they would catch it. My sister now has a child that I've never seen. They don't trust anything I try to tell them as reassurance about their ability to have contact with me. I'm not allowed to see *any* of the children, actually."

A nurse enters with a large stack of chocolate bars. He tosses one to Kevin and says, "Merry Christmas." Kevin fondles the bar and tells me, "we get so many presents on this ward. It's wonderful! People donate here a lot, it's an amazing hospital ward. I've met plenty of people with AIDS who wish they could be here."

"What's your relationship like with your Shanti volunteer?"

"We've had to teach each other about each other," he says. "The Shanti training, from what I can tell, is a wonderful experience, but it can't prepare them for everybody they work with. When we first met, Terry was pretty fresh out of the training. He used a lot of that Northern California attitude -- `how does it really feel to you?' I don't need that stuff. He was doing the best he could and I was a handful, frankly. The upshot is, though, we've learned how to be friends. I'm glad to have him with me.

"The first year I was diagnosed was a health honeymoon compared to now. I know the disease kills people, and I know it's not pretty. One by one, now, things are starting to happen . . . it's beginning. I don't know what that means on a calendar, I don't know what date, how much time . . . but I'm pretty realistic by now." He doesn't look away, even momentarily, as he tells me this.

"One very good thing about a Shanti volunteer," he says. "I can talk about anything with Terry. That lets me give my friends a break, if you see what I mean. It's nice to have a person you can talk to about AIDS without feeling you're a burden."

"You are having an extraordinary experience," I tell him. "What would you like to say to readers about it?"

"This is not a TV drama," he says. "It's happening right here. I bet we lose one AIDS person a day in this hospital. Those are real people, not just interesting stories. I know others have made this kind of appeal for help before. For research. For something to be done. But if you're giving me the chance to say something, I want to be sure that I've asked for the research too."

Linda Maxey - Shanti Counseling Coordinator - 5-B

She's a tall blonde, age thirty-eight, and is a registered nurse. She moved here from Cleveland ten years ago and likes San Francisco because of its "different ways of looking at the world. Orientals, Hispanics, there are so many more ways life is diverse here than in Ohio."

Linda established the Shanti counseling program for Ward 5-B. Shanti used to work with a number of life-threatening illnesses, she says. But AIDS is so demanding, it's become the full time focus of the organization.

"That's really sad. There are lots of other people who need this support." As it is, however, Shanti's 400 volunteers are stretched to capacity.

"`Shanti' is a Sanskrit word that means, 'inner peace.' Dr. Charles Garfield, a psychologist working on the cancer wards at the University of California, founded the group in 1974. He became aware that people with terminal illness have a lot of needs. It's when people who normally support you, your family and friends, go through their own issues about your illness. Shanti offers a supportive volunteer to counteract the isolation and abandonment that can occur with a terminal diagnosis."

"So it's care for people who are dying?"

"That's what the original brochure said. We've since changed it to 'life-threatening illness and grief.'" She explains that the finality of "terminal" is now often replaced with "life-threatening," which allows the possibility of hope. The change occurred primarily because of feedback from AIDS patients. They said, "You don't know much about this disease yet. Don't label us as though it's certain that we can't get better."

Shanti has become a role model for similar organizations around the country, especially since the increase in AIDS clients. "This is a very unusual program," she says about Ward 5-B. "I've never seen it happen before, that an outside organization helps to staff an institution like San Francisco General. We are under a city contract for both the inpatient and outpatient AIDS units."

A volunteer can't take the Shanti training without thorough screening first. The process begins with a lengthy questionnaire. What's been your personal experience with loss? Do you have a particular agenda for what people should do if they're disabled?

If the volunteer seems apt, extensive interviews follow, including role playing. How ready is the person to grow? Is the applicant prepared for Shanti training?

On a sudden impulse, I say to Linda, "Let's pretend that I'm interviewing with you. Can you set up a role play, so I can see what that's like? Then, after we've done it for a few minutes, stop and critique me honestly versus what you look for. Okay? What do you think?"

It's not so easy, she tells me. She'd be looking to my completed application as the basis of the role play. Am I opposed to particular treatments my client might favor? If I'm religious, how do I handle a client who says, "there is no God."

"We look primarily for strong agendas," she says. "Or people who are overly intellectual about the process. When someone's dying isn't the time to give them your theories. You give them your heart."

"I don't know which of my weaknesses is the best for you to go after," I say with a laugh. I am the only one laughing.

"We can do the role play," she says quietly. "I just didn't want you to think I had a pat one all set up." I wait and experience my growing tension as she considers my case. "Are you sure you're ready to do this?"

"No! I'm not sure at all."

"All right. She looks straight ahead, at the wall. I notice my own breathing. I'm tense as I wait in dead silence.

"All right. You're going to be the volunteer, and I'll be the client."

"Be a difficult client," I say, having come this far already. "Be a type of client people generally have trouble with."

"There are all kinds they have trouble with," she says. "I'm going to be a person who is newly diagnosed. I just got the results of my biopsy, and it is positive: I have KS. One of the lesions is on my face. I called Shanti, and I'm having a real hard time. This is our first session. I'm thirty-one years old and my lover died of AIDS six months ago. That's all you know."

"Okay," I say. But I'm no longer speaking to Linda Maxey. She has somehow changed her face. There is no life to her cheeks. Her mouth curls in a different way. Her eyes seem cold and empty. I think of the science fiction aliens who take over humans. My mind supplies a KS lesion on her right cheek. Only she doesn't seem like "she" anymore.

"Hi, I'm Mike Greenly. I'm here to be your Shanti volunteer."

"Hi, Mike."

(Pause.)

"What is your name?" I'm trying to show, with my voice, that I mean well.

"Tom." (Pause.) "I'm glad you came over." (Sigh.) "I don't even know why I called. Um . . . you know, my lover died six months ago, so I know what I'm looking at. I'm really not sure that I'm gonna deal with it the way he did. It was hell watching him go through that. I just don't think I can do it."

"Tell me more about how you feel."

"I don't know. I guess it's sort of like, I knew this was going to happen, and yet I didn't. I think I'm gonna make a different choice. I'm not going to go through it all like he did. He fought right to the end, and I don't think I want to do that."

"What do you want to do?"

"Well I think, you know, he's got some medicine left from, um, all the pain he had at the end. So I'm really thinking I'm just gonna take some of that medicine before it gets too late. I don't want to end up like him, where he couldn't even go to the bathroom. He was in constant pain. He couldn't even swallow because the lesions were stuck in the back of his throat. That's just not living, and I'm not gonna do that."

What do I say now? I have a fantasy of phoning Linda, wherever she is. Where are the pills he mentions and what am I supposed to do about his thoughts of suicide? Right now, he's not nearly in the final shape his friend was in. Not yet. Maybe if I get him to see that.

"But, how are you feeling now?"

"I just told you." I feel rebuked. "I don't wanna go through that."

(Silence.)

"Let's stop," I finally say. There she is again -- Linda. "I'll tell you what I'm feeling."

"Unh-huh?" At last, she is smiling.

"And then you give me some response."

"Great."

"I felt some panic at the fact that you wanted to kill yourself."

"Um-hmm."

"And I wasn't sure how I was supposed to handle it."

"Um-hmm."

"I didn't know whether you had a doctor -- could I get off the hook myself by referring you to your doctor? I was starting down a track of wanting you to see that you're physically not so bad now, and maybe things will get better. But that sounded hollow as I started to hear it in my own head — I don't, myself, believe it.

"When you said, 'well I already told you how I feel,' I was thinking -- 'gosh! I'm not doing this right.'" She is laughing now; I guess she's used to volunteers expressing this kind of uncertainty. "I was nervous, and felt as though . . . I could have used some more training."

"First of all," she says, as I relax back into my chair, "you've got a lot of what it would take to be able to do it. You learned a lot in doing the role play. You stayed aware of what was coming up for you, instead of blanking out or getting intellectual. That's significant. At this point I would say, you could learn it." Water after the dry spell.

"You've got the heart. That panic will come up, over and over, as a counselor. It comes up for me years down the line. The willingness to hang in there through the panic is really the key. It's hard to stay in there when someone's hurting, when someone's in pain. The willingness to do that is huge because, that's when most everybody else in his life leaves emotionally. It's human nature to avoid pain.

"Put yourself in the place of family and friends who don't have the training, and who are even more involved with the person. Imagine what it would be like if you were his lover, hearing that. You can imagine why people leave or don't know what to do. What you'd get in the training would be how to make some of your responses a little different.

"I liked your tone of voice. I thought that you were really there, and I felt your caring. That's important. I didn't feel you were emotionally distant, even though you didn't know what to say. You cared, and that came across.

"When you asked me again, how did I feel, that was when I knew you didn't know where to go. You didn't know what to say. A good response at that point could be, 'it seems pretty hopeless,' or 'that must be terrifying.'"

"To acknowledge it," I say.

"Yes. Just call it, right out there. Just, 'that must be really terrifying, seeing your lover go through this and now wondering about yourself.' That's the first step, just acknowledging what's happening. It's good you didn't play Pollyanna, I'm glad you knew that wasn't right and didn't do it. That would have been disruptive, you see.

"I would have shut down, and probably not shared with you any more. I'd be aware that you were really uncomfortable with my feelings of hopelessness, that you were trying to make it better, mostly to take care of yourself. It wouldn't have done much for me, except cut me off."

"But I didn't know what to say," I tell her, "about the pills."

"Um-hmm. It's good you didn't try to pass me off to the doctor right away. The most important thing to do is, STAY RIGHT THERE. Fear and all. Just stay right there and let them talk about it. When he mentions suicide, panic comes up for you, sure. What you'll get in the training is more comfortableness with hearing people express those thoughts. And you'll get more idea of how to respond. Because it's different if you hear someone newly diagnosed talking about suicide, versus someone who's been through so much more.

"Where I might have gone, after acknowledging the fear, is to try to separate out -- 'It must be difficult because that's the only image you have of what the disease is like for someone. It's probably hard for you to believe it could be different for you.' Then I might try, GENTLY, going in a direction of having him see, it *might* be different for him. He might have quality of life left."

"Well, I meant for him to deduce that."

"Yes, but first you have to acknowledge what he feels. Do that first, before you move on. If you point out that's his 'only' image, then he realizes maybe there are others. But go slowly, gently, in the direction of hope. You have time, you don't have to rush. I would have stayed with this client for hours. Before I left, I'd make sure he'd agreed not to try the pills right now. You'd be learning our Shanti policies on suicide, you'd have to report that to your group leader. You'd get training on all that.

"That was only one of hundreds of situations. Noncommunicative people. Very emotional. You'd find the areas of work you need to work on. A lot of the work is on yourself."

What would she like *you* to know?

"If there's a legacy of this epidemic, it will be that patients have rights. AIDS patients have spoken out more than any other group I've seen in health care. They've helped develop some incredibly fine models of health care. Not just for 'curing,' but for caring. And by a team of people who can also support each other. The legacy will be, we'll have bettered health care for everyone.

"Meanwhile, we're losing people who need our unequivocal support. And they deserve it."

Beverly Flynn - Shanti Volunteer

She's one of the volunteers assigned when the request is "a heterosexual woman, please." Ken Stevenson, a gay male with AIDS, is one of the clients who made that request. "I didn't want to take a chance on being attracted to my volunteer," Ken had told me in a phone conversation. "I needed someone with nothing `funny' going on in my head." He said with excitement, "She looks just like Jean Harlow, wait till you see here. She is gorgeous!"

Now I sit in her long, chilly office at the Pride Center, a drafty old mansion in a dilapidated neighborhood. This is where Shanti holds its volunteer trainings.

She tells me about the three types of functions that volunteers perform. First, there is office assistance for Shanti itself -- stuffing envelopes, clerical help, distributing tickets donated by local theaters. "People with AIDS usually can't afford entertainment," she says. "Many can't work at all. We keep a list of people to telephone when we're given free tickets."

A second category of volunteer assistance is "Practical Support," which is laundry, shopping, house cleaning, meal preparation, obtaining medicine. Whatever is needed.

Third is "Emotional Support," a peer counseling program. "You learn to listen," Beverly says. "To feel what your client feels and to let go of your own agenda. You meet the client's needs; yours are secondary."

"My first impression of Ken was that he was quiet. He was diagnosed two years ago and called for a counselor. I've always felt a few steps behind him. He figures things out on his own and then fills me in. I learned to accept that, although my desire at first was to be with him during a crisis. That was my personal agenda, so I could be sure I was

381

doing a good job. My previous client had always involved me during his crises, screaming, crying. But Ken has his own way of needing me.

"At first, my vision of being the perfect counselor was that Ken was supposed to call me twice a day. So in my support group -- it's mandatory for every volunteer, once a week -- I'd talk about my frustration. `I wish Ken would share more of his crisis with me! MY needs are not being met.' The more I verbalized it, the more I worked it out so I could be what he needed me to be and not some image I had."

"What Ken gives me is the ability to look at things differently. Working with him has helped me appreciate the quality of life more, see the beauty in little things that I used to overlook. He's helped me see different perspectives because he's had to do that for himself.

"For example, when I moved out here from New Jersey, my parents put a lot of pressure on me. They were calling me all the time, still wanting to be part of my life even though we were 2,400 miles away. I used to feel resentment toward those calls, I used to find them intrusive. Working with Ken, learning to listen to him, learning to appreciate other people more — now I'm able to put myself in my parents' position. I can look at things from their point of view, and feel the loss of their daughter who's moved across the country. So I stopped being defensive and opened up to them tremendously. Today I look at my parents as people I love, not just `my parents.' My experience with Ken, opening myself up as a Shanti counselor to other people's feelings, that's helped me with my own relationships. That is absolutely true. I can empathize more with others now, and I'm grateful for that."

Bev is an accountant. She tells me of her experience at a previous employer. When people learned she was a Shanti volunteer, she noticed that they quietly withdrew from her. Finally, she realized they were afraid of "catching AIDS" by having her in the office. She did her best then to explain that they needn't worry.

I ask her what message she would most like to pass on to readers. She doesn't hesitate for an instant.

"Don't run," she says. "Don't run. Just put your arms around these people and hold them. That's what they need more than anything else, love and understanding. That's what we all want out of life anyway. Especially when things go wrong."

Ken Stevenson - PWA

We meet for brunch in a noisy restaurant. The maitre d' sees we want to conduct an interview and does his best to give us a quiet table. This being San Francisco, with a high per capita incidence of AIDS — and this being a "gay part of town" — I have an inkling the maitre d' realizes my guest has the disease . . . with Ken's very pale skin and a tentativeness, a subtle weakness, as he walks. The maitre d' asks gently, several times during the meal, if the interview is going well.

After growing up in Maine, Ken moved to Tennessee, where his mother had moved with his stepfather. He did odd jobs for several years, until he had a "religious conversion experience." At twenty, he decided to join a Catholic seminary. He is now thirty-one.

He lived in the Toronto seminary for six years, studying to be a priest. "I always knew I was gay," he says. "At age three, or age five. I knew that I liked men, though I didn't know why. I liked to sit in their laps. I combed their hair, my father's friends, as a young, young child. In the seminary, it didn't take me long to discover that about 80% of the people I lived with were gay, at least in terms of their feelings. Many, I'm sure, never acted on what they felt and just stayed celibate. They would admit their true feelings only to other gay men, although not to our authorities. After a while I realized there was an underground gay network.

"You understand, in the seminary, it's still a sin to even masturbate. A sin! Try to be a school teacher and tell that to ninth-grade boys. I just couldn't say, `don't do it, it's a sin.' I wanted to tell them, `it's the most fun thing you'll be doing with yourself for the rest of your life.' But you're not supposed to do it at all; I know that is hard to believe."

When Ken was twenty-five, he says the "head honcho" whose office was in Rome came to Toronto as part of a North American tour. He called Ken aside and told him it was rumored he'd been frequenting gay bars. "Imagine my surprise," he says with irony. "I had gone to bars, but certainly not frequently." He'd been visiting local bars with another Brother. "We were just dancing, that's all. We didn't know enough to realize people met each other there to actually go home and have sex. I was so ignorant!"

"He said to me, `we think you have a problem with your sexuality.' I said, `what could that problem be?' No one would dare say the word. No one would say `homosexual.' They gave me a choice, leaving on my own accord or being dismissed. I didn't want to leave, really. I was genuinely growing there. If I could only have talked openly about my feelings, I think it's possible I could have come to terms with myself. Maybe I could have accepted my attraction to other men and also accepted celibacy. But I left before I could figure myself out.

"I left for San Francisco after six months back home in Tennessee. For twenty-five years, people had been telling me what to do. Finally, I thought, I'll start to make my own decisions."

He never discussed his sexuality with his mother. He left for San Francisco and found a clerical job to support himself. "I was so naive, I

383

was amazed that sex could be recreational. I had never looked at it that way. I looked at it, like the rest of my life, as spiritual. Here it was something to do, just for the fun of it."

It took him several years, he says, to accept the casualness of sex in this new environment. Nothing in his family or in the Church had prepared him. His wish was to "fall in love and live happily ever after." The actuality, however, was that he dated one man for a month, another for a few weeks. "Everything else was a one-night stand." In general over the course of his five years in San Francisco, he estimates, he had a sexual experience about once every three months.

Four times a year, I am thinking. Here was an unattached man in his late twenties, in a city known for the personal freedom of its lifestyles. Surely he was not "promiscuous" as locally defined. Here was a young man who didn't know, as a cleric in a seminary, that people went to bars for more than dancing. Cloistered for years, cautious in his sexual experience — and now he has AIDS.

"The exciting part for me," he says, "was just being able to touch another person, being able to be next to someone. The contact. The closeness. Whether or not I had an orgasm was less important than that."

In February of 1982, he went to bed — one time only — with a man he was very attracted to. John was a waiter, a year younger than Ken. The next month, John became "very sick." By late spring, he was diagnosed with AIDS. By late summer, Ken saw him in a bar and noticed John looked ill John. "I visited him during his illness," he says, "and got to see what it was all about. Now I've basically followed in his footsteps, step by step, with my own symptoms. John died the day I was diagnosed. That was November 15, 1983.

"It ruined my whole day," he says with a stagy laugh. "To say the least." How often has he been ironic like that about his condition? How often does he joke as he discusses the disease that will kill him?

"This is absurd," he remembers thinking. "I'm not one of those South of Market types. I'm not all of those things I've read in the newspaper. I have really not been very sexually active. And I have been good to people. I'm a good person. How can this happen to me?"

He tells me about his decision to ask for a Shanti volunteer. "I realized in my first week in the hospital, you don't deal with this alone. I found myself, frequently, so far hidden under my covers, I was down at the foot of the bed.

"I expected someone clinical as a Shanti volunteer. That's not what I got. I got someone I quickly realized was a friend, and she was listening to me. I hadn't expected to go out to brunch with her, or go with her just to walk her dog in the park.

"My regular friends were shocked, like I was. So it wasn't an easy communication with them. They never knew how much to ask. I wanted them to ask it *all* — like what the testing was like, so I could tell them how much it hurts. I wanted them to ask me what a lung biopsy is, because it's such a horrible experience. Tubes up the nose. It makes you cough, and it makes you choke. Physically and psychologically, it's as if you're drowning. I wanted my friends to ask, and no one did: I think they were afraid of the answers. But Bev knew.

"She will be there when I need her, I know that for sure. That's really important. And she does other things that matter, like hug you."

He tells me about watching TV from his hospital bed, hearing the news of Rock Hudson's death. Bev happened to enter the room at that moment and, this time, he allowed himself to let go. He chose not to control his grief and fear, and he was grateful to cry in her arms. "She had a beautiful blue silk dress on. I was worried I would stain it, but she just held me and let me cry."

"Shanti means a lot," he says. "I know I could say anything to Bev. I can tell her, `I'm tired of this, and I would like to die now.' She won't try to talk me out of it. Friends try to give you alternatives, as if you hadn't already thought of them, lying in bed twenty-four hours a day."

Before we leave the restaurant, I invite Ken to send you a personal message.

"I'd like to say that I feel cheated of my own death and dying experience. It isn't a socially acceptable disease, what I've got. If you have cancer, for example, you can tell people you've got it and they won't run away from you. They won't be afraid to touch you. They may even be willing to hug you.

"But when I tell someone I have AIDS, they'll say, `oh! how many times did you do it?' . . . like, `why weren't you more careful?' I wish, instead — I wish they'd look me right in the eye, really *look* at me and say, `I'm sorry you have a terminal disease, Ken.' Just say it to me and help me face the fact of it.

"Just once, I wish someone would say -- without even mentioning 'AIDS,' you know -- 'Gee, Ken. Dying must be difficult.'"

Chapter 33:
Hoffman LaRoche —
Two Scientists

I had interviewed the small pharmaceutical firm that makes Isoprinosine. Dr. Stan Bodner of Nashville, Tennessee -- an infectious disease specialist and reader of these interviews via computer -- suggested I also visit a larger company, Hoffman-LaRoche. Roche makes Bactrim, for example, which I've now seen tubed into the veins of many patients with PCP pneumonia.

My interest was not so much in specific medications as in the kinds of people working to respond to AIDS, and in the way they approach their goals. Roche is a privately held corporation with U.S. sales alone of over $1,000,000,000 and distribution of its products to over fifty countries worldwide.

I spoke to two members of Roche's staff, an M. D. and a research Ph.D. They have different disciplines, personalities, and assignments. Together, they added to my own understanding of the human side of scientists facing AIDS.

Paul I. Nadler, M.D.

He is wiry, intense, and a bundle of nervous energy. His thick pointed eyebrows look almost pasted on. He was born and raised in New York City and is now thirty-six. He responds to my first question with a coherent and organized presentation, hardly seeming to breathe for about twenty minutes.

He was a Chemistry major and English minor. He was named a Jonas Salk Scholar at City University of New York, completed his medical residency at Washington University in St. Louis, and worked five years at the National Institute of Health, taking care of cancer patients and doing basic research in immunology.

In his last year at the NIH, as an attending physician, he decided he no longer wanted to be an oncologist. He switched his emphasis to immunology and allergies and ultimately joined Roche in June of 1982. He is Director of Clinical Immunology, and he's worked on medications specifically being pursued in relation to AIDS, including Interferon and Interleukin-2. He is "the AIDS expert of Roche." I spot an award he received for an "original and inspired talk" he gave on the disease.

He remembers with fondness and admiration Dr. John Burns, the "humane and caring" Vice President of Research when Paul first came to Roche. Paul was asked to create some testing of interferon with AIDS. His budget was set at $100,000. "I felt we owed it to AIDS patients to do a controlled, randomized study, and that's what I designed." He also felt it was important to design a protocol for treatment of what are now known as ARC patients. When Paul had finalized his recommendations, the cost of all his proposals would grossly exceed the budget.

"Dr. Burns," he said, "I have $100,000 in the plan, but this is what I think we should really do. It's hard to design trials perfectly because we know so little about AIDS at all. I do know it's going to cost between $500,000 and a million dollars."

I can imagine how things might have been in my own corporation. "Ray, I know you're expecting our research on how people feel about Avon Representatives to cost $100,000, but . . . ." Fine, Mike, step out of the way please. I need to find a replacement who can stick to his budget!

Paul, too, was expecting "Can't you do it for $200,000? Have you considered fewer trials?" There'd been less than a thousand cases of AIDS back then, Paul reminds me -- a few IV drug abusers, a few hemophiliacs, and a lot of gay men. But Dr. Burns said, "AIDS is a terrible problem. We don't know the cause of it. If you think your design is a rational, valid thing to do, and if it will help answer some of the questions, then you've got it, Paul." Period. End of discussion.

"I was flabbergasted," Paul says. "He's one of those people who feels very strongly in a balance between market orientation -- there were many better markets to pursue for profit -- and science, especially for a disease with the morbidity rate of AIDS. I'd been at Roche for only six months and although I respected that man before, I left his office that day walking on air."

Researchers found that Interferon can be somewhat helpful in treating KS. Under some conditions, it is anti-viral and can also act as an immune modulator. There are further results still to follow that are not yet published.

I ask Paul to tell me more about his personal decision to leave the field of oncology. Originally, he says, he had fallen in love with treating cancer patients -- "they have a dire need for your services, and there's a tremendous amount to be done in research. You also have to be involved with every aspect of internal medicine, and I love that." He admired tremendously the oncology Fellows he worked with, people spending twelve to sixteen hours a day to keep cancer patients alive.

But the treatment of diseases like leukemia can make deathly ill people even more ill. The experience is grueling to both physician and patient. "There's only a certain amount you can do . . . I became what can only be described as depressed . . . for these people and for their families."

As a third year student, Paul hoped he would be less depressed when he reached a more senior level,. Maybe he'd then see fewer patients crying in the arms of their loved ones. Maybe he'd be present less often at the moment of death. Maybe he would feel less helpless.

But as a fourth year student, he was telling patients for the first time: "I'm sorry; you have cancer." Years later, as an NIH Fellow, he was the doctor a patient would turn to after treatment failed or when a cancer returned. "What do we do next?" people wanted to know.

"I found I cared just as much," he tells me. "But I was just as helpless. They turned to me now for the next experimental therapy. Often, there was nothing I could give them. I ended up in a room with the door closed doing what every oncologist is forced to do: discussing the importance of tying up loose ends and of saying good bye to people you love -- a realistic approach to the end of life. I was every bit, despite the years that had passed, as personally involved as a third year medical student. Every time one of my patients died, a little of me died. Many oncologists learn to see just the broad picture; I could not. I had to change my focus. As much as I loved oncology, I had to remove myself as a human being ."

He tells me he used to attend patients' funerals. He never admitted that habit to his peers, nor even his wife. It would have been considered unprofessional, although he took solace in showing bereaved families that the medical profession really cared. We agree on the irony: having left cancer, Paul now devotes his energy to the disease most often compared to it in devastation. But at least his present assignment is more distant than being the first to give bad news to a patient. He finds satisfaction in doing what he can so that fewer people will ever get the news . . . and in trying to create an answer for the patient who asks, "What can we do next, Doctor?"

"If I had to care for AIDS patients on a day-in, day-out basis, I'd be right back where I was and I wouldn't be effective. The people who treat it successfully find ways to get away periodically and not care . . . that's the only way they can then jump in again, rejuvenated, to treat each opportunistic infection, knowing they can do nothing about the underlying disease right now. That's the way they keep coming back."

I ask him about the perspective I've heard, that malaria isn't as attractive a disease as cat leukemia for pharmaceutical firms, given the poverty of its many Third World sufferers versus the relative wealth of cat owners.

"The feline leukemia vaccine was just licensed last year," he says. "It costs twenty-one dollars a shot, for three shots. I have to tell you, though, it turns out that Roche actually does do a lot of malaria research. Right now, we in Nutley, New Jersey are in collaboration with Roche in Basel, Switzerland and a fellow named Victor Nussenzvweig at NYU. He's done pioneering research identifying proteins that can help us come up with a malaria vaccine. So, we ARE working on that one! Roche, Basel made a judgement about malaria like Roche, New Jersey did about AIDS -- there may not be as much money in that particular disease, but it's an important one, and you have to have a balance. A vaccine for malaria would eliminate the disease worldwide!"

"There's not an iota of question, though, is there? Your company wants to make money."

"Absolutely. No question about it."

"When I worked on detergent at Lever, I knew the intensity of my competition at Proctor and Colgate. You have competition too, don't you?"

"Absolutely." He tells me about different companies that are all working with their own versions of Interleukin-2 for AIDS. "We're all tackling many of the same problems. Something to treat a disease that was never treatable before . . . that's a hard thing to find, Mike!" The simplicity of his statement makes me laugh. "We actually came up with a treatment like that -- in 1982 from the guys who are next door to me, the Dermatology people. We got a drug approved called Accutane, which is useful for a severe, terrible, recalcitrant acne. It was a genuine breakthrough.

"If you give Accutane over time to patients with terrible, disfiguring acne, eighty to ninety percent of them get a complete remission. That can change people's life experience. Now this drug is extremely powerful. If a young woman on this drug gets pregnant, despite your warning not to, while she's taking the drug, she could deliver a child with birth defects. If she waits till she's off the drug before getting pregnant, then there's no problem. We were very upfront about the risk and how to use it correctly. The drug, a genuine breakthrough, makes a 'good' amount of money. But I'll tell you, it's not like Valium.

"Valium was another breakthrough for its era in the 1960's. It was discovered here at Roche and it supplanted many more toxic drugs like phenobarbital. The company has made a fortune from it; many of the buildings here were created with Valium. Its success helps us research illnesses that may not be so lucrative but that are very important."

Paul contrasts his own situation at Roche with that of Dr. Glasky at Newport Labs, whose only product is Isoprinosine. The difference in options and resources is substantial.

"I guess we can afford, at Roche, to be more complacent. Suppose you ask me, for example, `is Interferon gonna work for AIDS?' I can afford to say, without pressure or excitement, `it has some activity in AIDS-related Kaposi sarcoma.' Does that mean it's effective and that the Food and Drug Administration will approve it as a drug for treatment of KS? I'm not sure yet, we'll see. Probably it will. I know they'll not approve any drug at all unless they're sure of its safety, beyond a shadow of a doubt. That requires extremely controlled studies of sufficient numbers of patients. Those studies, in turn, take financial resources."

Paul says he's not yet seen what he considers an appropriately controlled and replicated study proving that Isoprinosine does anything at all for any disease.

"And if you *were* now to see such a study on Isoprinosine, even though it's a competitor's product — if you saw a study that proved its efficacy?"

"Then of course, as a scientist, I'd acknowledge beyond question that it works."

"Dr. Glasky feels the medical profession is more geared to the 'Magic Bullet' approach, to anti-virals, than to trusting that the immune system can be built up sufficiently to tackle the AIDS virus itself. What's your perspective on that?"

"The virus infects the most important central cell in the immune system and kills it -- most of the disorders in AIDS follow from that. Until we inhibit the virus from replicating in cells, and then being transmitted from one cell to another, most immune modulators won't be useful enough — not unless they can *also* inhibit virus replication."

"But if Dr. Glasky is right that Isoprinosine helps the immune system build itself up and can, in fact, help protect against a number of different diseases . . . and if YOU are right that the virus needs special attention, isn't it possible that a good approach to AIDS might be something that builds up the immune system *and* something else entirely that knocks out the virus?"

"Sure, that's a valid approach. We're exploring that with Interferon and Interleukin-2, both separately and together. It may well take more than one drug to work with AIDS, and quite possibly drugs from more than one company."

I ask him now about a drug I've been hearing positive rumors about, "Compound-S" made by Burroughs-Welcome. "I will say for the record that Burroughs-Welcome has been absolutely the most effective company at developing anti-virals for the whole industry. At least for now, they've been the premiere company in the field." He says Compound-S is currently in clinical trials and is about to expand to more extensive testing. There is some indication that the product can halt the AIDS virus from replicating and may even help create immune system improvement. "I'm excited about that compound," he says. "I'm excited enough about it to wonder how it might work in combination with Interferon."

"Is it odd that you're 'excited' about a competitor's drug?"

"I'm not only interested in Roche's welfare," he says simply. "I'm a physician and a scientist. I'll do anything and everything ethical to develop Roche compounds that are important for disease. But I have nothing against some other company having a breakthrough that can help people."

"In the cosmetics business, at Avon, we wouldn't often be 'excited' by the success of Revlon's new fragrance."

"Mike, there are some fields of therapy we're not even involved in and don't do well. We're not involved, for example, in anti-fungals. When something is discovered that I can feel sure will help people, even if it's from a competitor -- then I do celebrate that. I'm a doctor."

Paul Nadler's message to you:

"There's nothing perjorative about having AIDS. It happens to have struck particular groups first, only because it's a blood-borne disease. As a society, we all need to get behind this disease together so we can solve it, not be divided in fifty ways. One doesn't get hostile to blacks because they have sickle cell anemia. One doesn't get hostile to Jewish or Mediterranean people because they get certain genetic diseases like Tay Sachs. AIDS is just a disease -- but it's having utterly serious affects on our medical system and society. We have to avoid being judgmental. We just have to fight it."

Dr. Robert Crowl

He could hardly be more different that Paul Nadler. He speaks in slow, flat tones with no emotion, while Dr. Nadler was electric. Dr. Crowl wears nondescript clothing, while Dr. Nadler was elegant. I see pictures of Bob Crowl in blue jeans, hiking with a backpack. I see crayon drawings by his children. His office has no "style" whatsoever, but the metalic and plastic furniture looks as though it withstands the effects of corrosive acid. I'm in a different part of the forest: the lab.

Bob Crowl has a Ph.D. in biochemistry. His training is molecular genetics and biochemistry. "I'm a specialist in producing foreign gene products in bacteria." His specialty is being applied to AIDS in two ways: finding better ways to diagnose when people have the disease, and searching for a vaccine to prevent it. "We're looking for a protein that can be tested for its capability of eliciting neutralizing antibodies," he says. I can see that I'm going to have to get him to talk more simply.

"You're one of those people who looks under the microscope, right?"

I am conscious, as I talk to him this way, of potentially insulting him by sounding too casual about his discipline. But I do not feel any personal chemistry between us yet, and I'm wanting to crack through his formality. I am not at all sure he's happy that I'm sitting here, distracting him from important research.

"That's right," he says, "I'm one of those scientists on the front line, but in a very narrow aspect against this disease. I work with things that are smaller than what you can see in a microscope. We analyze populations of molecules. For a diagnostic reagent, we're trying to produce proteins that can react with antibodies when they're present in the bloodstream of a person infected with the AIDS virus."

"Isn't it true there's a period when you're infected by the virus and your body hasn't yet made antibodies against it?"

"That's true."

"In that case, your test wouldn't yet show anything yet, right?"

"That's correct. And that's a problem. One solution is to be able to detect the virus directly. But it might be present only in very small amounts. Or it might be integrated into a cell which makes it harder to find."

"The virus also changes, doesn't it? It mutates. Wouldn't the changes also make it hard to test a virus directly?"

"These variants are diverse in only one small region of genetic material," he says. "That's within the 'envelope' gene, and that's the gene we're interested in. If you look closer within the envelope gene, the area of diversity is even more localized -- we've analyzed that. We know where those regions are within one particular gene of the AIDS virus. If you isolate variants of the AIDS virus from New York, San Francisco, Europe, Haiti and then clone their genetic materials . . . you can actually sequence them." (I remember the pages of identification letters I'd seen in Paris, a "sequence" being the way to describe a virus in detail.) "If you've read all the information contained within each virus variation and you compare them to each other, you'll see precisely where the changes have occurred.

"We focus on just those parts of the protein that are important, either to recognize the AIDS antibody if a person has it, or to actually make an AIDS antibody which is the goal of a vaccine. We're trying to find the common denominator of all those different virus variations, the part of the envelope gene thatremains the same."

"Let's talk about this idea of an 'envelope,'" I say. "I like to arrive at non-technical metaphors for the kind of work you do. When I was talking with Dr. Mathilde Krim, I began to imagine the AIDS virus as a mean, sneaky creature cloaked and hidden away behind a slicker, like a strong and protective rain jacket. But one could also think of the virus hiding inside of an 'envelope', I see."

"Either image can work. It's a defense mechanism for the virus. Not only does the virus protect itself with an envelope or raincoat, but the outer jacket also has a function. It directs the virus right to its target. That's the function of the envelope. In order to infect cells, the virus has to recognize a specific receptor located on the outside of them."

"Then it's almost as though the envelope has an 'address' on it. 'Deliver me to such-and-such a cell.' Like the mailing address of the cell it's going to go attack."

"Exactly!" he says. I can feel him begin to work with me to explore expressing his science in simple terms. We're like two kids on a beach. Having approached each other cautiously, we've begun sharing tools to build a castle. We can alter it, as the mood strikes us, just by shifting the sand.

"You know, in addition to information," he says, "we have to allow for a physical mechanism. Can we extend the image?"

"Well, if it's the raincoat idea, it could have a nasty hook on it."

"Exactly," he says, encouraging me now.

"A vicious hook right on its surface. A hook that fastens itself only onto particular kinds of cells with the right latch."

"And if we have a good idea of what that physical mechanism is," he says, "if we know how the hook operates, we can define our mode of attack."

"Tell me more about your vaccine search," I say.

"Okay. Because the envelope protein is on the outside of the virus, that's usually the predominate physical entity that's exposed in the bloodstream." I'm picturing a sealed envelope floating along on a red river, an address face up to the sky. PLEASE DELIVER ME TO THE FOLLOWING CELL . . . . VERY PERSONAL.

"That's what antibodies recognize," he says. "That's what they respond to."

"They 'see' the envelope, as it were."

"They see the envelope," he repeats dryly, listening to himself sound like a second grade primer with me. We laugh together at the way he's now talking.

"I know they don't REALLY 'see' it," I reassure him.

"Okay," he says. "So the envelope is the predominate physical entitity exposed in the bloodstream and that is what antibodies respond to.

You can use fact that in two ways. One, to detect antibodies that have already been generated as a result of previous exposure to the virus. And two, to find a way to elicit a class of antibodies that will not only bind to the envelope, but inactivate its function."

"You're talking about using a vaccine, then, to put a blank label over the address, so the virus is never delivered to the cell. Or, in the image of a raincoat with a deadly hook attached, you create an antibody strong enough to forcibly clamp itself over the hook, to deactivate it."

"Right! We already know there are antibodies that can at least recognize the hook. But they may not yet be able to stop it from working. We're looking for ways to generate antibodies that can go further. There've been studies, you know, that certain AIDS patients do already have low levels of neutralizing antibodies. That gives us hope for a vaccine possibility."

"So if you can already find antibodies that make a start at dismantling the hook, maybe you could make more of them, or make them stronger?"

"That's the exact idea," he replies. "The problem is, the targets of this virus are the very cells that control the production of antibodies *against* it! So our problem is quite tough. We've got to get cells to start making antibodies to neutralize virus, practically BEFORE they even see it coming!" It's like life-or-death tag. "If you give a patient a vaccine after he's already seen the virus, it could be too late."

"The virus might already have hurt his ability to defend himself."

"Right."

"That's the entire point of vaccine anyway, isn't it . . . giving it in advance."

"Yes. It's preventative, and that itself is an enormous problem. As perhaps Bob Gallo has mentioned to you, he advocates vaccinating the entire population. Which means the vaccine must be tested very thoroughly. You never know what potential problems can arise. The vaccine business is a risk. It's a business, but it's a risk."

"Because you'd certainly hate to come up with a vaccine that turns out to kill people."

"Exactly," he says. "That is a serious problem." I am beginning to enjoy his deadpan manner, his understatement in the face of my provocations.

"The approach we're taking, just producing a protein" he continues, "is a much safer way to make vaccine. Historically, vaccines are weakened forms of viruses, you know."

"I'll be getting a flu vaccine in a few days," I tell him. "So I'll be given a mild case of the flu to prepare my body to fight off the real flu if it comes."

394

"Right. But we're not working with the virus at all in this instance. We're working with *information* derived from the virus and, through genetic engineering, we're able to make in bacteria a *component* of the virus. Let's call it an 'artificial protein.' It looks, in molecular term, like the protein that's actually in the virus itself. So antibodies would then look at this protein and say, 'we've gotta make antibodies against this thing.' They'll do that, and if the real virus later infects the person, there'll already be protective antibodies to fight it off. That's the idea.

"With your raincoat image, Mike, we're injecting something that won't do a person any harm. What we inject *looks* like it's got that hook on the raincoat; we've simulated its appearance. The body then learns to immobilize the hook before the real one comes along. This is a new area in medicine, 'sub-unit vaccines.' A number of companies and institutions are working in this area. The malaria virus is another example.

"The problem with AIDS is, it's such an urgent problem you feel you've got to work so very fast -- and yet you've also got to be extremely careful. One has to strike a balance between speed and accuracy."

"Why did you choose this field in the first place?"

"I've always had an interest in science and in biology. This particular project on AIDS came to Roche from the National Cancer Institute, when Dr. Reddy joined the company from the NIH. He'd been working with Dr. Gallo."

"It's primarily, am I right, an intellectual interest that drew you into biology?"

"Oh, yes."

"The very effort that we're making, you and I, to be sure I understand you is an illustration of how cerebral your discipline is."

"Yes, that's fair. The scientific community's ability to cope with this disease is based on having prepared minds. Simply having an intellectual interest in the fundamental questions of biology and having information on hand at the right moment in time. Had this disease come about ten years ago, I promise you, we would not have been able to cope with it."

"Really?"

"That is absolutely correct. We would have been in much, much deeper trouble than we already are. We wouldn't even know, if it had come on the scene in 1970, we wouldn't know how to begin to deal with it. We wouldn't have scientific tools to even know what the cause is."

"I know that Dr. Gallo discovered the first human 'retrovirus.' And I know the difference between a virus and a retrovirus is the way that it replicates itself, which is where 'reverse transcriptase' comes in."

"Yes. That enzyme wasn't discovered until the early 1970's."

"What else is known now that wasn't known in 1970 but that's essential to how you're approaching the AIDS problem?"

"The entire technology to understand the molecular aspects of these viruses! What we call 'sequencing' was developed in the '70's. The first paper describing that technology was in 1975 or 1976. Only in the last five years has it become routine in virtually every laboratory. That technology is what's letting us know that there are different forms of the virus. It lets us find out just where the differences are. In order to sequence the virus at all, you have to be able to clone its genetic technology. That capability has only been available for the last fifteen years."

I imagine, at the outskirts of my mind, what would have happened if AIDS had struck the planet when none of these disciplines had yet been developed. I don't let myself take the fantasy very far . . . it's too overwhelming.

"This disease would have been devastating in 1970," he tells me. "The only reason our progress against AIDS has occurred with such speed is because of recent scientific preparedness. That's something you can't predict, you know. That's a really important fact I would like to stress to the public."

"Okay, this is your chance then. What exactly would you like to tell them?"

"They must know they've got to invest in scientific research without having totally defined preconceptions of what the research is going to be for. You don't know what problems are going to come at you in the future."

"It's a big issue, isn't it, in business of any kind -- if you can't see a tangible result, it's always harder to get funding."

"That's right. But that's a fundamental problem for scientists, that the public or governments don't understand how science works. Most of the time, things are unpredictable. Most of the time, advances are made through serendipity. They're just fortunate, that's all. There are thousands of instances where something important is discovered by luck. But in order to take advantage of luck, you must have prepared minds out there and on the scene. Minds that are simply motivated by intellectual interest in a problem. You never know when that interest, when that prepared mind, is going to make a valuable contribution to medical science."

"You are a prepared mind."

"In this particular field, yes."

"You entered it just because you found it interesting. Have you personally ever had any direct experience with AIDS and what it does to people?"

"No, I have not."

"I'm thinking that your kind of caring is different, a different kind of caring, than the nurse who cares for the patient with KS lesions, the patient who looks like an emaciated concentration camp victim."

"I have a desire to attack a problem on principle itself. AIDS is obviously an important public health problem. When you know your own scientific training can make an important contribution, that's enough motivation, whether you've had the emotional experience of the disease or not. I'm simply a scientist. The real satisfaction I derive is doing science. I don't really get satisfaction from publicity, for example. That's just my nature. I like doing science and seeing progress being made. I don't want to move up to sales management. I want to do science."

I am realizing how very glad I am that there are people who don't need to translate a virus into "raincoats" and "envelopes" to understand it. I'm glad that this man's kind of knowledge exists today.

Bob guesses that ten or twenty other companies have people and teams like his working hard on the AIDS virus objective. As I stroll through his lab on my way back to my car, I see a cartoon taped to a refrigerator. "THE AIDS TEAM," it says. Each member of his team is personified as a living test tube. Each person's name is written beside one of the little creatures.

As I turn to say goodbye, I see a sign over Bob's door, a banner I hadn't noticed on my way in. "ON A MISSION."

"It's been a pleasure, Mike," he says. "I'm glad you're helping to translate some of this work to non-scientists."

"The pleasure is mine," I say. And it is.

Chapter 34:
Bruce Voeller —
Mariposa Foundation

Public education has been an ongoing topic in these chronicles. Bruce Voeller heads the Mariposa Foundation which is specifically concerned with research and education on a broad variety of sexual topics. A portion of the author's royalties for this book is being donated to Mariposa. Reader contributions may be sent to: Mariposa Foundation, P.O. Box 36B35, Los Angeles, California, 90036.

It's probably not an exaggeration to say that this award-winning Ph.D. biologist from Rockefeller University is now, at age fifty-one, a celebrity in the history of the American gay movement. I remember the newspaper photos of him some twenty years ago — how thin and blond he was, with his Swedish and German heritage.

He's still blond, with touches of gray now, but he's heavier in a way that makes him solid and less ethereal. He is president of Mariposa which researches and distributes information about human (not just gay) sexuality. I am interviewing him in his West Side Manhattan apartment; he has another base in California.

He was one of the first gay men in history to sue for visitation rights to his three children, and he won. He was a founder of the National Gay Task Force in 1973. He successfully helped to cause the American Psychiatric Association to change the official definition of homosexuality, ending its classification as an emotional and mental illness.

Prior to age thirty, he'd never had one sexual experience with a man, even though he had "feelings" since adolescence. He remembers the only gay role model he knew about when he was growing up: a flamboyant "cross-dresser." He knew he wasn't one of those.

His Oregon minister assured Bruce that he would become a ridiculous figure in high heels and lipstick if he pursued his dangerous attraction to other males. A college psychiatrist told him he couldn't possibly be gay — his grades were too good, and he was an athlete. If he would simply date girls and get married and have children, some day he'd look back and laugh at his own foolishness. Bruce couldn't couldn't be such a fine skiier, for example, and be gay.

So he set his feelings aside and pushed himself into a heterosexual lifestyle: he got married at twenty-four. For six years, despite little interest, he performed sexually in his marriage. Sometimes he used fantasies of men to help him. At thirty, his wife divorced him for another man, a pediatric psychiatrist. She assured Bruce that he was heterosexual, though. They had, after all, had shared years of heterosexual relations together, resulting in children. That meant he was heterosexual.

Bruce has now been living with his lover, Richard, for seven years.

Today he's committed to the importance of societal role models — gay doctors, lawyers, judges, policemen, construction workes. He wants young people to realize they can be whoever they want to be and still be attracted to their own gender. He is also committed to accurate, well-researched information on human sexuality that is then made available to the media, to doctors, to priests, and to citizens at large. That's why, in 1969, Mariposa was created.

The name comes a flower that grows in both New York state and California. One of the organization's chief concerns was "violence linked to people's ignorance, misbeliefs, and misapprehensions about human sexuality." Violence against women, violence against gays, and violence in family relationships are all often tied, Bruce says, to a fear of sexuality or its expression. Another Mariposa interest became the use of information to help people avoid disease and even stress.

He reminds me that as late as the 1920's and '30's, there were still statements by prominent physicians warning that masturbation causes insanity, with explanations of the 'mental disease' in medical textbooks. "We felt we had a major job to do: putting out factual, honest, and forthright information of the sort that sex researchers like Kinsey and, later, Masters and Johnson had put out. We had an added focus of helping alleviate problems of violence and sexually-transmitted disease."

Mariposa began to use speaking engagements at colleges and civic organizations to get feedback from people on their most common questions about sexuality. An archive of information was established. Ads offering information on sexually transmitted diseases were planned.

Bruce and the co-founders of Mariposa envisioned a series of volumes, each on specific sexual topics. Each would update its research periodically and be available in both a scholarly version for researchers, and a simplified version for the public.

As he tells me these things, I hear the muffled, sneering thoughts in the back of my mind. This is a man who used to be on the barricades, I am thinking. He was in the thick of political struggle, pushing hard for civil rights and freedom as his personal conscience pushed him forward. Now he has apartments on both coasts and is in charge of a group named after a lily in which he can chat about sex and discourse at club meetings. What am I doing interviewing a middle-aged dilettante when my focus is the boiling epidemic of AIDS? What good is this discussion?

"If I were to say to you hardnosedly . . . . " I let my voice become harsh and crass. Indeed, I take pleasure in confronting this urbane academic with a loud, squawking voice as I imitate a skeptic: "Awwwwww, who NEEDS that? Whaddya we need YOU for? The media gives us more about sex to read as it is! What's the big deal?"

He's been observing my outburst, nodding his head.

"So what would you say, Bruce?"

"Almost the only area of major human experience for which you can't go anywhere and study and read up on, to become an expert — which even the experts, including physicians and ministers have never studied and have mostly 'street knowledge', just like you and me — is human sexuality. Kinsey, Masters and Johnson, C.A. Tripp, those kinds of people are the exceptions. But their knowledge is not part and parcel of what ministers, doctors, and teachers know. There is no obligatory course on sexuality for doctors-in-training at any medical school in the entire United States. We want to change that."

"You're saying, they should know these things because it's an important area."

"I'm saying it's one of the major parts of human life! Yes, they should study about it and learn about it in an organized way."

"Yeah, Bruce, but most people have survived, haven't they, century after century, merely by having friends and parents pass sexual information on to them. Who really needs you?"

"That's part of the problem," he says. "We have hand-me-down knowledge and pass-along information from kids in streets."

"But what are any real social consequences?" I ask him. "What's the difference?"

"People have enormous fears and anxieties about whether their 'performance' is right," he answers. "Or if they're 'adequate' because of the adequacy of their sexual expression. There is a huge amount of violence linked to this ignorance."

"Give me an example."

"Sure. Just the concept of fag-bashing." He's referring, I know, to gangs or individuals who look for people they believe are gay to, literally, beat up. "That's one link, from our point of view, to people who are unsure about their own sexuality. In the past few decades, that's been characterized by teenagers, or twenty-year-olds."

"Give me a non-gay example."

"Sure. All the kind of violence within the family."

"How is that linked to knowledge?"

"It's linked to the fact that men view themselves as 'top' and as having a role to perform. Women are seen as having a role to perform sexually and socially in a society where there's no intrinsic reason for these roles to be so rigid. So you have large numbers of men who really are uncertain about themselves — about how well they're playing their roles. Those men can resort to violence and force as a way of not having to deal directly with worry about their own performance or authority. Worry can come from lack of knowledge about their own adequacy."

It all sounds so theoretical to me, I'm not feeling much concern.

"Bruce, suppose I say, `well, okay. If you wanna do that, I guess it's probably okay. This is America, after all. But what have you done in six years? I've read a lot of magazines and I've never heard of Mariposa. I don't see Mariposa written up and credited on CBS news for doing anything about sexuality.'"

"That's actually not true," he says. "You have heard about us, you just don't realize it right now. So often, we remember the event but don't attach the source to it."

"Well, what have you done?"

He tells me about a George Segal sculpture his organization helped to organize -- I remember the photograph from both televison and newspaper. Two lesbians and two gay men, sitting on a park bench. The artwork is still not in Sheridan Square, in the Village, but is in the Museum of Brooklyn.

I am feeling crestfallen as he cites this example to me. Big deal. I remember that its purpose was to present role models showing that those types of people, male couples and female couples, do exist in our society. Fine, I think to myself. But I'm out here trying to finish a book about a killer, a monstrous disease. It's a December Saturday night and I could be home writing about somebody doing something that really matters.

"Last February 1st," he says, "to pick another example, the lead story on all three networks was, `Mariposa Foundation discovers way of killing the virus which causes AIDS."

He has my full attention now.

"`Nonoxynol-9,'" he continues, imitating the news, "`common component of vaginal spermicides, shown by foundation in New York and California highly effective in killing the AIDS virus.'"

"We have to go a little slower on this one," I say, interrupting him. We laugh at my acknowledgement that I am no longer quite so challenging.

I remember when I first spoke with Dr. Krim this summer and told her I earn my living as a marketing consultant. She said maybe I'd like someday to help figure out a "marketing" way to popularize nonoxynol-9, since it actually kills the AIDS virus.

And in the early fall, I became aware in my visit to Schmid Laboratories, of Ramses Extra, "the first condom with a spermidical lubricant for extra protection." Yes, that was nonoxynol-9. Brent Gulick, the product manager, had sent me a bar graphs comparing sperm activity within ordinary condoms versus the quick decrease in the number of "motile" sperm with nonoxynol-9. The condoms lubricated with spermicide were "thereby decreasing the risk of pregnancy if semen were to spill during withdrawal."

"It was the lead story in the media . . . " Bruce is continuing relentlessly with his trump card.

"I believe you," I say.

" . . . featured in every magazine, weekly, and daily paper in the country, *except* the New York Times."

"Does that mean -- is it true? -- that Mariposa discovered this?"

"Well, I did. And I'm Mariposa."

"How did you discover it?"

"That's a long story," he says.

"Well give me something closer to a sentence, and don't be insulted," I say.

"Okay. I'd been looking at spermicidal substances for a long time because they'd been anecdotally reported for a lower incidence of venereal diseases among women who use the vaginal foam containing nonoxynol-9 compared to other birth control methods." Bruce had already become involved with several AIDS commissions. He therefore contacted the CDC and asked them to work with him on a scientific test of whether the compound would kill the AIDS virus or not. They learned that it does.

"Laboratory studies?"

"Yes."

"Proof, positive."

"Yes. In less than a thirty-second exposure."

"So one of the things a heterosexual, female reader of mine can do, if she's worried about AIDS, is to use these foams that contain that ingredient."

"Yes."

"Could you state with confidence that if she uses the foam, but the man doesn't wear a condom, she won't get the AIDS virus?"

"No. Nor can I state with confidence that if he wears a condom alone, she won't get AIDS. I can state with a high degree of confidence, though, that if they use BOTH methods, their risk will be greatly reduced.

Either alone makes the risk reduction signficant. But both methods together makes a *dramatic* reduction. If one method fails, you'd still have the other. They are statistically much less likely to fail simultaneously."

He tells me about Mariposa's work to encourage more research on condoms. There are many kinds of condoms, he says, and the amount of protection can vary among them. "The fact that you can blow up a condom with air and water gives you a pretty good indication -- since those molecules are actually very tiny compared to a virus. It's like a marble versus a weather balloon."

"So a virus is HUGE compared to an air or water molecule?"

"Enormous. And the condom is able to trap the tinier molecules in, so that's a very positive sign. But there are also `real world' things to be taken into account in condom use." Sperm are far larger than a virus, for example. There are failure rates of condoms for pregnancy, so one assumes there is at least as great a failure rate with a smaller particle.

"The data," he says, "is that the failure rate on pregnancy ranges all the way from 35% down to 4% with highly motivated people. The generally agreed upon failure rate among most people doing contraception research with condoms is about 10%. In other words, 10% of women using condoms to prevent pregnancy actually become pregnant. I would remind you that women are fertile only a portion of each month, whereas you can be exposed to AIDS at any time."

I see, then, why he might recommend use of a spermidical foam *and* a condom. I ask him to tell me about the REASONS for condom failure rate — and therefore what people can do to maximize their effectiveness.

"It's not enough to say: `Safe sex? Use a condom,'" he tells me.

"Okay, let's make it safer. Give me more thorough information. Let's establish that I'm asking you on behalf of both gay and straight readers. I want to know, `how can I have vaginal sex with a condom and/or rectal sex with a condom, and be safer?'"

He delays, making me pay for having challenged him earlier. "First let me make a point," he says. "You asked about the need and value of sexual information that even physicians don't know. I challenge YOU to go back and ask anyone you've interviewed before me — ask them `how much anal sex do heterosexuals engage in.'"

"They don't know. I've already asked. Can you tell me?"

"Yes. I can give you a variety of published papers. One excellent example is data collected by a gynecologist in a broad-based study of Texas women from a range of socioeconomic backgrounds — Chicana housekeepers on through well-to-do society matrons. You should keep in mind that, with the exception of Kinsey, there hasn't been true statistically `random' research on *many* sexual topics."

"Okay," I say. "Now we've got two topics on the burner — heterosexual anal sex, and what anyone can do to make condoms more effective for anal or vaginal sex."

"Right," he replies. "The gynecologist's study found that 8% or 9% of women engaged in anal sex regularly, for pleasure. Something in the vicinity of another 10% had experimented with it. So consider: we may popularly think of anal sex as `gay' but roughly a similar percentage of the heterosexual population engages regularly in that practice. Not only is that one of the more obvious risk practices for transmitting the AIDS virus, but even in rectal gonorrhea — people always assumed women got it by wiping from vagina to anus after bowel movements — it hasn't been realized that a significant percent of the heterosexual population practices anal sex regularly."

"I'm impressed and glad to get some research indications," I admit to him. "It's a question I've asked many people in all these interviews. But now let's talk about how people can do what they want to do and be safer with condoms."

He tells me first about the Consumers Union and their *Consumer Reports* in 1979. They studied twenty-four brands of American condoms and 161 specimens of each and every brand. They measured for shelf life, porosity, stretchability, tensile strength, etc. They found enormous differences among brands. That was years ago, he emphasizes. There's just not as much good, reliable, *current* data as there should be in the midst of an epidemic. But here are some suggestions:

First, he reminds me, people should use both a condom AND a lubricant containing nonoxynol-9 -- for both physical and chemical barriers.

Next, when a man puts the condom on -- and if it doesn't already have an extended tip to trap semen -- he should pinch the tip with his fingers to create some "air" space. That minimizes the risk of leakage back along the length of the shaft of the penis. IF there is a tiny hole along the condom itself, creating a bit of room within the tip will reduce the risk of forcing semen back to where the hole or tear is. "A virus is orders of magnitude smaller than sperm," he says, "so it wouldn't take much of a leak to create risk."

Next, pull the condom on ALL the way down when you're first putting it on. "Don't just roll it partly down. Roll it down just as far as it will go, right to the base of your pubic hair. If you only roll it partly down, you are very likely to leave it inside the orifice — whether vagina or anus." That reason for slippage is one of the major reasons determined for unwanted pregnancy, he tells me. "He just didn't put it on all the way."

404

Next, based on actual sex research data, "many people stay together, inserted, after ejaculation. But — what happens after detumescence?" The penis has shrunken and the condom can slip off. Recommendation: withdraw fairly soon after sex, or at least while the man's penis remains hard. "If you stay hard a long time, fine. If not, get out."

Next, he says, there are men who are so physically large that ordinary condoms regularly burst on them. That is obviously unsafe. "The only solution I know to that is to use one of the Fourex lambskins. It's like sausage casing, from a lamb's intestine. All of people I know who have `two standard deviations from the mean' — large cocks — without exception they say the only one that works for them are the Fourex blue capsule ones. Not even Fourex in the individual foil units." He tells me of a pornographic film star, famous especially for his huge size, who uses this particular condom.

"I'll show you one," he says. He leaves the living room for a minute and returns with a small, blue plastic container. I can see the condom inside. As it happens, it's made by Schmid Laboratories.

Also, he tells me, aging can weaken a condom's protection. One should check a condom, always, to be sure it's not gummy or glued together. If it's hard to unroll, then it's likely to offer diminished protection and be subject to breakage.

"You're probably not aware," he tells me, "that the average heterosexual male ejaculates very quickly, often in less than sixty seconds of penetration. Three quarters of the population ejaculate within two minutes. That's in Kinsey. Masters and Johnson confirm it. Almost ALL the data verifies it."

"So — men who are inside a woman for two minutes and then worry about it — they shouldn't fear that they're 'abnormal'?"

"Yes. Many men worry that they have 'premature ejaculation' because they come so quickly, even though almost everybody else is doing the same thing. It takes women, on the whole, much longer to reach that kind of high-phase state. It's only been in the last fifteen or twenty years that there's been such serious discussion of female orgasm. Why don't women have more orgasm? Because men are so quick, before women are near the peak. The lower you go down on the socio-economic scale, the less foreplay there tends to be with the spouse — the mother of your children — as opposed to 'other' women.

"Why do I bring this up? It's another example of what most people don't know. Second, this is one place where there are often significant statistical differences between gay men and heterosexual men. A lot of gay men have learned to protract ejaculation; they've developed the expertise to last longer.

"That's relevant to our condom discussion. For the gay AND straight males who do stay in the penetration state a long time, it's important to select a condom with durability to withstand friction, reducing breakage and therefore disease. That's another reason the porno star I mentioned uses that particular Fourex condom in the blue case — he uses it for what he calls 'marathon sex,' meaning lengthy sessions in which he's concerned to minimize chances for breakage.

"You can't put all this into a small flyer, obviously. But one can certainly go into detail with physicians and sex counselors. Mariposa focuses on passing along this kind of information to the medical profession. I spent all Thursday in Ithaca, for example, talking with 300 physicians and nurses. Information really matters, Mike."

By now, I'm convinced.

He tells me about doctors from New York and elsewhere who visit him in California and ask his help in going to Mexico to obtain Isoprinosine and other drugs for their patients. He tells me of his personal belief that it's important for people to have the blood test for the AIDS virus. He gives me his impression that there isn't nearly as much hyper-concern or panic in Hollywood as some of the media had reported.

He also says the danger of AIDS to heterosexuals has been somewhat overplayed. Bisexuals, heterosexual IV drug users — those are genuine ways that the virus can be transferred to other heterosexuals. But "most heterosexuals are in very limited danger. If you are a person who has sexual contact with someone in a very high risk group, or if you have sex with a large number of people and therefore with people you don't really know, then it is wise to take some of the precautions we've discussed — condoms used carefully, and spermicides. But if you're basically monogamous, or outside the heavily urban areas of the U.S., then the odds just aren't as high for you to get AIDS."

What would he like to add directly as a message to the public?

"I'd call on people to really familiarize themselves with information, to take the trouble to discover that it's an extremely difficult disease to catch and not a danger in the social context or workplace or to children in schools. Hysteria just isn't warranted. Talk of quarantine, that kind of reaction, is simply and totally inappropriate.

"Don't support research funding because you're terrified of getting the disease — support it because you care about other human beings."

Chapter 35:
"Cliff" — Last Meeting

Cliff was the first person I'd interviewed after Dr. Grossman, six months ago. I had not yet actually seen a person with AIDS when I met this man whose lover, Aaron, has the disease.

As of this final meeting, Cliff had still not told his friend about our interviews. By the time this book is published, Aaron will know.

Today we're having lunch in a Mexican restaurant, a contrast to the raw cold December outside. There is something different about the way Cliff looks today. His hair's longer, he says. That's probably what it is.

"I've been doing . . . somewhat well." I hear the pause. "There've been occasions when, out of nowhere, comes a sadness. I'll watch TV, some piece of trivia, and start to weep. I'm repressing things, I know. I guess that's how it comes out. Deep inside, somewhere, I'm grieving.

"Outwardly, I guess we still don't accept what we hear in the media as being inevitable. So we cling to positiveness, even as the national statistics go up. Just yesterday, Aaron started radiation therapy. It's largely cosmetic. The KS lesions in his mouth are now sufficiently extensive that a wide smile makes them evident."

I think about what it would be like, being afraid to smile freely lest people see you have cancer in your mouth.

"He has a faint place on his forehead, too. Faint. The radiation may remove it. One concern with his mouth is that the lesions could spread to his sinus cavities. The growths could close in. It would be hard to breathe or swallow. He's had none of that, so far, but it could happen. The doctor was alarmed after not seeing him for several months; the KS had spread further inside his mouth. The doctor said we had to start radiation right away. That, I admit, was frightening.

"They want him to go to chemotherapy, too. I don't think we're going to. I have yet to find anybody who'll speak favorably about the outcome of chemotherapy. Even the hospital, when you ask about people in the experiments, all they say is, 'it's the best we know to do.' Living with that treatment, losing your hair, I -- I don't know. The alternative, doing nothing . . . ." He laughs, a short, helpless titter. "That doesn't take you places, either."

"His energy level drops each month," Cliff says of his friend, "but it's slow. I guess we're constantly in a struggle between inevitableness and hope. I'm afraid to let myself be hopeful, even as I want to. I find myself thinking more about . . . life after Aaron, more than I used to. I feel guilty about that, but it's a way of preparing myself, you see? I haven't gone to any group therapy. Maybe I should. How busy I am at work, that's a help.

"Mostly I avoid the really hard moments except for direct medical experience, or something unpleasant you can't escape in the media. Last night there was a story about an addict with AIDS dying alone in a flophouse. We were eating dinner, watching the news. You think to yourself, is that going to happen to him? Here is this addict who's going blind. He can't swallow. What do you say to Aaron about that?

"It's been a year since diagnosis. We've come in touch with so much more in ourselves and together, much more than in a 'normal' relationship. There's a richness now, a tender caring. It's made me grow in a way I never had before."

My fork plays with the tostadas and refried beans. "Last time we were together, you were telling me about your macrobiotic diet with him. How is that?"

"Mostly we've stuck to it, although not during the holidays. Actually we modified it a bit. I don't think we could invite our teacher to dinner. We let ourselves have dessert once a week. We'll add fish to the meal. We've found a middle ground. The most interesting thing is how angry and defensive some of the doctors become when they hear we're doing it at all. The thing I find best about the diet, myself, is all the stuff about 'oneness with the universe.' I seem to need that. It's a kind of comfort. Your basic nutritionist doesn't give you that philosophy."

Our waitress — an Irish woman with a lyrical brogue — brings me another coca cola. For a half-second I suspect myself: have I ordered this gooey mess on my plate, am I recklessly drinking full-calorie cokes like some Speakeasy High Life, as if to separate myself from Cliff? He sits across from me now with his meagre salad and a diet drink. I'm not on a macrobiotic diet. I don't have a lover who has AIDS.

I don't like even playing with such an image of my own unconscious impulses. I shove the thought aside like leftover beans.

"You mentioned that you may be repressing your own grieving. If that's so, if you're in fact smothering feelings, do you have any inkling of their coming out in other ways?"

My own training in therapy has made it very clear: you do not escape your feelings, whether you know it or not. I know that Cliff is seeing an analyst right now, so it seems possible he may be in touch with an answer to my question.

"Yes, actually," he says. "I have a very light trigger on my anger at the moment. That's something new. At Christmas, with the stress of holidays and Aaron, I blew up one day at the office. I shouldn't have, I was embarrassed, but I came unglued. I'm trying to watch myself — that kind of temper isn't normal for me.

"I'm taking tranquilizers more now, once or twice a week. They used to be very rare backups. I've had some numbness lately in my hand. I think that's constricted blood vessels, and I guess if you analyze it, I'm 'constricting' my feelings. I'm keeping a lid on. I'm just hanging on and trying to keep things even. I've had a significant increase in my blood pressure the last few months. I guess it's all 'biofeedback' to myself. But what is my alternative? I'm functioning this way. I'm keeping it going, somehow."

"Cliff, when you think about the future — those thoughts you feel guilty about — do you ever discuss those feelings with Aaron?"

"Oh, no. Not with Aaron. Not with anybody. For a variety of reasons lately, it seems we've mostly been socializing with his friends. I won't discuss it with them, I wouldn't want anything to get back to him. I wouldn't want him to misunderstand. I'm not always sure it's even right for me to feel what I'm feeling."

Suddenly, I know it's not my imagination: Cliff *does* look different and isn't just his haircut. The way he carries his body, his shoulders, his hands. He has less life, now. He seems weaker. It's been months since I've seen him and, just now, I perceive the change.

"Except for my therapist," he continues, "and today's lunch with you, I haven't told anyone. I should do something, I suppose. Keeping it all in probably isn't good. Lately I've been telling myself, it's okay what I'm feeling. I've got to be feeling something!

"One of the questions I privately ask myself is, would I ever be open to another relationship, having gone through what I have. I'm so exhausted right now . . . at first I said, no, I'd turn to my work. Then I asked myself, what was the purpose of all the growth, all the self-understanding, if — whenever — I close myself up again. I hope I could someday . . . ."

"Everything okay, boys?" says the waitress cheerily? "Something more for your waistline?" she asks me pointedly. I am liking her less now.

"Cliff, tell me. If you were in another relationship, someday, how would you be different, having experienced what you have?"

"I'd make many fewer demands on another person now. I'd be more prepared to allow someone else to be just who they are. I know more what I have to give. I respect myself more than I used to. I think I could be less needy now, toward somebody else. I wouldn't need them to be, so much, just exactly how I'd want them. I've had to accept so much in this situation . . . I could be more accepting in general.

"I'll tell you something I think about. One of the things I wanted, at the start of my relationship with Aaron, was closeness, tenderness. Well we have so much of it now. But I never thought I'd be getting it this way. I never wanted to have those feelings this way. There's a lesson there for me. Getting love and support from someone, it can't be about that person changing — it's got to be accepting them for who they are, for being themselves. Do you understand me? I'm not even sure I understand me, myself. I've learned something about acceptance."

He stares down at his salad. "As much as this last year has meant," he says to his plate, "as close as I've gotten to Aaron now, I'd trade it, I'd trade it in an instant — for him only not to have this disease."

It's happened to me before, what's happening now. The conversation I'm having, the feelings I'm feeling, they're out of context with the festive, bubbling atmosphere around us. The tape is turning, sitting next to the sugar bowl. It is soaking up the 1950's music and our silence.

"You do the best you can do when your lover has AIDS," he says. "I tried very hard to be perfect, and I know I'm not. I'm not as strong as I thought, but I'm trying to make the most of it. `Be happy with what you've got when you've got it' — that's what I'm learning, too.

"I know there are people, friends, willing to be supportive of ME. I used to want to be so strong I wouldn't need them. Maybe I'll admit I could use that, too. Aaron now understands: I am not going to desert him. I love him.

"The thing about AIDS is, it makes you face whether you're really doing what you want to do or not. Like, I've always wanted to do something helpful for people, to do some good. I haven't done a thing about that impulse, you know? I wonder how much longer I'm going to wait before I do. Not long, I hope. It's important to do the things one really cares about.

"It's important to let someone else do what *they* really care about, too. He didn't want the chemotherapy, and I'm glad I never tried to force it on him. Lately, he's been discovering more of his spiritual nature, going back to the Catholic church. It's not always comfortable for me, but I go with him. It's important to him, and I want to support him in what's important.

"You know, I was raised a Southern Methodist. My mother, when she was in her last years, she had cancer. She wanted, all of a sudden in her seventies, she decided to experience the freedom she'd never let herself have. She'd been demure, you know, with gloves and her autumn haze stole. Now she wanted to go to the churches where you clap. As an older lady, now she was clapping and singing. My father, he never taught me by words but by doing. He — "

His eyes are moist. His hands rest, limp, on the table.

"It wasn't easy for him. For him, it was radical, those religious services she wanted to go. Now I understand — " I see the tears. "It was an act of great love. He went with her. He sat by her. He was there when she was clapping and singing. He wanted to be there for her, to help her be who she wanted to be. That was love. Just to go. Not to judge. Just to be there. I took that act as my model. You accept. It wasn't what he wanted to do, you know. But he went because he wanted *her* to know: it was okay.

"I went myself, once or twice. In my pompous, judgmental way, I was embarrassed that she was going to these kinds of services. I hadn't learned yet. I hadn't learned how to be there, just to be there, for somebody else. You don't have to always understand. You don't have to contribute something active. But you have to be there. You have to NOT withdraw.

"So if Aaron wants to go start going to Catholic services all of a sudden, then I'm going too. I'm going to be there for him for whatever there is. For as long as I've got."

Chapter 36:
Dr. Grossman — December

We were at the end of the chronicle together. I'd be submitting a manuscript to my publisher. I would be moving on, and he would continue to live what I'd been writing. "But I also saw an ingrown toenail today," he said, reminding me that it isn't only AIDS he treats each day.

When I started this experience in May, "doctors" as a category were like noble paperdolls to me — a distant stereotype. So, I guess, were "AIDS patients."

I don't feel that distance any longer.

He's obtained permission for my involvement and is preparing me now for the housecall. I come along, just for perspective, as he visits an older, non-AIDS patient.

"At age sixty-five," he tells me, "the lady took up golf and became a champion golf player. At seventy, she took up fine art. At seventy-two she was part owner of her own gallery. Her work has been shown in galleries all over the country. Here she is, this photo, a couple of years ago. Mind you, she is eighty-one now."

She stands by one of her paintings. She has a wonderful, confident smile. The day of her sudden hospitalization, he says, she swam and had played tennis. She was in radiant and productive health, just the way we'd hope to be. Her only problem was a slight forgetfulness.

"Is that a photograph of an eighty-year-old?" he asks me. I'm not good at this, but I know she looks sensational. "Would you agree, she's the youngest old person you've ever seen?"

"Yes. Of course."

"You're going to see her very deteriorated now. Not mentally, just physically."

Jeffrey, an assistant, insists that he show me a note from her:

"We both want to thank you so very much for saving us a whole day and night of concern about the results of the test, by calling instead of waiting for the next day's appointment. You are just wonderful for us and we love you. Bea."

One year ago, she'd lost the power of coherent speech. She was the guest at her eightieth birthday party that night. Somehow she got through the evening without her guests seeming to know -- nodding, smiling, murmuring.

"`Marked expressive aphasia,'" he tells me, reading from her chart. "She knew what she wanted to say, but couldn't come up with the words. They were garbled and somewhat as gibberish. `Patient accutely aware and embarrassed.'"

I think about how I would feel if I couldn't communicate. At this moment, I do not think about people who are dying at twenty-two or thirty-eight or twenty-seven. It is nice to go out on a house call to a woman who is now in her eighties.

"She smiled so sweetly at her party," he is continuing. "Afterward, we took her to N.Y.U. They found an enormous brain tumor occupying most of the cerebral hemisphere. Surgery was completed at about 4:00 on May 10th. I went to see her at 10:00 the next morning." He laughs in admiration and wonder. "There she was, sitting up in bed, having breakfast and feeding herself." He laughs again and is misty-eyed.

"In an intensive care unit full of vegetables, she was sitting up, independent, looking around as if to say, you know, `why am I here?' Of course she couldn't talk at all now. On top of the tumor, she had swelling from the craniatomy. I'll never forget her, with her white bandage and a little bottle of fluid bobbing -- it's a suction device that drains the fluid and it bobs -- just like an earring.

"She was told by the surgeon . . . I'm sorry to tell you, Michael, she was barely recovering from the surgery and he assembled her and the family to announce she had six weeks to live. The family is at their rock-bottom most vulnerable when he tells them this. 'Six weeks.' Could he not wait to at least get her out of intensive care? As a doctor, you need to rely on cues from people, on sensitivity. Of course, you are honest. But you need to factor in the needs of the people you are talking to. Timing matters, you know. It can help people handle things the way they hope to.

"When I saw her sitting up and feeding herself, I said to her husband, 'no, Lee. She's stronger than that. You'll see.' That was six MONTHS ago. She still can't talk, but she's there. The communication is there, emotionally."

We taxi down to the Village. Lee meets us at the elevator, in pajamas and bathrobe. "I'm living a nightmare," he says. "I love her so much." They've been married forty-eight years.

413

I'm introduced to Bea. She is meagre, a swaddled rag doll on a divan. She makes a warm and gurgling sound of welcome. Dr. Grossman jokes about the turban wears; she lost her hair from recent therapy. I see her eyes laughing when he teases her. He removes the turban and checks her scalp. I note the gentle way he touches her shoulder and, now, her hand. I feel the persistence of his physical contact.

Lee and a nursing assistant from India bring Bea slowly into the bedroom where Dr. Grossman will give her an injection. I am alone in the living room, surrounded by strikingly varied artwork. The only painting she didn't create is a portrait of herself, done by her art teacher. This Bea on the wall under a spotlight is a virtual Joan Crawford, strong and elegant.

Dr. Grossman confers with Lee about medication, while Lee wants also to talk about his business. He can hardly pay attention to it, he's so concerned about Bea. He always wanted them to make it to their fiftieth wedding anniversary. He pours out his worry. Dr. Grossman says something soothing, then something teasing. He has no recommendations for what should happen to the business, but he is listening and he cares. Lee keeps a hand on Dr. Grossman's overcoat as he shuffles with us back to the elevator.

We have dinner in an Italian restaurant. We talk about Bea. We talk about AIDS. And we agree to have our final dinner of this chronicle, one week from tonight.

~ ~ ~ ~ ~

I assumed he'd be late. I've eaten my own dinner already and have set aside his portions of various concoctions. He arrives at10:00.

He teases me about a plastic goose, a lamp in my window. It is an unglamorous contrast to the gorgeous Manhattan skyline, but it's a sentimental goose lamp for me. I tell him I have a clearer idea of his own sense of humor, now, by schlepping around with him these past six months.

We talk about the huge increase in public attention to AIDS, largely because of Rock Hudson. And how science seems more optimistic now than when we started. He has hopes for Isoprinosine, for example, even though he's not yet authorized to 'break the code' of his test. He mentions promising drugs — Compound S, HPA-23, Ribavirin — and other names, unknown to me. Naltraxone. Imreg. To be able to cite so many, he tells me, gives him hope he didn't have at our first dinner.

"You don't know this, Michael, we haven't talked about it, but our 'walk' through this chronicle has actually helped me. It has certainly allowed me to shed any embarrassment, any reluctance, any shyness about what I powerfully feel: the importance of reaching out to help people in desperate need and, at the same time, helping those who don't have the disease understand its human meaning. The book has helped me. I'm not afraid any more of talking about life and death and reaching out."

"What do you mean?" I am startled to hear him talk this way.

"It's just this powerful, inner feeling I have now, that people *need* to KNOW the true story. The courage. The fight. The fact that people with AIDS are all different from each other, and have nothing to do with the newspaper statistics that lump them together. Or with people's automatic pictures.

"You remember the fellow I told you about who would put on a suit and go to work every day with 104 fever? Well I've watched you hearing these things, seeing all this — the guy in Intensive Care, for example, and Daniel, and Philip, and Jan, all of them. As I watched you, it's helped me see what you were seeing more clearly.

"I've somehow been reminded of my real commitment here, Michael. I used to sense the fear so many people have — an atavistic fear, an almost primal fear — of even *hearing* about AIDS. Like superstition: `Don't talk to me about it! I might get it.'

"But the way we've discussed these individuals together . . . it's helped me perceive something more important than public fear. Now I notice that everyone who walks into my office, for no matter what trivial complaint, hungers to talk about *this* disease. Even if only for an instant. Everyone. Gay, straight, old, young. If I used to sense their fear, now I also sense their need. It's the medical topic of this time."

He is thin, this doctor of mine. He would probably prefer "trim." His hair was black when I first became his patient those years ago. Now it's mostly silver.

"Ron, let's talk about the chart you drew for me that first night."

"The numbers may not be as high as I feared back then, especially if science keeps progressing so rapidly. There've been very positive changes in the gay community. Like many other doctors, I am impressed at the fall-off in ordinary, sexually-transmitted diseases.

"I have a high percentage of gays in my own practice, you know. I will wind up 1985 with one twentieth of the number of cases of gonorreah I used to see, and maybe a hundredth the incidence of syphilis. That can't help but be encouraging.

"Mind you, in some statistics, VD is actually on the rise in heterosexual women. There are still unknowns about the curve I drew that night. Some strictly 'logical' methods of reducing disease — like distributing sterile needles to drug addicts — are blocked by political or social factors. Another example: factual education of the public about sexuality is an option whose aggressive use is dampened by social factors.

415

Still, I'm more optimistic than I was, that's true. As a society, we haven't addressed all the issues we need to, but we have made progress.

"I did fear then, as I do fear now, a limbo that people with AIDS could fall into. It's sad enough that these people will cease to exist as human beings in their prime. I fear lest they also be forgotten. I fear that people will unconsciously *need* to forget them because of the disease. `Yes, I miss Richard, but — gosh, he had AIDS, such a horrible disease. Maybe it's just as well we don't think of him on the anniversary of his death. Let's think about grandma.'

"That's my fear, that these people will be lost. For those around them, the people who've lived through their disease and death, it may be difficult to think about later. I don't want them forgotten.

"I made a summary for you, Michael, of my patients with CDC-defined AIDS. 146 people as of now. Eighty-seven of them are dead."

He shows me a chart on a small piece of note paper. It compares his AIDS patients with Kaposi's sarcoma alone, the ones with opportunistic infections (like pneumocystis pneumonia,) and those who've suffered both types of illness.

Diagnosis	Living	Dead	Totals
KS	24	3	27
KS-OI	7	26	33
OI	26	53	79
Lymphomas	2	5	7
	59	87	146

I can see, myself, how much more dangerous it's been to have an opportunistic infection, either alone or with KS. His first patient died in early 1982, he says. By the middle of 1983, he'd lost only eight. Most have died in the last two and a half years.

"But what does this chart show you?" he says. It shows you no more than a newspaper clipping. Those eighty-seven people are people I knew well, you understand? I knew their families, their friends, their aspirations." I can feel the tension in his voice and how steadily he is controlling it.

He rustles through a notebook. He shows me his crinkled summary of people with AIDS — a far longer record than he once expected would be his sad memento.

"For the longest time," he says, "my entire chronicling of their deaths was right here. Now I use a computer, because I need better access to the data." He clears his throat.

"This is a sloppy piece of paper, Michael. It's only how I started. For quite a while, I unconsciously put a little cross by a name when someone died. Then one day I realized the entire page was lined with crosses. I would stare at the paper and say, 'this can't be. I can't have known all these people.'"

I am sitting still and listening. I do not want to interrupt him. He needs to talk. I need to hear.

"What shall I tell you about them? What talent? What promise? The jerks? The ne'er-do-wells? Do you want to know about suffering? Do you want to know about treasure? Families who don't have a son, and don't have a penny.

"My gray chicken scratches on this piece of paper are people." (Pause.) "Were." (Pause.) "I guess the important thing is what I said before: I don't want them lost. We don't have to build a stone monument to 'Tom' — we have to build it to the *concept* that these were thinking, living, thriving, promising people. We are less for their loss.

"There is a world class makeup artist here, Michael. I may have joked with you about him once. How many can there be? How many people get a call in the middle of the night from a diva who says, `You've GOT to be in Rome tomorrow morning!'"

I laugh at the urgency in the diva's voice. He does, too.

"`No one else can do my makeup!' she said. And he did it. There's humor in that, isn't there? Just as Jan is an important wedding gown designer. Did you ever know a wedding gown designer? I didn't.

"There is on this list, a barber. A free-lance barber. I'm sure he never reported his income to Uncle Sam. I am sure, since he used to cut my hair, that he is sorely missed by his clients.

"I don't want it erased, the moment I took their hands, whenever I could, and ushered them out. They tell us so often in Medical School, `Death is the great Foe. Do not take it personally when you lose people.' Guess what. I didn't follow that advice. Nor did I have the remotest idea that it would get piled on my head this way."

His silence is tender.

"Well, you let yourself get involved," I finally say.

"Yes."

"With eighty-seven people." And climbing.

"On occasion, Michael, these deaths come in bunches. It produces a most unusual experience for myself and my staff. These are Hollywood words, but `We reel under the blow.' Three and four deaths in two days. You think cosmic thoughts then.

"There was a night I walked out of Bellevue. We'd lost an incredibly promising young dentist, thirty-one. He fought like a son-of-a-gun. I liked him a lot. I walked out of Bellevue on a starry summer night with a direct view of Heaven. For a moment, I was yelling at God, I couldn't help myself. I'm sure I must have looked like a 'bag lady' lost on the sidewalk.

"Michael. None of these people is here any more!" I listen to Ron as occupations roll by. His finger finds the crosses on the page.

"Advertising executive of great success. Turned bartender when he realized he was never happy. Helluva good bartender.

"Pharmacist. Fought like the dickens for the folks in the hospital not to know. Unaware that when they finally did, they would shower him with caring.

"Owner of popular shop on Fire Island. Inundated with well-wishing of friends and clients.

"Young actor, never made a name for himself. Went down bitterly complaining of not enough time to fulfill the career.

"Owner of a restaurant.

"Founder and long-time director of an animal shelter.

"Manager of his own small construction firm. Artist and ceramic designer of great promise. Corporation executive. Attorney. University professor. Actor-producer.

"Young, black clerical worker. He always asked you how you were before you could ask him first.

"Dancer.

"Founder of a Puerto Rican theater. News magazine executive. Press secretary to Mayors.

"Jewelry designer — all his pieces were frogs.

"Twenty year veteran of the U.S. Postal Service. Living quietly with his lover in a house in Queens. The antithesis of whatever you think of as 'gay man.'

"My very best and closest friend. An unsuccessful entrepreneur in the theatrical world. Loved by everyone that he was unsuccessful with.

"Greek immigrant. When I asked him what he did for a living, he said, 'mink operator.' His friends explained to me that he designed mink coats.

"Baker. When he could no longer pay his bills, he brought me home-made cakes. They were inscribed. His English was so bad, they were always misspelled. Jose, I *miss* you!"

His list continues. The man across the table reads an occupation and shares a memory of another of his patients who is gone.   It is a midnight reading from his private, pencilled Scripture, and Dr. Grossman's voice reverberates as I listen and watch him in silence.

Behind him, a gentle mist has softened the nighttime Manhattan skyline.   The goose lamp sits poised against the window; its reflection glows back into the room.

He was a waiter.

Word processor.   Wig designer.   Street hustler.

He was a writer.   He edited film.   He was in real estate.

This one was a friend named "Manny".

This one, an actor who got sick, right on stage.   He always used to say, "we'll beat this one, won't we, Ron?"   He went blind but, with a friend's help, he went home one more time to "see" his parents.

The list continues and, finally, we are done.

"I hope people see this not just a list," Ron says.   We are both talking thickly from fatigue as we say good night.   He is muffled under the weight of his overcoat.

I am alone.

I bring his dinner plate into the kitchen.   I leave my manuscript notes in the living room.

I let the goose lamp shine all night.

End of the Chronicle

An experiment in computer conferencing became a cause that took over my life.

When I began, I thought I'd be bringing a candle to a mostly hidden topic. It didn't stay hidden for long; Rock Hudson changed the planet's response to AIDS. His public acknowledgement switched on the camera lights, unleashed the headlines, created the cover stories. For the public attention and action it caused, his revelation will surely have saved lives.

The subsequent media focus helped me personally understand my own wish to contribute something quite different than the everyday news. Someday, I assume, "AIDS" will be a faraway acronym. For example, I have never seen a case of smallpox. I have seldom seen someone with polio. Those older diseases are now mostly controlled: you get a vaccine, and that's that. On some future day, when we are routinely vaccinated for AIDS, I hope to have helped something of this time be remembered.

Not the "facts." They were hard to get, anyway. The reader has found contradictions between one medical expert's comments and another's. What is "safe sex" in 1986? How fast and how wide will this epidemic spread before it's controlled? Precisely how safe is the blood supply? Exactly how accurate is a blood test? I did my best to garner such perspectives, but they are secondary. What I hope is more enduring is, "the human side of AIDS."

I am much more humble about that tag line today. What began as a few interviews became a daunting, sometimes crushing task. I know I failed to capture it all. For example, one of the few points on which almost all medical authorities seem to agree is the lack of danger to school children of "catching" AIDS in the classroom. But where are my interviews with the parents, the teachers, or the children themselves? To chronicle their feelings and fears?

I couldn't get to it, it's that simple.

Where are my interviews with a mother whose son died of AIDS? A father, sister, brother, or wife. Where is my chat with a hemophiliac? Or a single, heterosexual woman worrying about her love life. A Senator on a medical appropriations committee. Executives at the FDA or the CDC. People in Houston, Dallas, Atlanta, Chicago, Detroit, Boston. Everywhere. Where is the Rabbi, Catholic priest, newspaper reporter, policeman? Where is a talk with a hospital orderly or an insurance executive?

None of them happened. I ran out of time.

I did gain a lot from the effort, nonetheless — from the generosity of the people who shared themselves for it, and from what I learned, saw, experienced, and understood from them. The people I encountered are surely symbols of so many more I couldn't meet.

I have a changed attitude now toward death and dying, because of this experience. Regardless of age, regardless of cause, I will be a better listener for someone very ill in the future.

I have a richer understanding now of scientists and some of the human needs that drive them. I feel a heightened respect and gratitude for their skill and their diversity.

I have a clearer sense of what it means to be a doctor or an addict, a prostitute or a foster mother, a bishop or a nurse, a bisexual or an evangelist. So while I know how much I couldn't accomplish, I also know how very much I've gained.

To the volunteers who raise funds, answer phones, clean bedpans, and simply listen: I admire you. Gay Men's Health Crisis and Shanti are symbols for me now of the *many* people in the many organizations I could not personally encounter. From the inspiring people I've met, I know there are thousands and thousands more who are making a difference every day.

I believe some good must come from the caring and even the suffering I have learned of and attempted to chronicle. More humane health care. Scientific discoveries. Volunteers who become surprisingly enriched by the work they do for others. Families and friends who learn to love more deeply, despite the differences and separations that divide them.

It is the first week of a New Year as I write this to you. In local news, Mother Teresa, the Roman Catholic nun, seeks a hospice for state prisoners with AIDS. How many of my former stereotypes about religion, about science, about addiction, about whatever --- need to keep changing? Can I become still more open to learning about human experience? Can I be more able to look past labels to individuals? I hope so. I would like to be a person who continues to grow.

May AIDS have produced a legacy that will help us all understand each other, more lovingly and more truly.

May the memory of people with AIDS — and of the people who cared, and of the people who fought — live on when this disease is dead.

May their memory flourish when the suffering has ended.

I thank you for joining me in this chronicle.

Mike Greenly
New York City
January 6, 1986

421

About the Author

Mike Greenly grew up in Beaufort, South Carolina and obtained his B.A. in English Literature from Duke University, where he graduated Phi Beta Kappa. He moved to New York City in 1965 and joined Scholastic, Inc., where he became Assistant Publisher.

After six years of study, simultaneous with his fulltime career, he obtained a Master's Degree With Distinction at New York University Graduate School of Business, specializing in Marketing and International Marketing. He had meanwhile been a writer and then a product manager at Lever Brothers, and joined Avon Products, Inc. in 1970. In 1977, he became the youngest Vice President in the history of the company, working in a number of marketing and communications assignments. He also received formal training as a Gestalt psychotherapist, and is a member of the New York Institute for Gestalt Therapy.

Mike was profoundly influenced by *The Third Wave* by Alvin Toffler, a book about the transformational effects on world society of modern computer communications. Influenced by the new perceptions this book created in him, Mike resigned from Avon in the fall of 1983 to start his own marketing consulting firm, Mike Greenly Marketing. By that time, he had become an avid user of computer communications networks including The Source and many others.

As he began attending computer and software trade shows as a way of finding clients, he also sent back reports to users of the computer conferencing section of The Source, Participate. Because this new form of communication allowed readers to write back to him and dialogue with each other, he became known as "planet earth's first *interactive* electronic journalist." With two colleagues, Sherwin Levinson and Diane Worthington, he founded TRANSCOASTAL Electronic News Service. Together the team became the first reporters in history credentialed to cover the Democratic and Republican political conventions via the new communications medium.

Today, Mike makes his living by helping companies of all kinds create and market products and services, by conducting focus group interviews of consumers, and by writing speeches and scripts. His articles on various subjects have been published in a variety of magazines around the world.

CHRONICLE is his first published book.